BIG SCIENCE

The Growth of Large-Scale Research

BIG

*Edited by Peter Galison
and Bruce Hevly*

SCIENCE

*The Growth of
Large-Scale Research*

STANFORD UNIVERSITY PRESS
STANFORD, CALIFORNIA

Stanford University Press, Stanford, California

© 1992 by the Board of Trustees of the Leland Stanford
Junior University. Copyright in this work does not extend
to Chapter 11, which was written as a work of the United
States Government and is in the public domain.

Printed in the United States of America

Original printing 1992
Last figure below indicates date of this printing:
03 02 01 00 99

CIP data appear at the end of the book.

Preface

Big science has brought research an unprecedented strength and vulnerability. After the development of radar and nuclear weapons in World War II, science occupied an unparalleled position of prestige and power. Other coordinated efforts built on those accomplishments, capitalizing on broad public and political support: weapons projects like the hydrogen bomb and guided missiles; huge particle accelerator centers that ushered in a new understanding of matter; space programs of moon missions and unmanned interplanetary craft; massive efforts in controlled fusion; and a plethora of large-scale scientific-industrial projects in new materials, electronics, computing, and pharmaceuticals.

In the years since, the blurred domain between science and technology has demanded—and received—more than popular attention; it has required ever larger fractions of national budgets in the United States and elsewhere. Perhaps inevitably, the rising scale of science collided with economic constraints. Even without the catastrophic explosion of the space shuttle *Challenger* and the near meltdown of Chernobyl, big science was in for questioning. With such events, reflection on the nature and wisdom of large-scale science has been rife—from the pages of scientific journals to the halls of government. Scientists, scholars, and the public, willingly or not, must now confront basic issues about research priorities, and where scientific effort is best put.

In this broad context, a diverse mix of scholars assembled at Stanford in 1988 for a small interdisciplinary workshop on the origins and practice of large-scale research. Representing (among other fields) history of science, particle physics, space science, anthropology, and business history, the group focused on the opportunities and dilemmas presented by the growth of big science. Not surprisingly, the style of the authors' inquiries differ; it was just this mix of policy, history, and anthropology that we were after. Together, the essays address some basic questions: How did big science begin? How did (and do) national characteristics shape its execution? What are the difficulties and costs of doing research at the industrial scale? How do industries, government agencies, and universities interact in the production of such scientific enterprises? While a volume of this size can only begin to pose questions about the nature of big science, it is the authors' hope that these questions will help raise the debate beyond the simplistic language that lumps all large research into a homogeneous mass and comes out for or against it. It goes without saying that there are vast areas of research left untouched by these chapters—the human genome project is but one. We hope others will take up these and other questions soon. For faced with the possibility of staggering costs and enormous possible benefits, both the public and the scientific sector will be making fundamental decisions about where we are going with orchestrated research; to do so we will need a nuanced understanding of how we came to have the infrastructure of big science that exists today.

The organization of this meeting and preparation of this volume were based in part on work supported by the National Science Foundation under Grant nos. DIR 8553245 and DIR 8807868. Any opinions, findings, and conclusions or recommendations expressed in this material are those of the author(s) and do not necessarily reflect the views of the National Science Foundation. In addition to the authors represented in this volume, all of us at the workshop benefited from many helpful comments and criticisms by others who were present: David Berley, Program Director for Particle Physics, NSF; Stanley Wojcicki, Chairman of HEPAP; Spencer Weart, Center for History of Physics, AIP; and Joan Warnow, Center for History of Physics, AIP. For additional support of the meeting and preparation of this volume, the editors wish to thank the Stanford Centennial Operating Committee and the Howard and Frances Keller Fund, University of Washington. Peter Galison conducted part of the work during a leave at the Center for Advanced Study in the Behavioral Sciences. The authors and editors are grateful to Barbara Kataoka for assistance at all stages of the project—from the workshop to manuscript preparation. We are also grateful to Henry Lowood, who was immensely helpful throughout our research. Our thanks go as well to Gwen Loosemore and Shannon Temple for help with photographs and other editorial matters, and to Barton J. Bernstein and Betty Ann Kevles for their aid in the process of bringing this book to completion.

P.G.

Contents

Contributors

C. W. F. Everitt is Professor (Research) with the W. W. Hansen Experimental Physics Laboratory, Stanford University. He is the Principal Investigator of NASA's Gravity Probe B program and is author or coauthor of several works in the history of science, including *James Clerk Maxwell: Physicist and Natural Philosopher* and *Maxwell on Molecules and Gases* (with E. Garber and S. G. Brush).

Peter Galison is Associate Professor of Philosophy and Co-Director of the History of Science Program at Stanford University. He is the author of *How Experiments End* and is now finishing a book on the growth and role of instrumentation in modern physics.

Bruce Hevly is Assistant Professor of History at the University of Washington. He is working on a book entitled *Expanding the Spectrum*, about the relation of technology and science at the Naval Research Laboratory.

Lillian Hoddeson is Visiting Associate Professor of History and Senior Research Physicist at the University of Illinois at Urbana. Among her contributions to the field of big science are two co-edited essay collections in the history of modern physics, *The Birth of Particle Physics* (with L. M. Brown) and *Pions to Quarks* (with L. M. Brown and M. Dresden).

David A. Hounshell is Henry W. Luce Professor of Technology and Social Change, Carnegie Mellon University. His works include *From the American System to Mass Production* and *Science and Corporate Strategy: Du Pont R&D, 1902–1980* (with J. K. Smith), winner of the 1990 Newcomen Book Award.

Robert Kargon is Willis K. Shepard Professor in the History of Science Department at The Johns Hopkins University. Among his books are *The Rise of Robert Millikan: Portrait of a Life in American Science* and *Science in Victorian Manchester*. He is currently engaged in a study of the development of high-technology regions.

Daniel J. Kevles is Professor of History at Caltech. His published works include *The Physicists: The History of a Scientific Community in Modern America* and *In the Name of Eugenics*.

John Krige has a Ph.D. in Physical Chemistry and a Ph.D. in the Philosophy of Science. His first book, *Science, Revolution and Discontinuity*, was published by Harvester Press, Brighton, U.K., in 1980. In 1982 he began working on the history of CERN in Geneva, while remaining attached to the Science Policy Research Unit at Sussex University. He is presently leading a project, hosted by the European University Institute in Florence, to write the history of the European Space Agency. John Krige and Dominique Pestre are the main authors of two volumes of the *History of CERN* published by North Holland (Amsterdam) in 1987 and 1990.

Stuart W. Leslie is Associate Professor in the History of Science Department at The Johns Hopkins University. His works include *Boss Kettering: Wizard of General Motors* and a forthcoming study of academic science and the military entitled *The Cold War and American Science*.

Rebecca Lowen is an NSF postdoctoral scholar at The Johns Hopkins University. Her primary interest is in the relationship between academic discipline formation and the structure of university funding and politics.

Allan A. Needell is Curator of Aeronautics and Astrophysics in the Department of Space Science, National Air and Space Museum. He has worked in the history of quantum physics and the national laboratories and is now finishing a book on Lloyd Berkner.

W. K. H. Panofsky is a high-energy experimental physicist at Stanford. He was Director of SLAC from its creation until 1984 and served on the President's Science Advisory Committee.

Dominique Pestre studied physics and history in France and got his Ph.D. at the Ecole des Hautes Etudes en Sciences Sociales in Paris. He published a book in cultural history in 1984, *Physique et physiciens en France, 1918–1940* (Paris: Editions des Archives Contemporaines), and worked on the history of CERN from 1983. In 1990 he published a study on the solid-state physics school built by Louis Neel in Grenoble after the war, *Neel, le magnetisme et Grenoble, 1940–1965* (Paris: CNRS, Cahiers pour l'histoire du CNRS). He is currently coordinating a major study on the reconstruction of French physics after the war. John Krige and Dominique Pestre are the main authors of two volumes of the *History of CERN* published by North Holland (Amsterdam) in 1987 and 1990.

Erica Schoenberger is Associate Professor in the Department of Geography and Environmental Engineering at The Johns Hopkins University. She has published studies on flexible manufacturing, business strategy, and high-technology industry, and is currently applying the techniques of economic geography to analyze the formation of high-technology regions.

S. S. Schweber is Professor of Physics and History of Science at Brandeis University. He has just completed a book on the history of quantum field theory from the 1920's to the establishment of quantum electrodynamics and early meson theory after World War II.

Robert Seidel is director of the Bradbury Museum of Science at Los Alamos National Laboratory. He is coauthor with John Heilbron of *Lawrence and His Laboratory,* vol. 1. The second volume is now in preparation.

Robert W. Smith is Associate Professor of History of Science at The Johns Hopkins University and also holds a position in the Department of Space Sciences, National Air and Space Museum. He is author of *The Expanding Universe: Astronomy's 'Great Debate,' 1900–1931* and *The Space Telescope: A Study of NASA, Science, Technology, and Politics.*

Sharon Traweek is Associate Professor of Anthropology at Rice University. Her book *Beamtimes and Lifetimes* is an anthropological analysis of high-energy physics, focused on the younger members of the community as they enter professional life.

BIG SCIENCE

The Growth of Large-Scale Research

The Many Faces of Big Science

Peter Galison

The huge scale of scientific research in the second half of the twentieth century is hard to ignore. Large-scale, coordinated science occupies whole regions of the United States—Silicon Valley, Route 128, the Research Triangle; it consumes a substantial fraction of all federal expenditures on research. Defense laboratories sprawl over thousands of acres and employ tens of thousands of workers. Some particle physics accelerators encircle whole towns. Seen from the outside, big science has, by its very scope, entered the realm of public debate. Questions are being asked about the implication of the huge scientific/technological projects—such as the Superconducting Supercollider (SSC), controlled fusion, and Star Wars—for the rest of science and for their effect on society.

Seen from the inside—from the scientists' perspective—big science entails a change in the very nature of a life in science. Teamwork and hierarchy increasingly characterize daily work at the big particle accelerators. Indeed, all but the very newest entrants to the field of high-energy physics, for example, have witnessed radical changes in the character of research even over the last few years. Teams of five or six researchers have been replaced by teams of tens; teams of tens in the more recent past now exceed one hundred. With the introduction of the SSC, teams will include some 500 Ph.D.'s on a single experiment. Since there are somewhat more than 2000 high-energy physicists in the United States, and at least two experimental teams planned for the SSC, it does not take much mathematics to see that a sizable fraction of high-energy physicists will be working in one experimental site. Big science is big relative not just to what scientists knew before, it is big relative to all science.

The rapid growth of big science in the half century from the 1930's through the 1980's has not occurred without resistance. The life of the experimenter has shifted as experimental practice has been increasingly coordinated with subcontractors, review committees, military demands, and the complex social order of running what amounts to a small scientific community *on a single experiment*. As the scale has increased, frequently at the cost of individual autonomy, some protested, some fled from what they considered a "factory" work style, while others struggled to find ways of working that would avoid the necessity of such massive teamwork or reliance on outside funding. At the same time, in each generation there have been physicists and engineers who have embraced the changes as affording new opportunities for research— opportunities to see deeper into space, more finely into the structure of matter.

Perhaps because of its sheer size, historians, sociologists, and scientists have all tended to think of large-scale research as being all of a single type. One of the principal goals of this volume is to go beyond the recitation of the often startling budgets of large-scale research and to explore the many kinds of activities that are subsumed under the term "big science." How does a coordinated effort change direction when new scientific results arrive? Who controls research when sponsors and scientists have different intentions? How does the organization of the research team reflect the wider culture in which it is embedded? For above all, the change in the scale of science has required scientists to align their activities with broader elements of the society. Whether big science derives its support from designing patents, working for industry, contracting to the federal government, or building weapons, the demands of the wider society cannot be ignored. Academic, military, and corporate cultures are not all the same; particle physics in the United States, Europe, or Japan is not a single, monolithic enterprise. It is to the analysis of these different facets of big science that this volume is addressed.

What unifies these various studies is their effort to understand how the expansion of science has forced scientists to confront the world outside their disciplines. But the experience of these scientists has been diverse, just as the "big" in big science connotes expansion on many axes: geographic (in the occupation of science cities or regions), economic (in the sponsorship of major research endeavors now costing on the order of billions of dollars), multidisciplinary (in the necessary coordination of teams from previously distinct fields), multinational (in the coordination of groups with very different research styles and traditions). Alas, just as the enterprises we have begun to sketch are large, so is the scope of what could have been included in this book.

Our hope is that by combining the insight of the historian, the scientist, the geographer, and the anthropologist we can draw attention to some of the leading issues and indicate methodologies appropriate to the task.

Part I: The Big Physics of Small Particles

As Robert Seidel points out in Chapter 1, big science in California did not begin with the increased defense outlays of World War II. On the contrary, large-scale research arose to cope with the problems of providing hydroelectric power to the burgeoning state in the 1920's. Industry and universities allied themselves from the earliest stages of the expansion: Stanford, Caltech, and Berkeley all were involved in the problems of power production and distribution.

E. O. Lawrence, in many ways the guiding force behind prewar big science, worked with indigenous California industries such as the Pelton Waterwheel Company, which supplied power needs of many of the state's industries, especially mining. Pelton in turn helped Lawrence build the magnet for his earliest big cyclotrons; in total, industry provided 48% of the capital for Lawrence's pre–World War II research. Although it may surprise some who think that the federal government turned to aid physical research only during World War II, before 1940 Berkeley received 22% of its capital and operating budget from the federal government, 40% from the state of California, and 38% from private philanthropy. Less evident were the hidden resources siphoned to the cyclotron: the donated labor of students, postdoctoral, and visiting scholars that fueled the enterprise during the lean depression years. Resources, however, are only part of the story. Without the cultural fascination of Americans in general for the large, the goal of building ever larger scientific facilities might have remained peripheral to other concerns. The depression-era delight in gigantism is apparent in the Golden Gate Bridge, the Hoover Dam, and the Empire State Building. It was in this spirit that the Rockefeller Fund called Lawrence's 184-inch cyclotron "a mighty symbol, a token of man's hunger for knowledge."

In the years of scarcity, experimenters looked outside university walls for support, and with that outside support came constraints on how research was conducted. For the physicists who participated in the early years of big science, these issues of control were central among their concerns. As Galison, Hevly, and Lowen show, Stanford, like Berkeley, began to pursue large-scale, sponsored research *before* World War II. From 1935 to 1941, physicists at Stanford worked with the Sperry company to acquire the resources needed to exploit the microwave technology they had begun to create. In some ways the collaboration with industry worked wonderfully—it allowed the inventor/physicists to protect ideas with patents and garner money for future research of a "purer" sort. Soon, however, the constraints imposed by industry (and some-

– outside support – constrains research

Money over scientist

times by protective university administrators) became more apparent: there were secrecy restrictions that accompanied the patent business, and these began to chafe. Worse, as Sperry and the university put pressure on the scientist/inventors to patent their work, the *character* of research began to change. Instead of exploring new phenomena, the physicists found themselves increasingly spending their time searching for ways to pursue patentable ideas for economic rather than scientific reasons.

After Pearl Harbor, the Stanford microwave team turned to war duties, but soon its members began contemplating the postwar configuration of their research. As Hansen recorded in his notes, the tension between opportunity and burden was very much on his mind:

> Some help should be obtainable from the outside, e.g. Sperry.
> What can we sell them?
> Not our soul.
> Consulting.
> Students. . . .
> Terman thinks they will pay, and so do I, but how much and for what are questions.

The radar, counter-radar, and atom projects showed that the federal government offered an alternative to private subventions, and the national coffer appeared free from the heavy hand of the patent business. It was therefore with considerable enthusiasm that the physicists began planning for federally funded accelerator and microwave research in the postwar era. But soon a price appeared on even this bonanza: restrictions on disclosure for reasons of national security and *de facto* limits placed by the technological needs of the armed forces.

Accelerator designs tumbled out one after another, each capable of boosting particles to ever-higher energies and therefore of exploring the structure of matter on an ever-finer scale. But just as some physicists at Stanford had bridled over the loss of control of research to Sperry in the 1930's and to the federal government in the 1940's, in the 1950's Felix Bloch and others began to worry that the scale and bureaucratization of even "pure" research would themselves transform physics into an "industrial" rather than academic form of investigation.

To some, American gigantism made large-scale physics research in the United States seem inevitable. If there had been no Lawrence one could easily imagine others following the astronomers, bridge makers, dam builders, and skyscraper architects in searching for a big physics. And, some would say, if research had not reached for the very large before the war, then surely the experience of the big war projects would have tilted the balance. Could things have evolved differently? John Krige and Dominique Pestre, in effect, argue that de Tocqueville was right—there is an American Particularism. These two historians of the European Center for Nuclear Research (CERN) oppose the traditional view that, following World War II, there were powerful forces at work in Europe that could not help but create a laboratory like CERN— centered in particle physics, multinational in character. The traditional view contends that politicians had to have a Europe-wide effort to heal the wounds of a catastrophic war, and that the physicists naturally needed bigger equipment to conduct the most fundamental research and to compete with the United States. Since the scientists, country by country, could not afford such huge accelerators, they allied themselves with the politicians and founded CERN.

On three principal grounds Krige and Pestre contest this picture of the inevitable rise of a multinational accelerator. First, they argue that it was crucial that CERN was the *first* such attempt at building a multinational scientific program. Had a European space program come before the nuclear physics laboratory, CERN could have been shunted aside or built smaller and considerably later. Second, at the end of the war, there were relatively few powerful state organizations for the pursuit of science, leaving individuals with a great deal of autonomy in organizing postwar research. Third, unlike accelerators in the United States, CERN did not grow out of a long and continuous national tradition of scientific or scientific–military concerns. Instead, the laboratory was constructed by an *ad hoc* alliance of several nations and could easily have been derailed by the actions of any of several key individuals at many points along the way.

Once the laboratory was built, the differences between the European and American big physics laboratories became apparent to everyone. To the Europeans' frustration, the laboratory in its early years seemed forever to be losing prestigious discoveries to the Americans, particularly to the Brookhaven National Laboratory. At the time, many Americans ascribed their successes to their freedom from the conservative traditions of the past, to their willingness to try new, unproven methods. But as is apparent from the cases of Berkeley (see Chapter 1), Stanford (see Chapter 2), and Du Pont (see Chapter 9), American physicists had an entirely different relation to engineers than did their European counterparts. In particular, the Americans considered the joint physics–engineering projects of accelerator building to be a worthy collaborative endeavor. Some people criticized Lawrence's laboratory for paying too much attention to engineering. European physicists, by contrast, tended to segregate engineering tasks from physics concerns, and the physicists in the early years tended to shun the "dirty" details of engineering. As a result, the engineers worked to bring apparatus to a standard of engineering design that the Americans did not, and the European physicists concentrated on physics questions that were often *less* conservative than those addressed by their overseas colleagues. Pestre and Krige conclude that the stereotypical characterization of Europeans as too conservative is inadequate. When they lost many of the early particle physics "races" to the Americans, it was as much because of their refusal to dirty their hands with "standard" engineering tasks such as beam transport and secondary beam separation as because of their conservatism.

No matter how distant the style of European big physics may seem from its American counterpart, they are near analogues when seen beside the striking cultural contrasts illustrated in Chapter 4 by Sharon Traweek. Traweek, an anthropologist, reports on her field work at KEK, the Japanese high-energy physics facility that serves as host to teams from around the world. On one level, the experimental halls seem unproblematic as a site for cross-cultural interaction. After all, the various groups were pursuing a common set of technical goals. But, as Traweek shows, the international language of physics vastly underdetermines the interpretive structures different groups deploy. How, she asks, do the different laboratories negotiate a sense of where "center stage" is in the world of physics? How is hierarchy established among nationalities? How does the style of work depend on cultural background?

The results of such an anthropological inquiry can be surprising, and serve as a useful corrective to the view that the conduct of research is dictated by hardware alone. In one striking episode, Traweek recounts how a multinational team confronted the opportunity to test their equipment before the detector system was fully operational. To the American team from Lawrence Berkeley Laboratory, a preliminary test seemed a splendid opportunity to debug their apparatus. But to the Japanese groups, such a move loomed as the very pinnacle of poor taste: it would only expose to public embarrassment the incomplete preparation of whichever groups had not yet readied their subsystem.

Even the fact of collaboration itself had different significance for the different nationalities. For the Americans, working in Japan carried the risk of being "too far from the center of the action." For the Japanese, working in America (or in Europe) carried a far greater liability—losing one's cultural identity as a Japanese, and therefore risking one's place in society. Other differences immediately struck the experimentalists themselves as they encountered one another in their work. To the Japanese, the American social organization of large-scale research teams looked highly hierarchical, even dictatorial, whereas their own decision-making process was profoundly democratic. To the Americans, Japanese decision-making was needlessly encumbered with the need to achieve consensus and save face; Americans saw their own organization as flexible and resourceful.

Pief Panofsky has, for many years, been a particle physicist and an often-consulted advisor to the American government. In his essay here, he uses his experience at the Stanford Linear Accelerator Center (SLAC) as a jumping-off point to comment on some of the trends and problems associated with the growth of large-scale particle physics research. The comparison and contrast of the Stanford accelerator with other facilities is revealing. For example, one might think that as the facilities have grown larger they take ever longer to build. Not so. Because of what Panofsky calls "the relative invariance of muscle to inertia" many big projects take about the same time—on the order of ten years. Thus while SLAC was a project of approximately a hundred million dollars, and the Superconducting Supercollider will, if built, cost on the order of $7 billion, their expected construction time is similar. But the political context of big science has not remained the same. At the time policy-makers debated the merits of SLAC, the budget for science was growing so fast that competition among sites and laboratories was not a decisive factor in its authorization. Technical objections were. Some physicists considered a large linear electron facility to be tangential to more fundamental questions that could be addressed by means of protons, a prejudice that Panofsky argues kept SLAC from becoming a "truly" national facility, as the National Accelerator Laboratory (later Fermilab) was supposed to be in the early 1970's.

Reflecting on the problems raised by SLAC, later laboratories, and the proposed SSC, Panofsky and many other physicists have recently raised a host of questions about the effect of big physics research on the research scientists themselves. Fundamental questions have arisen, such as how one can identify an individual's contribution when it is buried in the collective effort of a hundred (and in the SSC, five hundred) physicists? How can universities evaluate young physicists' careers according to a tenure clock when the time scale for a big experiment now extends for much longer and demands months at a time away from the home institution and its teaching and administrative demands? Given the growing technical challenges of accelerator and detector design, can universities adapt thesis standards to accommodate research work that focuses increasingly on instruments rather than physics "results"? Finally, now that detector design and construction come to demand such extensive computer resources and construction plants, can individual universities maintain their previous partial autonomy from the national laboratories? Is it worthwhile to equip individual universities so that they even have the possibility of building significant components of new instruments?

For Panofsky, as for many physicists, the constraints of big physics arise inevitably from nature. As he puts it, "We simply do not know how to obtain information on the most minute structure of matter (high-energy physics), or on the grandest scale of the universe . . . or statistically elusive results without large efforts and large tools." Despite these changes, Panofsky sees the underlying motivation to do science as being the same, whether it is the probing of matter in a desk-top experiment or through participation in a five-hundred-strong team of physicists awaiting results from a national or multinational laboratory. Claims like these have not gone unchallenged. Some, such as opponents of the SSC, have contended that we make choices about how to address the structure of the world, and the choices leading to particle physics and therefore big machines are not unique. Others have argued that the nature of experimentation has changed with big science, and the newer mode favors a certain type of team worker over the tinkerer of experiments past.

Part II: Sponsored Research and External Interests

In this section, we step back from the experience of individuals confronting the changed conditions of the large-scale laboratory in order to understand more completely how programs with specific "missions" function. When we come to the case of the space telescope or Gravity Probe B, the specifically mission-oriented nature of some kinds of big science becomes quite clear. In the case of a university it is, of course, much harder to identify what the mission might be, given the heterogeneity of programs, departments, and autonomous individuals within the institution. Nonetheless, there are contrasts that can be drawn between different types of universities, and how they situate themselves with respect to the powerful external forces of industry and the military. The first chapter of this section, by Silvan Schweber, focuses on the question of a university's alignment with respect to outside interests and specifically examines the effect of this alignment on the conduct of physical research in two very different institutions: the Massachusetts Institute of Technology and Cornell University.

From its inception, MIT was designed to work with industry. It began as a vocational school that stressed entrepreneurship. During the 1920's MIT's leaders created a Technology Plan specifically to strengthen ties to industry; the construction of a Division of Industrial Cooperation and Research was to pursue this goal. For the Institute, this division would, for a fee, lend MIT's "scientific and industrial experience and creative aptitude" to industry. During World War II, ties between the MIT Rad Lab and industry were rather easily expanded upon the Institute's prewar commitment to industrial–academic coordination. Simultaneously, with the infusion of hundreds of millions of dollars of government money, ties to the military also grew strong.

In direct contrast to MIT, Cornell was designed from its start to restrain movements toward militarism and mercantilism. When World War II began, the presidents of the two institutions reacted oppositely. Karl Compton of MIT was certain that technology would prove decisive. More particularly, he contended that the race to a more sophisticated electronics would determine victory on the ground. MIT, he reasoned, could and should play a central role in the war effort. By 1943, MIT had administered some $25 million of government contracts, and Compton could tell his board of trustees at the war's end that "the value to our country of this type of institution in a time of emergency [is enormous]. . . . Its war value is parallel with that of a fleet or an army." Within a short time other institutions modeled on the Rad Lab had sprung up at the Institute; in the process the centralized government-funded enterprises radically reshaped the character of research in the physical sciences.

During the 1930's, Cornell's president, Edmund B. Day, a social scientist and economist, was equally opposed to the fascist threat, but, as Schweber puts it, he "saw the world in terms of men and women, their hopes and frustrations . . . and he gave primacy to values, commitment, and morale over gadgets and technologies." Consequently, he insisted that America needed more than new weapons, it had to bolster itself against internal divisions by improving the social and economic lot of its citizens. Universities could contribute by fortifying a cultural life—reinforcing the fundamental values of the liberal tradition. In physics, this meant supporting basic research, even when it deviated from the path of clear application. In practical terms it meant that, after a brief skirmish, the department, with the strong backing of the administration, brought to it Hans Bethe, one of the best of the European theoretical nuclear physicists, and M. Stanley Livingston, a colleague of E. O. Lawrence who had helped construct the earliest Berkeley cyclotron. By the mid-1930's, Cornell had established one of the strongest nuclear physics groups in the country and embarked on a decades-long commitment to this branch of research.

Following the war, MIT and Cornell continued along their separate trajectories, though the scale of both had been transformed by the big physics of the war projects. MIT committed itself to major investments and expansion in electronics (especially with military application) and to the development of nuclear reactors and nuclear power. MIT's was a decision to carry physics to engineering. Cornell, by contrast, set about building an accelerator in the pursuit of less applied goals. The Cornell Nuclear Studies Laboratory continued Day's tradition of a liberal university, insofar as it could, in the context of big physics.

Accelerators such as those built at Berkeley, Stanford, KEK, and Cornell were, of course, not the first massive scientific instruments. The great optical telescopes, such as those that grace Mount Wilson and Mount Palomar, were not only astonishing technical accomplishments, they brought American astronomy to international prominence and set an example for scientists and philanthropists of how large instrumentation could be funded and executed. Yet while the telescopes could be built only by coordinated teams of engineers, scientists, and industrialists, they were used primarily by small groups of observers. Prewar astronomy had come to demand large-scale equipment while remaining traditional at the level of scientific practice.

Like postwar physics, postwar astronomy (and astrophysics) began to look to the federal government for funding, and at the same time began to create an infrastructure for the research itself. In part this transition accompanied the growth of radioastronomy with its new electronics, but the funding needs of even large radiotelescopes were dwarfed by those of the space science made

*Apolitics
shaped
use*

possible by rockets. Space-based astronomy demanded the kind of multi-disciplinary team efforts that the ground-based astronomers had avoided. In his chapter, Robert Smith examines the most costly and in some ways the most ambitious experimental system attempted in space: NASA and the European Space Agency's $2 billion Hubble Space Telescope. His concern is to trace how the scientific constituency for such a massive project was assembled, how the project advanced through the decentralized funding structure of NASA up through the White House, Congress, and the Office of Technology Assessment, and how the politics of this process shaped the design of and use of the instrument itself.

The advocates of the Space Telescope needed an education in politics. Mostly from the East Coast (where optical observing was nearly impossible), they learned to avoid alienating their West Coast colleagues by not impinging on ground-based observing projects. Even among their fellow space-based observers, the Space Telescope defenders had to avoid making their project a threat to the Jupiter Orbiter probe, which meant delicately handling relations between those parts of NASA backing the Space Telescope and the Jet Propulsion Laboratory (headquarters for the Jupiter Probe).

Two of Smith's examples nicely illustrate the entanglement of political and scientific issues. When the first proposals for an optical space telescope came to NASA, the instrument was to be used exclusively by the principal investigators (the scientists who would build it). After encountering resistance by the astronomical community to the monopolization of such resources, the project's leaders widened their scientific constituency by opening up the space telescope to "guest" researchers, making the device a "national facility." This move radically altered the proposed use of the instrument. Here is Smith's second example, one that illustrates how the instrument was physically altered for political reasons. In the midst of their efforts to widen the scientific appeal of the Space Telescope, its boosters encountered opposition from the planetary scientists, who feared that the deep-space scientists would slant the instrument *technically* away from the planetarians' need for a device that could observe in the red. At the level of materiel, the split divided this way: the deep-space people wanted a Secondary Electron Conduction (SEC) Vidicon, whereas the planetary observers wanted a red-sensitive Charge Couple Device (CCD). The working out of a compromise was the hardware embodiment of the politics of large-scale research.

*politics
affect
science*

Complementing Smith's chapter, Francis Everitt tells of his own decades-long struggle to put an experiment in outer space to test general relativity. If Gravity Probe B is lofted on schedule, it will have taken several hundred million dollars, 35 years from conception to flight, and the coordinated effort of physicists and engineers from a variety of domains. These include theoretical physics, cryogenic experimentation, inertial guidance engineering, management consultants, and the sustained efforts of NASA and Lockheed.

Some of the problems encountered along the way were purely technical:

how to read the precise direction along which a gyroscope is aligned, how to suspend the gyroscope on earth and ensure its survival despite the rigors of the launch, how to keep a suspended, fast-spinning gyroscope from exploding, how to manufacture a gyroscopic rotor ten times more perfectly spherical than any ever made. Other difficulties were political, and resemble the trials and tribulations of the space telescope. Still other challenges, as Everitt reports, issued from the bureaucratic structure of NASA and its allied institutions.

One such bureaucratic consideration had to do with the fine points of accounting. For example, there were several possible laboratories that could have conducted the cryogenic work—research that typically costs $120,000 per person-year. It turns out, however, that NASA's accounting procedures are such that work conducted at the Marshall Center by its own staff is considered "internal" and billed at only $14,000. Though the saving is fictitious, because it is buried in other budget lines, it became real enough to shape the distribution of major portions of the probe design. Other management decisions had a subtle effect on morale—and consequently on the results of team efforts. Everitt relates one example:

> Take power. Ask an engineer how much power he needs and you will get one answer. Tell him how much he can have and you get another . . . a 100-watt task may not be feasible with 0.1 watt, but offer 20 watts and once the screaming and the shouting have died down there will often emerge an ingenious solution to meet it. Do not be so foolish, however, as to apply the limit only in one area: you will get nothing. Everyone must feel the pinch.

By pinching everyone's budget for space, weight, and power, a kind of integrated elegance arises. People begin to solve problems in ways that help others, in ways that simplify assembly and disassembly, in ways that require just the precision needed, and in ways that avert the risk of failure of the whole system. Such systemic considerations alter the "feel" of research as the scale of the enterprise increases. The coordination among different, quasi-autonomous groups becomes central to the success of the whole.

As the Gravity Probe B team began to transform itself from benchtop tinkering to flight preparation, the makers of the probe learned—often the hard way—how different the world of NASA and Lockheed was from academia. Science conducted subject to deadlines and review panels was a shock, if often a salutary one. For industry, however, the problems of scaling up to big science was a step already taken. David Hounshell's contribution to this volume is a chapter addressing the case of Du Pont's management of big research and development, one of the first—and most important—industrial confrontations with large-scale science-based technology. And large-scale it certainly is: on sales of $33 billion, Du Pont spends over $1.4 billion on research and development.

Hounshell zeroes in on Du Pont's prewar invention and production of nylon, and shows how it served both as a successful—and disastrous—model of how to transform a scientific idea into a major commercial operation. Nylon was discovered by Wallace H. Carothers, a Harvard chemistry instructor who had been enlisted into an elite corps: Du Pont's fundamental research program established in 1927 by Charles Stine, the head of the company's central research organization. Exploiting their experience with the mass production of ammonia, the company moved swiftly to capitalize on the discovery. With the miracle fiber in hand, Elmar Bolton, the new head of the Organic Chemical Department, slowed fundamental research and launched a crash effort to produce the material in bulk: he established a steering committee to coordinate and review the work of the different groups, he froze the design of individual components of the production network when they seemed to promise "good enough" results, and he insisted on the development of intermediate-scale (semi-works) plants to test the integrated production system. To hasten the product into the market, Bolton managed the nylon project in parallel rather than in series—if one production component was not ready others simply "black-boxed" it and proceeded under the assumption that the missing element would succeed with time. Together these elements of a management of big science constituted what one might call Du Pont's "nylon strategy." It soon paid off handsomely. In the 50 years after its invention, nylon had earned Du Pont some $20 billion.

During World War II, Du Pont invoked its nylon strategy for a very different end. From early in its history, the Manhattan Project planned two very different species of atomic bombs—the uranium bomb and the plutonium bomb. Only the plutonium bomb could be mass-produced, and it could be produced in bulk only if the newly discovered element plutonium could be manufactured in tens of kilograms, not micrograms. Using the techniques of nylon manufacture (semi-works, steering committee, review meetings, parallel development) and even key personnel from the nylon project, Du Pont established the plutonium plant at Hanford, Washington, at a cost of some $350 million. The imposition of corporate managerial control on a group of nuclear physicists habituated to a great deal of autonomy did not come easily. Nor did the physicists' adaptation to the ways of industrial big science: they strenuously objected to the development of a semi-works plant (though most all later conceded its necessity). And the project almost certainly would have failed had the Du Pont engineers followed the nuclear physicists' advice and left little room for error in the reactor design. As in the case of Stanford's physicists, the nuclear physicists of the plutonium project had to reorient their vision of research to accomplish their collective mission. For some, like John Wheeler, the experience with Du Pont, Hanford, and Oak Ridge left a lasting impression of how science could be done.[1]

1 On Wheeler's modeling of his postwar research strategy on the model of his experience with the Manhattan Project, see P. Galison, "Physics Between War and Peace," in E. Mendelsohn, M. Roe Smith, and P. Weingart, eds., *Science, Technology, and the Military* (Dordrecht: Kluwer, 1988).

The plutonium was manufactured, and in bulk, as the devastation of Nagasaki demonstrated. Not surprisingly, Du Pont took its successful Hanford plant as yet further testimony to the virtues of the corporation's nylon strategy. Modeling on success can, however, be a difficult proposition. When the company mobilized its nylon strategy to produce Delrin acetal resin, a polymer it hoped to manufacture as a plastic, disaster struck. Spending over $50 million in research and development alone, Du Pont soon found that its skyrocketing research costs drove the price of Delrin out of the market. So badly did the product and others like it fail, the research reserves of Du Pont were rapidly depleted. The huge demand for nylon and the inelastic demand for plutonium turned out to be poor models for the soft market Delrin soon entered. By the mid-1970's the company threw in the towel and began to curtail its high-risk, decades-old commitment to fundamental research.

Part III: Big Science and National Security

It is manifestly impossible to examine big science without addressing the science of war. Even in earlier sections, the military's role has intruded: the transformations of physics at Berkeley, Stanford, Cornell, and MIT were all profoundly affected by the massive weapons projects of World War II; the creation of CERN had to be designed so as not to infringe on French and German national interests in atomic energy; Du Pont's corporate research strategy was reinforced by its experience with the Manhattan Project. In the third section of the book we turn to face directly the question of national security and the evolution of big science.

Popularizations of the Manhattan Project often obscure the fact that there was not one but two atomic bomb projects: one to separate the easily fissionable isotope of uranium (U-235) from its more common variant (U-238), and the other to assemble a bomb from the recently created synthetic element plutonium. As Hounshell shows in Chapter 9, the production of plutonium was a task of gargantuan proportions; conducted away from Los Alamos, the manufacturing used a sizable fraction of the Manhattan Project's $2 billion (1945). We begin this section of the book with Lillian Hoddeson's analysis of the plutonium atom bomb.

Hoddeson's essay spotlights what happens when a mission-directed laboratory hits the impassable wall of a physical law. For in the spring of 1944, with the laboratory already deeply involved in its work on atom bombs, utter failure faced the secret New Mexican facility. Emilio Segrè's group discovered that plutonium spontaneously fissioned at a rate far above what anyone imagined, producing five times the number of neutrons the laboratory had expected. This meant that before the plutonium could be rammed into a critical mass and detonate as a bomb it would begin to explode. Such a predetonation would blow the weapon apart, releasing only a tiny fraction of the planned explosive force. The laws of neutron emission and spontaneous fission now obstructed the multibillion dollar enterprise.

Suddenly a small, peripheral group in the laboratory became central. Its task had been the exploration of an alternative assembly of critical mass, one not predicated on the gun method (in which two pieces of subcritical material are explosively driven together). Instead, it sought to develop techniques to implode a spherical shell of subcritical material with a myriad of synchronized explosions outside the shell of "active" material. Hoddeson traces how the implosion group, previously considered to wield no more than a "backup" technology, moved toward the mainstream of the laboratory, and how its task eventually became the single most important problem faced by Los Alamos as a whole. Along the way she draws lessons about the strategies invoked by the physicists and chemists as they faced the nearly overwhelming task of designing a bomb based on a combination of physical and technological processes none of which was particularly well understood.

At the end of the war, the leaders of wartime science—Vannevar Bush and Frank Jewett—wanted desperately to reinstate the prewar scientific institutions they so valued. In speech after speech, they emphasized the temporary nature of wartime dislocations and advocated a shift from big, federally funded scientific projects to private, philanthropic support, administered by a network of honorary and advisory committees. It was not to be.

Allan Needell's chapter addresses the career of one of the first of the new breed of postwar scientific administrators, Lloyd Berkner. Berkner resisted the dismantling of the federal and military connections of science, and prospered in the new infrastructure of large-scale research. Berkner was, for example, executive secretary of the Joint Research and Development Board, which took over, after the war, the wartime work of the Joint Committee for New Weapons and Equipment. In this capacity, Berkner created committees to pursue the nuclear propulsion of ships and aircraft, guided missiles, chemical and biological warfare, communications, radar systems, and much else. Later in the 1940's, Berkner helped establish the Weapons Systems Evaluation Group (attached to the Joint Chiefs of Staff), one of the most important postwar links tying civilian physicists to the provision of new weapons systems to the military. He worked on project HARTWELL (dealing with transport in the face of enemy submarine attacks), TROY (unconventional warfare), CHARLES (air defense), and many other endeavors bringing civilian science to solve military problems.

Even when he served with the Associated Universities, Inc., which, among other things, oversaw Fermilab, the Brookhaven National Laboratory, and the National Radio Astronomy Observatory, he guided it toward a mixed role encouraging both military and basic science tasks. Indeed, throughout his career, but especially after 1950, Berkner came to view the World War II enlistment of science for national defense as the necessary model for scientific life in the Cold War. Others resisted. Lee DuBridge, who had headed the MIT Radiation Laboratory during the war, dissented, contending that the military-scientific establishment of Berkner's dreams would take on a life of its own. So, with particular vigor, did Merle Tuve. But as the Cold War began burning in Korea, the national security link to science grew stronger.

Daniel Kevles argues that the Korean War was as crucial in transforming the relationship between physics and the state as the conflict was in the more frequently studied link between military and industry. The physicists' ambivalence toward state-sponsored research discussed by Needell only deepened as the national security apparatus pumped ever greater funds into science. Times had changed since the early days of World War II, when there were high officers skeptical about the usefulness of scientific work. Now, as President Conant of Harvard put it: "The military are no longer the conservatives . . . at times they seem to be fanatics in their belief of what the scientists and the technologists can do." Others, like Lee DuBridge, protested that science should not feed from the crumbs dropped by the military. Yet at the same time DuBridge himself continued to serve in key positions of coordination between scientists and the military, such as his membership on the Atomic Energy Commission's powerful and elite General Advisory Committee and the Science Advisory Committee to the Office of Defense Mobilization (ODM). In general the quandary faced by the leadership of the scientific community was this: if they cut the civilian scientific community off from military planning, the arms race would proceed without their influence. If they joined the various coordinating boards, they bound (*de facto* if not *de jure*) civilian science to military goals.

When, in 1949 and 1950 tension between the United States and the Soviet Union grew so bad that politicians began talking about a third world war, there was little chance the scientific community would remain outside the general increase of military preparedness. The Berlin blockade, the Czech coup, the "fall" of China, and the Russian A-bomb all played a role in generating support in political and military circles for NSC-68, the report that recommended an enormous expansion in military expenditure. Korea then boosted the budget and locked the expansion in place. As Kevles argues, these events set the stage for the mobilization of civilian science. Some argued that the new National Science Foundation (NSF) ought to address military needs, along with pure science; others argued for the creation of a new Office of Scientific Research and Development (OSRD).

At the center of many of these debates was William Golden, a New York investment banker who was committed to making science as useful as possible to the national interest. Kevles follows him as a barometer of the changing times. A civilian, Golden took on the task of interviewing dozens of military officers, as well as academic, industrial, and governmental scientists. To all, he posed the question, "How can civilian science best be enlisted for defense work?" The response, Golden found, seemed to indicate that a new OSRD was not called for, though a science advisor to the president was. There was opposition from some academics who feared such an advisor would distract political attention from the NSF; more resistance came from military leaders who wanted any such advisor to be subordinate to the director of the ODM. Compromising, President Truman got an advisor, of higher rank than at least one general wanted, but located squarely within the ODM. In a way, Golden's experience could stand in for that of the scientific community at large: the defense mobilization of the Korean War brought them recognition at the highest level of government, but at the price of working within the constraints imposed by an enormously augmented military establishment.

Our collection of essays ends with an analysis of big science on geographical regions. Robert Kargon, Stuart Leslie, and Erica Schoenberger make an important distinction between what they call the "vertical" dimension of big science—its hierarchical character when deployed in large research teams—and its horizontal component—the spread of science cities over substantial geographical areas. Such cities have long existed in the utopian imagination: one thinks of the splendor of Tommaso Campanella's *City of the Sun*. In a certain sense science cities existed in the nineteenth century, when industry and university collaborated in such places as Trafford Park near Manchester, England. But the modern science city that constitutes the authors' major interest is, not surprisingly, Silicon Valley. For it was in that complex of academic and industrial research that the electronics industry first exploded into a major economic force in the postwar world.

Central to the academic component of Silicon Valley's development is Stanford University. But while the story of the growth of the valley from the academy outward has been told many times, Kargon, Leslie, and Schoenberger sketch how the massive scale of electronic and aerodynamic engineering efforts in industry have acted back on the structure of teaching and research in the university. In part, the coordination of industry and the academy has occurred through programs bringing industrial researchers on campus, such as the industrial affiliates program and the honors cooperative program, and more recently the Center for Integrated Systems. Even more strikingly, Lockheed presents a case study in the restructuring of research. In 1953 Lockheed was desperate to enter the burgeoning field of guided missiles. With the help of a retired general, the aerospace firm tried to create its own research center in southern California, one that would approximate the style and organization of a university. When that failed, the company began to see Stanford as affording a research base that, with the appropriate resources, could do a job no company could undertake alone.

Soon both company and university found a joint interest in pursuing an educational program that would meet both their needs and the needs of an increasingly technological weapons business. In an effort to fill the suddenly expanded demand for intercontinental ballistic missiles, Lockheed turned to missile production, and through its auspices the Stanford aerodynamic engineering program turned, on a large scale, to questions such as the effect of high temperature on superstructures, gas flow, and heat transfer. For these were what one needed to know to design nuclear warheads that could withstand the conditions of reentry.

The science region, Kargon, Leslie, and Schoenberger conclude, is not something that can be understood without a highly interactive model of university, industry, and the military. It is not enough to account for technology as an offspring of fundamental research that flows unilaterally from university to industry, and from industry to its market. Rather the shaping of knowledge, the fashioning of university departments, texts, and institutes, must be seen as responding to as well as guiding the powerful forces that demand high technology. The United States is now littered with failed copies of Silicon Valley and Route 128, efforts that testify to the complexity of their workings, to the myriad connections of large-scale research to other institutions. It is a pattern of linkages not easily understood or replicated.

By its very size, big science cannot survive in isolation from the nonscientific spheres of society. It has become an economic, political, and sociological entity in its own right. With that transformation, the practitioners of large-scale research have drawn, sometimes consciously, sometimes unconsciously, from the resources of their societies. In different ways the authors of this volume have sought to explore this context—the technological, military, and cultural context—of big science.

PART I

THE BIG PHYSICS
OF SMALL PARTICLES

CHAPTER 1

The Origins of the Lawrence Berkeley Laboratory

Robert Seidel

I f we seek the origins of big science in physics, we must look to the period between the two world wars. As Dominique Pestre and John Krige point out in Chapter 3, a fusion of pure science, technology, and engineering emerged between the 1930's and 1960's in America, most particularly in the group surrounding Ernest Lawrence at the Radiation Laboratory at the University of California in Berkeley.[1] Many of the elements of this style of American big science were established in the period before the war. National prestige, interdisciplinary efficiency, military-like hierarchies, autocratic leaders, committees, and money all played their roles in the prewar Radiation Laboratory.[2]

The Radiation Laboratory, as it was known in the 1930's, became a national and international center of nuclear science in only ten years. In that short period, the cyclotron became the principal tool of nuclear science as

---

1 Pestre and Krige, Chapter 3, this volume.

2 This list of characteristics, taken from Lew Kowarski, is explicated by Sharon Traweek in Chapter 4. In *Lawrence and His Laboratory,* John Heilbron and I have explored the early history of the Radiation Laboratory with an eye to explaining these developments and the contrasts between the new practice and that of European centers like those Kowarski was familiar with before the war.

practiced in Berkeley and many other research centers. Ernest Lawrence won a Nobel Prize, membership in the National Academy of Sciences and its Comstock Prize, honorific lectureships, and a position of leadership in American science for this accomplishment. More important, his work was emulated by others in many places throughout the world. Lawrence's cyclotron brought new prestige to American physics.

In the 1930's, nuclear medicine and nuclear chemistry emerged at the University of California Radiation Laboratory as physicians, biologists, chemists, and others made use of the cyclotron to manufacture substances and propagate beams for use in experiment and therapy. As the machine itself grew, engineers added their own expertise to this interdisciplinary mix.

As the Radiation Laboratory grew, assistant directors, crew chiefs, and other components of a formal hierarchy arose in order to operate the machine as productively as possible. This structure, although much changed during the war, was reinstated after it to guide a larger laboratory. Lawrence was always the leader, though committees and new offices might use his delegated power, for it was he who raised the funds that made the Laboratory and its machines grow (see Fig. 1.1).

Lawrence could not have succeeded had not he been singularly blessed by talent, charm, and his environment, which gave play to that charm and talent in a way that permitted him to assemble the resources and use them in the pursuit of nuclear science.

The Radiation Laboratory's technological environment offered opportunities for Lawrence to use the products of high-voltage technology, radio engineering, isotope separation, and mechanical engineering in cyclotron construction. These technological resources were supplemented by less tangible but important elements in his organizational and economic environment. This infrastructure permitted Lawrence to transcend the boundaries of big science fully as much as did the hardware that was made available to him. The confluence of these environmental factors in California favored the emergence of big science there, and it then spread when the larger environment of American science was transformed by war.

The first technology significant for the development of the Radiation Laboratory was high-voltage transmission of electrical power, central to California's development of hydroelectric generation in the early twentieth century. The need to bring hydroelectric power from remote stations in the mountains of California to centers of population in the central and coastal regions of the state eventually involved the state's universities, the California Institute of Technology, and Stanford University.[3] Although at Stanford the physics department at first held itself aloof from these developments, at the California Institute of Technology, Pasadena, physicist Robert Millikan, who

3 For the development of long-distance high-voltage transmission in California, see Hughes, *Networks of Power,* pp. 263–66, and Coleman, *PG and E,* pp. 102, 107, 144–48.

Fig. 1.1. Ernest Lawrence and M. S. Livingston with the first working cyclotron. This device first operated in December 1931. Photo courtesy Lawrence Berkeley Laboratory, University of California.

came to the Institute in 1921, tackled many problems of high-voltage electricity in a million-volt laboratory built for him by Southern California Edison Company. To bring power from the projected dam on the Colorado River to Los Angeles, the company planned to increase the capability of its high-voltage lines to 220,000 volts. Only General Electric and Westinghouse had laboratories that could match that of Southern California Edison. Millikan used it at first to carry forward his studies of electrical behavior and to "approach . . . the conditions existing in the stars . . . through the application to matter of immensely concentrated energies . . . through the operations of electric fields of the highest possible potential."[4]

Later, this technology was applied to high-voltage X-ray tubes and particle accelerators by C. C. Lauritsen and John Bennett, providing a challenge to Lawrence, who, at the University of California, sought to achieve both a million-volt X-ray tube and acceleration of protons to high speeds without the use of high energies. Accomplishing this would permit Lawrence to avoid many of the problems encountered in the early attempts to apply high voltages directly to particle acceleration.

4 Seidel, "Physics Research," pp. 135–38, 319–21 (quote). At Stanford, this technology was later turned to the development of the klystron. Galison, Hevly, and Lowen, Chapter 2, this volume.

High-tension accelerators stretched the power of insulators and the nerves of physicists to the breaking point. Surges of electrons from the cathodes of the Caltech tube ripped metal from them as thousands of amperes traversed it. Millikan and Lauritsen, who became an expert on field emission of electrons in the process, went to elaborate lengths to insulate and shield their tube, which produced radiation detectable up to 100 meters away.[5]

The high-tension accelerators also taxed the finances and furnishings of the few institutes in which they were developed. They demanded unusual electrical service, special apparatus and safety precautions, and above all, space, a commodity more precious even than money in the laboratories of the time. The construction of the Caltech testing laboratory cost Southern California Edison $105,000 plus 10,000 kilovolt-hours of electricity per month. Westinghouse helped build the transformer. It filled a room 50 feet high and covering 300 square feet.[6] So it is a small wonder that at the Cavendish Ernest Rutherford pined for "an apparatus to give us a potential of the order of 10 million volts which can safely be accommodated in a reasonably sized room and operated by a few kilowatts of power."[7]

An obvious way to relieve the tension on men, material, and money was to accelerate particles in several steps, each requiring only a moderate electrical force, so that the high-voltage energy would be accumulated on the particles, not on the apparatus. Resonant acceleration was attempted by Rolf Widerøe at Aachen, E. T. S. Walton at the Cavendish, and Merle Tuve at the Carnegie Institute of Washington. This was also the way Lawrence chose, because he thought it would require only "relatively modest laboratory equipment."[8] But the problems of keeping a beam of accelerated particles together required focusing techniques then unknown.

5 Charles C. Lauritsen, interviewed by Charles Weiner, June 26, 1966, p. 6, Center for History of Physics, American Institute of Physics, New York; Lauritsen and Bennett, "A New High Potential X-Ray Tube"; Lauritsen and Cassen, "High Potential X-Ray Tube"; Coolidge, "Some Past Developments."

6 Fleming to Hale, Mar. 17, 1922, G. E. Hale Papers, microfilm ed., 14: 72–74, California Institute of Technology Archives, Pasadena; Sorenson, "Development and Characteristics of a 1,000,000-Volt Cascade Transformer," and "California Institute of Technology's Million-Volt Laboratory." Not to be outdone, General Electric built Harris J. Ryan at Stanford a larger testing laboratory in 1926. Sorenson, "Dedication of the New Ryan Laboratory"; Lusignan, "Ryan Laboratory Opens Untouched Field of Electrical Investigation," "Stanford University's Experimental Generators Tested," and "2,000,000 Volt Research Facilitated at Stanford University." Early laboratories at Pittsfield (General Electric), Ivry, France, and Freiburg, Germany, are described by Fleming, "High Voltage Laboratories"; Peek, "Lightning—Part I," described the GE 5-million-volt laboratory.

7 Rutherford's speech at the opening of a new high-tension laboratory at Metropolitan Vickers Electrical Company, quoted by Eve, *Rutherford*, p. 338.

8 Lawrence, "Evolution of the Cyclotron"; Wideroe, "Über ein neues Prinzip zur Herstellung hoher Spannungen"; Walton, "The Production of High Speed Ions by Indirect Means"; Breit, Tuve, and Dahl, "Atomic Physics."

   The challenge was that of a negative salient, to use the happy term of Tom Hughes.[9] Enough voltage was available for stepwise acceleration of particles thanks to developments in electrical engineering, and the means of generating those particles was at hand. The problem was to overcome their tendency to scatter into the walls of the accelerating tube before they could be accelerated. Another element from Lawrence's technological environment, radio engineering as practiced in California, permitted Lawrence to solve the problem. He used a radio-frequency electric field to accelerate protons and a magnet to bend their paths into big circles, permitting their step-wise acceleration to high energies. An 84-ton relic of radio engineering, the massive magnet used in the larger Poulsen arc generators developed by the Federal Telegraph Company of Palo Alto, California[10] (see Fig. 1.2) to generate intercontinental radio waves, was reconfigured for Lawrence by a mechanical engineering firm, the Pelton Waterwheel Company of San Francisco, which had come into existence to supply the power needs of the California mining industry. The Pelton water-wheel had increased the speed and efficiency of the conversion of the power of falling water into electricity.[11] The reconfigured magnet, when "shimmed" by Lawrence's student M. S. Livingston, efficiently focused protons into a beam that could be accelerated to high energy.

   The first radio-frequency oscillators were built by Livingston and Lawrence's other graduate student David Sloan, who had learned his trade at the Westinghouse Research Laboratory. Later radio tube-maker Charles Litton of Palo Alto assisted the Radiation Laboratory in the construction of oscillators for the large cyclotrons. Trained at the Federal Telegraph Company, and introduced to Lawrence by Leonard Fuller, who left the company to teach at Berkeley, Litton made important contributions to the art of tube design not only at the Radiation Laboratory but also in the embryonic electronics industry of the West.[12]

   The electrical and electronic industries in Lawrence's California environment contributed unique equipment and expertise to his development of the cyclotron. These technological resources were supplemented by less tangible but equally important elements in Lawrence's organizational environment.

   The development of astronomical observatories and of research laboratories in chemistry and physics at the University of California and the California Institute of Technology offered both scope and suggestion for organizational

   9 Hughes, *Networks of Power*, p. 79.
   10 For the development of the Poulsen arc generator, see Aitken, *Continuous Wave*, pp. 110–17.
   11 Smith, "Origins of the Water Turbine"; Constant, "Scientific Theory and Technological Testability."
   12 Norberg, "The Origins of the Electronics Industry"; William Brobeck, interviewed by Robert W. Seidel, Mar. 27 and Apr. 15, 1985, Bancroft Library, University of California, Berkeley.

Fig. 1.2. Federal Telegraph magnet. A magnet like the one shown here was given to Lawrence to build his first large (27-inch) cyclotron. Photo courtesy Lawrence Berkeley Laboratory, University of California.

innovation.[13] The construction of the Lick and Mount Wilson observatories and the creation of first-class research departments in physics and chemistry had accustomed Caltech and the University of California to the expenditures necessary to sustain independent research organizations. In response to Lawrence's enthusiasm and energy, the president and patrons of the University of California channeled state and private funds to Lawrence's enterprise to augment those offered by philanthropic organizations in greater measure than ever before.

The small and large philanthropic foundations, whose support Lawrence also successfully cultivated, also provided increasing resources as their programs evolved in response to opportunities provided by his enterprise. From the Research Corporation's decision to concentrate contributions earmarked for the University of California to the 27-inch cyclotron to the Rockefeller

13 Seidel, "Origins of Academic Physics Research in California."

Foundation's commitment to $1.15 million to support the construction of the 184-inch cyclotron, foundation support rose from $10,000 to $75,000 per year in the 1930's.[14] The support of the Research Corporation, which drew its revenues from the patent of an invention from the University of California chemistry department, was especially crucial.

The values of these eleemosynary institutions were measured by increases in the size of the machines and in the production of X rays, neutron rays, and radioisotopes. Lawrence had to overcome scruples against securing a financial interest in his discoveries for the Research Corporation, and he had to develop a rationale for high-voltage X-ray and neutron therapy that would appeal to private and, ultimately, to federal patrons. Confessing privately that there was "not much point in X rays above a half a million volts for therapy purposes," Lawrence continued to publicize the million-volt X-ray tube his laboratory developed as "a high voltage X-ray machine which alone is as effective as all the radium in the world for the treatment of cancer."[15] Neutron therapy was promoted in similar fashion, with results that were at best disappointing and at worst disastrous for patients. In this way, Lawrence responded to the opportunities provided by the Research Corporation's desire to raise funds for research through patents on academic science inventions and the growing philanthropic support for cancer research and therapy in the 1930's. This adaptation of scientific to cultural and political values was to become characteristic of big science.[16]

Lawrence enjoyed budgets that were an order of magnitude larger than those of his colleagues. Patent-pools like the Research Corporation and the Chemical Foundation, which were interested in scientific products to sustain their coffers, and foundations interested in the application of physics to solve medical problems (and to fund academic science research) provided what was needed to supplement state and private support.

The federal government also contributed importantly through the National Advisory Cancer Council, the state expression of the growing philan-

14 Heilbron and Seidel, *Lawrence and His Laboratory*, table 5.2.

15 Lawrence to Wood, Sept. 3, 1932, "A Brief Statement Concerning the Radiation Laboratory of the University of California," Sept. 12, 1933, Ernest O. Lawrence Papers, Bancroft Library, University of California, Berkeley.

16 "New Neutron Ray More Powerful Than Either the X-Ray or Radium," *New York Times*, Jan. 17, 1934, pp. 1, 11; "The Irresistible Neutron," *New York Times*, Jan. 18, 1934, p. 20; "Neutron Projectiles," *New York Times*, Jan. 21, 1934, section IX, p. 5; "The Neutron Ray," University of California radio broadcast no. 996; *University Explorer* no. 38, Feb. 5, 1934, University of California Archives; Field, "Historical Survey of Radiobiology and Radiotherapy"; Stone, "Neutron Therapy." Compare the comment by Everitt, Chapter 8, this volume, that "in big physics, individual ideas must be related to the grand idea and those who raise funds must be alert to human affairs. But there is a further subtlety. Those two very different realms of discourse intermingle. Demands for money must simultaneously address technical truth and political truth."

thropic interest in medical problems that might succumb to technological solutions. A surprising 22% of capital and operating expenses for the development of the cyclotron before 1940 came from the federal government, while the state of California contributed 40% and foundations contributed 38% of the operating expenses. The federal government thus came to play a role in big science well before World War II.

Individuals and corporations contributed 48% of the capital expenses, although this reckoning does not include contributions such as the building that housed the original Laboratory, a gift of the University to match the gift of Lawrence's 84-ton magnet.[17] To the total of $550,000 that came from these sources prior to 1940 can be added the $2 million pledged in that year for the 184-inch cyclotron, of which 58% came from the Rockefeller Foundation and 42% from the state. This total of $2.55 million equals the entire sum going to support all of academic physics, exclusive of new plant, in 1900, and about 2% of the entire sum spent in nonindustrial physics (government, higher education, and private research) in 1940.[18]

The sources of the Radiation Laboratory's finances provide an image of the financial physiognomy of an early form of big science. They tell the complexity of the political economy of the prewar physical sciences. The patenting of discoveries from research funded for the general welfare, the hawking of therapeutic applications of newly discovered neutron rays, mass production of radioisotopes for research and therapy, and the creation of advisory councils to channel federal dollars into scientific laboratories all played a part in securing unprecedented support for the Radiation Laboratory (see Fig. 1.3).

These sums are the more remarkable because they were raised not in the heady environment of the postwar economic boom but in the depths of the Great Depression. Despite the misfortunes of scientists who sought support at the highest levels of government and industry, there was money in the 1930's for the kinds of costly scientific enterprises now associated with big science.

Big science requires concentrated labor as well as capital. The Radiation Laboratory relied upon an increasing number of paid and unpaid staff members to build, repair, and use its cyclotrons. Some of the unpaid were victims of the Great Depression, unable to find jobs but willing to support themselves in order to participate in the development of the cyclotron and carve out an acceptable career in physics. The other main source of labor for which Lawrence did not have to raise money consisted of doctoral students and postdocs on extramural fellowships. On average, at least three unpaid graduate students, two unpaid postdocs, one professor on sabbatical leave, and three holders of extramural fellowships worked in the Laboratory at any one time. The resulting free-labor contribution, some $150,000 in the 1930's, was significant in the development of the Laboratory. Appointments in the phys-

17 Heilbron and Seidel, *Lawrence and His Laboratory,* chapter 5.
18 Weart, "Physics Business," p. 306.

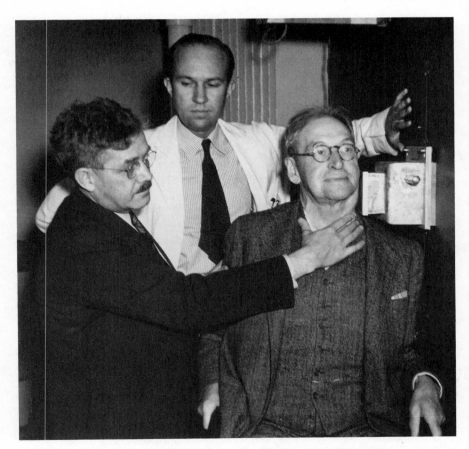

Fig. 1.3. Neutron therapy. Robert Stone and John Lawrence treat Robert Penney with neutrons from the 60-inch cyclotron. Photo courtesy Lawrence Berkeley Laboratory, University of California.

ics department, state-funded positions after 1936, medical funding, and the Works Project Administration provided stipends for which Lawrence did some or all of the fund-raising.[19] Of the Radiation Laboratory's staff, 20% were supported by the state, 25% by intramural research funds, 37% by external funds, and 25% by their own resources.

The Radiation Laboratory's staff of approximately 60 members in the period 1938–40 was modest compared to that of postwar big science laboratories but large for academic research laboratories of the time. It required means of regulating and socializing the work force to inhibit small-science

19 Heilbron and Seidel, *Lawrence and His Laboratory,* chapter 5.

TABLE 1.1
Cyclotroneers in Partibus, 1932–40

Name	Date left	Destination(s)	Class[a]
Abelson, P. H.	1939	Carnegie Inst.	A
Green, G. K.	1938	Carnegie Inst.	B
Henderson, M. C.	1935	Princeton	B
Hurst, D. G.	1937	Cambridge	B
Kinsey, B. B.	1936	Liverpool	B
Kurie, F. N. D.	1938	Indiana	B
Langsdorf, A.	1939	Washington U.	B
Laslett, L. J.	1937	Copenhagen; Indiana	A
Livingood, J. J.	1938	Harvard	B
Livingston, M. S.	1934	Cornell	A
Lyman, E. M.	1938	Illinois	A
Paxton, H. C.	1937	Paris; Columbia	A
Richardson, J. G.	1937	Michigan; Illinois	A
Simmons, S. J.	1939	Pittsburgh	A
Snell, A. M.	1938	Chicago	B
Thornton, R. L.	1936	Michigan; Washington U.	B
Van Voorhis, S. N.	1938	Rochester	B
Walker, H.	1937	Liverpool	B
White, M. G.	1935	Princeton	A

[a]A, Berkeley Ph.D.
B, Postdocs from other institutions

research, to make production of radioisotopes routine, and to facilitate the construction and maintenance of the cyclotrons. Shift work on crews and assignments to search for new radioisotopes in the Radiation Laboratory marked a new departure in academic physics research.[20]

This elaborate group structure, a consequence of the forces at play within the interdisciplinary laboratory and of the need to meet external commitments, was a foretaste of the roles the Laboratory and its dispersed staff would take on during the war, when Lawrence helped organize the Massachusetts Institute of Technology's Radiation Laboratory, the University of California's underwater sound laboratory at San Diego, and Los Alamos, and after, when the National Laboratories set up similar facilities around accelerators and reactors.

Discontent with the increasingly structured regime was common. It was, however, minimized by close social ties, by seminars and colloquia on wider subjects, and by the satisfaction of cooperative work toward an important objective unrealizable by a single individual. Morale stayed high. As a member of the Laboratory passed through his apprenticeship, Lawrence assigned duties and stipends, approved research projects and the publication of research results, and, most important, found jobs for journeymen cyclotroneers. Liv-

20 Kurie, "The Cyclotron: A New Research Tool for Physics and Biology"; Cooksey to Lawrence, Nov. 30, 1936, Lawrence to Cockcroft, Aug. 11, 1936, Lawrence to Woolridge, Aug. 12, 1936, Lawrence Papers; Abelson, "A Sport Played by Graduate Students."

ingston found work first at the University of California hospital, where he helped install a million-volt X-ray tube; Luis Alvarez and Edwin M. McMillan found posts as assistant professors in the physics department; David Sloan eventually joined the College of Engineering. Lawrence's brother, John, was hired by the Medical School, and Donald Cooksey, a former associate from Yale, became assistant director of the Radiation Laboratory when it was formally organized in 1936.

Manpower was also exported to other laboratories to build or perfect their cyclotrons. Twenty-nine of the 54 regular members of the Laboratory in the 1930's found jobs elsewhere by 1940. Of these, nineteen built cyclotrons at other laboratories, as shown in Table 1.1. They took with them those features of Radiation Laboratory practice that could be exported, as well as the cyclotron, planting the seeds for the growth of big science elsewhere.

The New Species

The environment that favored the evolution of big science in the 1930's tells us a good deal about the origins of this species of scientific work. A few further remarks about it may better characterize the relations between science and technology, the interdisciplinarity, the bigness, and the cultural significance of the new organism.

The Blurred Distinction Between Science and Technology

As the Radiation Laboratory grew, the distinction between science and technology became harder to draw. If operationally defined, that is, as what scientists do, the big science of the Radiation Laboratory progressively became cyclotron technology. After William Brobeck and W. W. Salisbury joined the staff in 1938, professional expertise in mechanical engineering and vacuum-tube oscillators was available for the construction of the 60- and 184-inch cyclotrons, supplementing the assistance formerly rendered by Charles Litton. The transition was not an easy one. According to Salisbury, Lawrence at first refused to allow him to join the Laboratory, relenting only when Salisbury proposed to increase the voltages on the 60-inch cyclotron by using coaxial inductances.[21] Brobeck went unpaid throughout the period, and avoided challenging the physicists on scientific, as opposed to engineering, questions in his support role: improving the cooling system, scheduling maintenance, and providing mechanical engineering expertise for the 60- and 184-inch cyclotrons.[22]

The absorption of radio engineering techniques, vacuum engineering development, and other arcana cost time and effort but paid off when the

21 W. W. Salisbury, interviewed by James Culp, October 1981, Salisbury to Livingston, Feb. 24, 1940, Lawrence Papers; Brobeck interview.

22 Salisbury interview, October 1981, Salisbury to Livingston, Feb. 24, 1940, Lawrence Papers: Brobeck interview; Alvarez, *Adventures of a Physicist*, pp. 44–45.

TABLE 1.2
U.S. Cyclotrons by Size, 1940

Size[a]	Magnet (inch/ton/ton)			Commission dates			Builders
	Poles	Fe	Cu	Plan	Magnet	Beam	
Baby (1–2 MeV)							
Cornell	16	3.5	0.5	Fall 1934		July 1935	Livingston[c]
Illinois-1	16	3.5	0.5	Feb 1935	Sept 1935	July 1936	Kruger,[b] Green
Washington	13			Winter 1935–36		May 1938	Loughbridge
Small (3–7 MeV)							
Rochester	20	15	2	Winter 1935–36	Apr 1936	Aug 1936	DuBridge,[b] Barnes
Rochester	27	17	2			Feb 1938	DuBridge,[b] Barnes, Van Voorhis[b]
Yale	27			June 1937	Aug 1937	May 1939	Pollard
Medium (8–12 MeV)							
Bartol	38	62	10	Winter 1935	Aug 1936	Jan 1938	Allen
Berkeley	37						Cooksey et al.
Chicago	41	60	10.5	Spring 1936	Mar 1937	Nov 1938	Newson;[b] Snell[b]
Columbia	35	65	7	Feb 1935	Spring 1936	Aug 1938	Dunning, Anderson, Paxton[c]
Harvard	42	70	16	Spring 1934	Nov 1937	Oct 1939	Hickman, Evans, Livingood[b]
Illinois-2	42			Winter 1938–39			Kruger,[b] Lyman,[c] Richardson[c]
Indiana	45	70	10	Fall 1938	May 1939	Spring 1941	Kurie,[b] Laslett[c]
MIT	42	70	16	Spring 1938	Feb 1939	Spring 1940	Livingston[c]
Michigan	42	80	15	Aug 1935	Mar 1936	Aug 1936	Cork,[b] Thornton[b]
Ohio State	42			Dec 1937	June 1938		Smith, Pool
Pittsburgh	47			Fall 1939			Allen, Simmons[c]
Princeton	35	40	8	Fall 1935	Mar 1936	Oct 1936	White,[c] Henderson[b]
Purdue	37	50		Fall 1935	Nov 1936	Jan 1936	W. J. Henderson
St. Louis	42			Fall 1939			Thornton,[b] Langsdorf[b]
Large (16 MeV)							
Berkeley	60	196	22	Spring 1936		June 1939	Brobeck, Cooksey, et al.
Stanford	28	~11		Winter 1939–40	Fall 1941		Bloch, Staub
Carnegie	60	~11	~11	Spring 1939	Sept 1939	1944	Tuve, Roberts, Green,[b] Abelson[b]

[a]Livingston, "Cost Estimates," ca. Nov. 1, 1940 (Lawrence Papers 12/12), established the size categories.
[b]Postdoctoral experience at the Berkeley Radiation Laboratory.
[c]Berkeley Ph.D.

transfer of cyclotron technology became an enterprise of physicists. We can measure the results in terms of beam current and energy or in the transfer of the technology to other laboratories at home and abroad (Tables 1.2 and 1.3). The development of cyclotron technology in these laboratories produced information that improved the design of larger machines at Berkeley. Much of this feedback was the work of physicists who traveled between Berkeley and the new centers, supplying technical information in person, much in the manner of the artisans of the early industrial revolution. Livingston, who left Berkeley to build the Cornell cyclotron, improved the old cathode ion source by adapting the Tuve capillary fountain source used in his Van de Graaff machines to yield 500 microamps of positive ions. Lawrence adopted the innovation in the 60-inch cyclotron. The transmission-line dee system was adapted from the cyclotron built at the University of Illinois by Green and Kruger, both of whom brought their expertise to the Radiation Laboratory.[23]

The system of transformers, rectifiers, transmission lines, oscillators, electrodes, ion sources, vacuum chambers, pumps, probes, and oscillators demanded much from Lawrence's apprentices. In the early years, their activity suggests the shop culture of nineteenth-century American technology: by empirically shimming the first cyclotrons with iron plates, for example, Livingston discovered the focusing effect of the magnetic field. Cut and try was the only way to improve cyclotron performance until Brobeck's engineering, and Robert Wilson's analysis of cyclotron focusing, provided systematic guidelines. Even then, the knowledge proved difficult to transfer.[24] It was only after World War II that commercial cyclotrons became available.[25]

It was in part because of the empirical nature of the technology that it had to be transferred by its practitioners to other laboratories: even with the help of advanced engineering firms like Metropolitan-Vickers, it was hard to put a cyclotron together without the direct help of a man trained in Berkeley. It is scarcely an exaggeration to say that a week's sweating over a Berkeley cyclotron was worth six months' immersion in its blueprints. To European visitors, American accelerator laboratories seemed to squander time on mere technical improvements, to lust after machinery, in an unscientific if not uncivilized fashion. This fascination with hardware, like the subordination of individual to group science, was to spread from accelerator laboratories to other parts of physics and from the United States to the rest of the world, and to make science

23 Livingston to Lawrence, Dec. 2, 1936, Cooksey to Barnes, Jan. 28, 1937, Cooksey to Lawrence, Sept. 29, 1938; Lawrence to Livingston, Dec. 15, 1936, and Feb. 21, 1939, Lawrence Papers; Livingston, Holloway, and Baker, "A Capillary Ion Source for the Cyclotron"; Kruger and Green, "A Million Volt Cyclotron"; Heilbron and Seidel, *Lawrence and His Laboratory,* table 5.5.

24 Wilson, "Magnetic and Electrostatic Focusing in the Cyclotron"; DuBridge to Lawrence, Jan. 25 and Mar. 9, 1938, Lawrence Papers.

25 Brobeck went into the business of manufacturing cyclotrons when he founded the Cyclotron Corporation. The market was not what he anticipated, however, and the corporation was dissolved in the early 1980's. Brobeck interview.

TABLE 1.3

Foreign Cyclotrons by Size, 1940

Size[a]	(Magnet inch/ton/ton)			Commission dates			Builders
	Poles	Fe	Cu	Plan	Magnet	Beam	
Small (3–7 MeV)							
Leningrad-1	24					Sept 1937	Rukavichnikov
Tokyo-1	26	23		Sept 1935	Spring 1936	Apr 1937	Yasaki,[b] Sagane,[b] Watanabe
Medium (8–12 MeV)							
Cambridge	36	46	8	Spring 1936	1936	Aug 1938	Cockcroft, Hurst[b]
Copenhagen	36	35	3	Winter 1935–36		Nov 1938	Frisch, Jacobsen, Laslett[c]
Heidelberg	40	80	80	1937	Spring 1938	Dec 1943	Gentner[b]
Leningrad-2	40			1937?		1939?	
Liverpool	36	46	8	Spring 1936	1936	Mid-1939	Chadwick, Kinsey,[b] Walke[b]
Osaka	40					1939	Kikuchi
Paris	32	30?		1936	Nov 1936	Mar 1939	Joliot, Nahmias, Paxton[c]
Stockholm	35			1937	Sept 1938	Aug 1939	von Friesen[b]
Large (16 MeV)							
Tokyo-2	60	196	22	1936		>1941	Yasaki,[b] Sagane[b]

[a]Livingston, "Cost Estimates," ca. Nov. 1, 1940 (Lawrence papers, 12/12), established the size categories.
[b]Postdoctoral experience at the Berkeley Radiation Laboratory.
[c]Berkeley Ph.D.

and technology one. As Krige and Pestre indicate, however, it required several decades for European physicists to adopt this style.[26]

Interdisciplinary Research

If the lines between science and technology blurred, so did those between the disciplines, as chemists, biologists, and physicians joined to exploit new radioactive substances, high-voltage X rays, and neutron beams against disease. The result was a new interdisciplinary enterprise: nuclear science, which combined radiochemistry, radiobiology, nuclear physics, and nuclear medicine.

Radiochemistry grew in direct proportion to increases in deuteron energies, which made new radioactive substances available for study. Radiobiology was a response to concerns about the physiological effects of the neutrons the deuterons produced from beryllium in copious quantities and about the opportunities of a new radiopharmaceutical line. Nuclear medicine, which used neutrons for therapy and radiopharmaceuticals to treat diseases like leukemia, flourished under the patronage of medical interests and John Lawrence's fraternal leadership. These directions of research and the pace at which they were pursued reflected pressures of the financial and organizational environments discussed above: the University's patrons, as well as the foundations, expected Lawrence to redeem his pledges of synthetic radium and radiotherapy for cancer and other diseases.

Because of these demands, reliability of production was required of the cyclotrons, and the crew system of organization supported this reliability. Here the manpower environment of the Laboratory was crucial, since it permitted a satisfactory response to the growing need, which Ernest Lawrence stimulated through tours and publicity.[27] The stress upon the Laboratory eventually led to an adaptive change in practice, as Martin Kamen and Robert Wilson designed an internal target that could be inserted into the cyclotron to permit efficient use of a beam that could not be withdrawn. This cooperation, of a chemist and a physicist creating a mechanical technology to satisfy biologists and doctors using the cyclotron, is a fine example of the degree of interdisciplinarity achieved in the Radiation Laboratory before the war. This interdisciplinarity proved difficult to achieve at some other laboratories, such as CERN,[28] but was to spread to the national laboratories of the Atomic Energy Commission after the war.[29] The problems of interdisciplinary effi-

26 Pestre and Krige, Chapter 3, this volume.
27 "New Neutron Ray More Powerful Than Either the X-Ray or Radium," *New York Times*, Jan. 17, 1934, pp. 1, 11; "New Department at the University of California Has Possibilities in Medicine and/or Building New Elements from Lighter," *New York Times*, Jan. 17, 1934, p. 1; Lawrence, "Report to the National Advisory Cancer Council," Oct. 12, 1939, Lawrence Papers.
28 Pestre and Krige, Chapter 3, this volume.
29 Seidel, "A Home for Big Science."

ciency in big-science laboratories were faced in the Radiation Laboratory long
before they were addressed elsewhere in high-energy physics.

The Bigness of Prewar Big Science

It was not only economies of scale that Lawrence sought in his cyclotrons,
which were claimed to produce greater beams and more radioisotopes more
efficiently. By his own admission, the 60-inch cyclotron was oversized, a
monument to megavolts and money. The 184-inch cyclotron transcended
theoretical limits for fixed-frequency accelerators imposed by relativity and
the boundaries of philanthropic programs. In planning his giant machines,
Lawrence was driven not so much by theoretical considerations of the energy
requirements of certain nuclear reactions as by the resources he perceived to be
available. The poles of the Federal Telegraph magnet, which served as the
cradle of the 27-inch cyclotron, were expanded to 37 inches as soon as funding
permitted. Lawrence had planned to expand it even before Livingston got his
first beam from the machine. The 60-inch cyclotron was made wastefully large
because he had the money to do so. The Rockefeller interest in a large
cyclotron produced plans for machines ranging from 150 to 205 inches in
diameter, and the 184-inch cyclotron was restricted to that size by available
funds and commercial steel plate, not by any consideration of the relativistic
limits on particle acceleration.

In large measure, Lawrence succeeded as builders of laboratories and
observatories had before him. The Crocker Laboratory, which housed the 60-
inch cyclotron, like the Lick Observatory, which housed the University's
largest telescope, immortalized its patron, who was flattered by having the
"world's largest" scientific instrument of this kind named after him. The 184-
inch cyclotron, like the Palomar Observatory, was to the Rockefeller Foundation "a mighty symbol, a token of man's hunger for knowledge, an emblem of
the undiscourageable search for truth which is the noblest expression of the
human spirit."[30]

Adoption of such scale in scientific instrumentation brought Lawrence into
closer touch with the culture of the larger industrial technology of his time,
first as a supplicant, later as a taskmaster. In this he was aided by Alfred
Loomis, a master of finance and a jack-of-all-physics, by Leonard Fuller, radio
engineer and Federal Telegraph executive turned professor, and by the president and regents of the university. His growing comfort with the captains of
industry reflected many shared values: the esteem of growth as an end, a
respect for the power of finance, a faith in the applications of science, and an
appreciation of the art of marshaling capital, labor, and knowledge to build
new enterprises.

Lawrence's enterprises "helped to establish high-energy physics as the

30 Fosdick, *The Rockefeller Foundation*, pp. 36–41.

most fundamental area of science," according to Stephen Brush, "but this status was earned in a particular historical situation, and is not inherent in the rise of science."[31] An examination of this particular historical situation reveals why high-energy physics became a big science in other ways.

First, as is often maintained, small science is more effective in doing some kinds of research at the frontiers. Routine production and identification of isotopes, the focus on transmutation, and the need to balance the researchers' needs for publication with minimal cyclotron beam time per experiment all mitigated against painstaking and thorough efforts of the type that led to the discovery of the positron, the neutron, artificial radioactivity, and the meson. These discoveries, inherently significant in science's quest for the fundamental entities of nature, were not made with accelerators. Nuclear physics continued to be pursued with particles from electrostatic accelerators and even from natural sources long after Lewis and Lawrence smashed atoms with deuterons, and it was only toward the end of the period that the weight of nuclear medicine, radiochemistry, and medical money tipped the scale in favor of the cyclotron and changed the overall direction of nuclear experiments. What, then, accounts for accelerators' predominance in modern high-energy physics?

By 1940, the power and stability of the 37-inch and 60-inch cyclotrons were adequate to demonstrate the superiority of the new direction for high-energy physics. Kamen and Ruben were able to harness both to their successful search for carbon-14, and McMillan and Seaborg brought fission studies full circle by creating transuranic elements, including a fissionable one. Plutonium, which demonstrated its terrible power at Trinity in 1945, depended upon the cyclotron for its discovery, just as the separation of the other nuclear fuel, uranium-235, depended upon the wartime cousin of the cyclotron, the calutron, an electromagnetic isotope separator. Although cosmic-ray studies continued to be important in high-energy physics for a few years after the war, the growing usefulness of accelerators, with their increasing energy, gradually eclipsed them.

Second, the organization of scientific work in the Radiation Laboratory was another significant contribution to the modern culture of big science. Despite the perturbations and expansions of World War II, Berkeley's pattern reasserted and replicated itself in later high-energy physics laboratories. Often singled out as the archetypal form of big-science work units, the interdisciplinary team proved a persistent species in accelerator laboratories. Cyclotroneers were influential in organizing and leading the MIT radar laboratories as well, and would carry the notion to other endeavors. The crew system, concocted in a meeting remote from the Laboratory by the self-designated platoon leaders of particle physics, was a matter of chance as well as of technological necessity. Although cyclotron laboratories elsewhere clung to a more relaxed and disci-

---

31 Brush, "The Scientific Value of High Energy Physics."

plinary organization of research, reflecting their own cultural influences, in this period, the pace was accelerated at Berkeley in time with the demand for radioisotopes and neutron beams to satisfy the expectations of the Laboratory's patrons. Once they had been fulfilled at Berkeley, the pilgrims of the production cyclotron who sought to turn it to their individual ends might snatch a moment or two for individual research, but soon this too required team efforts.

Third, an explicit *quid pro quo*, which would serve as a model for big science, was worked out at the Radiation Laboratory. As with technological advances, patents provide a useful barometer of the pressure of patronage based on commercialization. The Research Corporation's purpose for these patents and the disputes arising between those purposes and the traditional norms of academic science are of great interest in showing how weak were the latter in the face of the drive for commercial products of a science business. When the federal government replaced the private patron, patents were made available to the economy at large, until it was found this would not suffice. The *de facto* socialization of nuclear physics during and after World War II blocked the path to more widespread commercialization of accelerators and their products, but it would not be impossible, in the light of the success the Research Corporation's patents of accelerators have had, to envisage a radiopharmaceutical industry arising on the basis of patents taken out in the 1930's. In any event, the tendency of big science to profit from its applications was well established in the scientific culture of the 1930's.

The mobilization of science in World War II has often been taken as the origin of modern big science. This rests on the notion of "big science" as a well-defined entity. An alternative view might be that big science, as we know it today, evolved more gradually over the course of the nineteenth and twentieth centuries in organizations like those of the German chemical industry, Rutherford's Cavendish laboratories, and the Radiation Laboratory, providing a range of models for research organization in wartime and postwar science of which high-energy physics was one of the earliest.

The war required an expansion of the engineering and technical support that the Radiation Laboratory had relied upon in the construction of the 60- and 184-inch cyclotrons. The organization of the machine-building effort was described by Brobeck in 1937:

> The work of building each group of apparatus is given to a *committee* for which a *leader* is appointed. . . . He may divide the work as he wishes. . . . *Supervisors* are to be appointed for definite lines of the work and their approval must be obtained by the committee leaders for all work included in these lines. Committee leaders, supervisors and others needed are to meet periodically with the directors of the Laboratory . . . [as] the directing committee.[32]

32 "Suggested Organization for the Construction of the 60-inch Cyclotron," Nov. 10, 1937, Lawrence Papers.

Such committees dealt with the design and construction of the magnet, vacuum chamber, vacuum pumps, and oscillator for the 60-inch cyclotron, and supervisors oversaw mechanical design, vacuum systems, wiring, and radiation lines.[33]

The directing committee was initially composed of Ernest Lawrence, Donald Cooksey, who took charge of chamber and ion source design, Edwin M. McMillan, who oversaw low-voltage power and wiring, Luis Alvarez, who directed radiation protection and electronics, Art Snell, who supervised controls and instruments, and Brobeck, who was responsible for the magnet and mechanical engineering of the 60-inch cyclotron, and came to include John Lawrence, who took all responsibility for medical matters. Its members also headed the crews operating the 37-inch cyclotron while the 60-inch was being completed.[34]

This organization was amplified for the building of the calutrons used to separate uranium isotopes for the Manhattan Engineer District. Brobeck's engineering organization expanded to around 100 engineers and draftsmen including electrical engineers from the movie industry and supplemented by Westinghouse, Allis Chalmers, General Electric, and Tennessee Eastman, the industrial contractors who built the Y-12 plant at Oak Ridge. As before the war, these worked directly with the physicists to solve the design problems of the devices under construction. The directing committee, known as the process engineering committee, met daily:

> And when Lawrence was in town, he sat in a large upholstered chair in one part of the room; the rest of the people in the room all sat around on ordinary furniture. But he was very much on a sort of a throne. . . . And the subject was the results of what had been tried in the last 24 hours and what was going to be done next.[35]

Some twenty members of the committee directed experimental groups building components of the calutrons, operating the 184-inch magnet, and operating the experimental calutron magnets and, when Lawrence was not on his throne, managed the effort. The research and development groups, operations, engineering, laboratory liaison, chemistry, and medical divisions began to formalize the hierarchies and charismatic direction characteristic of the 1930's.[36]

Mechanical and electrical shops operated on much the same basis as the prewar shops that contributed to the construction of the cyclotron. According to Brobeck, "It was like about twenty or thirty cyclotrons being built at

33 Cooksey, memorandum on committees, Nov. 22, 1937, and Brobeck, "Suggested Maintenance Operations," July 29, 1938, Lawrence Papers.

34 Brobeck, notes on directing committee meetings of July 15, 19, and 29, and Aug. 24, 1938, Lawrence Papers.

35 Brobeck interview.

36 Lawrence to members of the Process Engineering Committee, Nov. 11, 1942, MED 76/160C, Box 4031, and Laboratory Organization Charts file, Lawrence Berkeley Laboratory Archives.

once. . . . As more people came on, they did the same thing as I did as individuals, then as groups of draftsmen, and so on, headed by somebody who knew what was needed, usually one of the physicists."[37]

The wartime organization of the Radiation Laboratory was, however, more complex. To the research and development effort was added an organization for operations under Donald Cooksey, who had been assistant director of the Radiation Laboratory since the organization of the 60-inch cyclotron effort in 1936. The Operations "Division" dealt with security and safety, health protection, space, 184-inch plant maintenance, electronics, and the shops. The last four functions involved a combined total of 398 individuals by the beginning of 1944. Operations shared some functions with another new organization, "Scientific Personnel and Relations with Allied Contractors," which a new assistant director, astronomer C. D. Shane, supervised. In addition to business and office management, payrolls, purchasing and expediting, accounting, receiving, and stores, this division handled personnel, patents, and reports, and maintained a liaison with the industrial contractors building Y-12. Some 274 people worked for this division. The Research and Development effort, directly under Lawrence (as was the whole Radiation Laboratory), included an engineering group of 110, an "operating physicist" group of 86, a 40-man reassembly shop, a ten-man "Fundamentals Study Group," a fourteen-man magnet group, seven men to operate the 37-inch cyclotron, a four-man insulator group, a six-man pump crew, and a fourteen-man theoretical group, for a total of 166 physicists and technicians. The Chemistry group, under physicist F. A. Jenkins, numbered 82, while W. M. Latimer led a group of 34 other chemists on a related contract, and J. G. Hamilton and 21 scientists carried out war-related medical and radiological research. Excluding 144 persons furnished for guard duty and maintenance, the Laboratory staff totaled almost a thousand at the height of its wartime effort, about twenty times its prewar staff.[38]

The wartime organization did not fit the mold of the prewar Laboratory, even though it grew out of it. First, the Radiation Laboratory was intimately connected with the operations of other aspects of the Manhattan Engineer District, especially the electromagnetic separation plant at Oak Ridge. Its effort was chiefly developmental: to scale up the calutrons and make them reliable. The predominance of technicians and engineers, who outnumbered the physicists, chemists, and other scientists by more than two to one, shows the applied nature of the work. This technical work force was, of course, supplemented by the work of many industrial engineers assigned to the project. This was big technology but, in its aims, not big science.

37 Brobeck interview.

38 Dr. Shane's wartime directory of the Radiation Laboratory, Jan. 1, 1944, Lawrence Berkeley Laboratory Archives; Heilbron and Seidel, *Lawrence and His Laboratory*, table 5.6.

Indeed, in looking to the postwar era, neither Lawrence nor his associates associated this level or the organization of the wartime project with the future of accelerator physics. From a wartime expenditure of $692,000 per month, Lawrence expected to drop to an annual budget of $85,000. Although he expected to add a Division of Medical Physics to the Radiation Laboratory, this would only consolidate work interrupted by the war. In the postwar reorganization, as I have indicated elsewhere,[39] the scientific effort was decentralized as Alvarez, McMillan, Glenn Seaborg, and Robert Thornton each took responsibility for different aspects of the scientific program. Instead of being associated with one machine, this effort was associated with four: the completed 184-inch cyclotron, improved by McMillan's wartime invention of phase stability, which Thornton ran, the linear accelerator conceived by Alvarez at the MIT Radiation Laboratory and built adjacent to the 184-inch with Manhattan Engineer District money and surplus equipment, the electron synchrotron built by McMillan on his new principle, and the 60-inch cyclotron, which was largely given over to medical uses. By 1948, the Bevatron was added to this armamentarium by the Atomic Energy Commission, although it was not completed until 1954 (see Fig. 1.4).

The engineering and support services of the Laboratory, in contrast, remained centralized. Brobeck's engineers, reduced in number to three senior engineers and a handful of assistants, resumed work on accelerator building. Brobeck completed the 184-inch cyclotron and began design of a 10-billion-electron-volt machine that eventually became the Bevatron. As before the war, the big accelerators remained the tools of physicists, chemists, biologists, and physicians pursuing the ramified subdisciplines of nuclear physics, and the Berkeley Radiation Laboratory was divided into a series of organizations grouped around them and their applied functions in chemistry and medicine, with a clear disciplinary focus. Big science took what it could from big technology in this stage of its evolution but retained many of the elements from the prewar stage.

The postwar Radiation Laboratory was modeled on the prewar one, although it was now somewhat larger. And it was this laboratory at Berkeley that served as a conscious model for the postwar nuclear research laboratories,[40] as well as the leading high-energy physics laboratory throughout the 1950's.

By studying the evolution of this model, we may be more precise about the roots of big science in its prewar technological, organizational, and economic environment and the nature of its successful adaptation to other environments. If, on the other hand, we abstract the Radiation Laboratory from this

---

39 Seidel, "Accelerating Science."

40 DuBridge, "Role of Large Laboratories in Nuclear Research"; see also Seidel, "A Home for Big Science."

Fig. 1.4. Accelerator alley. The modern Lawrence Berkeley Laboratory with its LINAC (left), Bevatron (center), 88-inch cyclotron (lower right), and 184-inch synchrocyclotron (upper right). Photo courtesy Lawrence Berkeley Laboratory, University of California.

environment, concocting a definition[41] common to other and later stages of big science, we substitute for historical specificity only debatable generalizations because the very size, diversity, and dynamism of big science threatens constantly to make obsolete any such abstraction.

For example, the argument that the modern form of work organization associated with big science emerges with the large subatomic particle detector overlooks the work organization associated with the construction of the early cyclotrons, which also required "extensive collaborations among physicists and engineers."[42] The early cyclotrons also "altered the kind and quantity of

41 Weinberg, *Reflections on Big Science,* pp. 78–80.
42 Galison, "Bubble Chambers," p. 311.

data that had to be analyzed," as did the later large detectors.[43] The changes in work organization are as fundamental a part of our story of the development of the cyclotron as they are of the development of the bubble chamber into an instrument of big science at the Radiation Laboratory.

If the issue is cast in terms of the control of research, as Galison, Hevly, and Lowen suggest,[44] we find the same disputes over time on the machine, proprietary secrets, classification, teaching duties, and administrative autonomy in the prewar history of the Radiation Laboratory. The change is one of scale and degree, but not of essence.

In exploring the origins and development of the Radiation Laboratory through World War II, the temptation to define big science in terms of rigid categories must be resisted. By seeking rather to characterize an evolution of the art that has long been associated by scientists with the Radiation Laboratory, it is possible to understand not what the platonic definition of big science is, but what its historical definition can be. This historical definition reflects the dynamic character of the art. In work organization, the reliance upon capital-intensive scientific instruments and interested patrons, national prestige, and interdisciplinary efficiency, the early Radiation Laboratory made important contributions to big science. It evolved into the canonical institutional expression of big science. And although big science has ramified institutional expressions as it penetrates into new disciplines, it is to the Radiation Laboratory that we must look for a historical understanding of this phenomenon.

43 *Ibid.*
44 Galison, Hevly, and Lowen, Chapter 2, this volume.

References Cited

Abelson, Philip. "A Sport Played by Graduate Students." *Bulletin of the Atomic Scientists* 30 (1974): 48–52.

Aitken, Hugh F. J. *The Continuous Wave: Technology and American Radio, 1900–1932.* Princeton: Princeton University Press, 1985.

Alvarez, Luis W. *Alvarez: Adventures of a Physicist.* New York: Basic Books, 1987.

Breit, G., M. Tuve, and O. Dahl. "Atomic Physics." *Carnegie Institute of Washington Yearbook* 27 (1927/28): 209.

Brush, Stephen. "The Scientific Value of High-Energy Physics." *Quests with U.S. Accelerators—50 Years: The High-Energy Physics and Nuclear Physics Research Programs.* Hearing before the Subcommittee on Energy Research and Production of the Committee on Science and Technology, U.S. Congress, House of Representatives, 96th Congress, 2nd sess., July 23, 1980. Washington, D.C.: GPO, 1980.

Coleman, Charles M. *P. G. and E. of California: The Centennial Story of Pacific Gas and Electric Company, 1852–1952.* New York: McGraw-Hill, 1952.

Constant, Edward W. "Scientific Theory and Technological Testability: Science, Dynamometers, and Water Turbines in the 19th Century." *Technology and Culture* 24 (1983): 183–98.

Coolidge, W. D. "Some Past Developments and Future Possibilities in Very High Voltage Vacuum Tubes." *General Electric Review* 31 (1928): 184–85.

DuBridge, Lee A. "The Role of Large Laboratories in Nuclear Research." *Bulletin of the Atomic Scientists* 2, nos. 9 and 10 (Nov. 1, 1946): 12–13.

Eve, A. S. *Rutherford (1871–1937), Being the Life and Letters of the Rt. Hon. Lord Rutherford, O.M.* New York: Macmillan, 1939.

Field, S. B. "A Historical Survey of Radiobiology and Radiotherapy." *Current Topics in Radiation Research Quarterly* 11 (1976): 1–85.

Fleming, A. P. M. "High Voltage Laboratories." *World Power* 6, no. 31 (July 1926): 16–26.

Fosdick, R. B. *The Rockefeller Foundation: A Review for 1940* (1940).

Galison, Peter. "Bubble Chambers and the Experimental Workplace." In Peter Achinstein and Owen Hannaway, eds., *Observation, Experiment and Hypothesis in Modern Physical Science,* pp. 309–73. Cambridge, Mass.: MIT Press, 1985.

Heilbron, J. L., and Robert W. Seidel. *Lawrence and His Laboratory: A History of the Lawrence Berkeley Laboratory.* Vol. 1. Berkeley: University of California Press, 1989.

Hughes, Thomas P. *Networks of Power: Electrification in Western Society, 1880–1930.* Baltimore: Johns Hopkins University Press, 1983.

Kruger, P. G., and G. K. Green. "A Million-Volt Cyclotron." *Physical Review* 51 (1937): 57–58.

Kurie, Franz. "The Cyclotron: A New Research Tool for Physics and Biology." *General Electric Review* 40 (1937): 272.

Lauritsen, Charles C., and Ralph D. Bennett. "A New High Potential X-Ray Tube." *Physical Review* 32 (1928): 850–57.

Lauritsen, Charles C., and B. Cassen. "High Potential X-Ray Tube." *Physical Review* 36 (1930): 988–92.

Lawrence, Ernest O. "The Evolution of the Cyclotron." In M. Stanley Livingston, *Development,* 136–37.

Livingston, M. Stanley, ed. *The Development of High-Energy Accelerators.* New York: Dover, 1966.

Livingston, M., M. Holloway, and C. Baker. "A Capillary Ion Source for the Cyclotron." *Review of Scientific Instruments* 10 (1939): 63–66.

Lusignan, J. T., Jr. "Ryan Laboratory Opens Untouched Field of Electrical Investigation." *Journal of Electricity* 57 (1926): 403–7.

———. "Stanford University's Experimental Generators Tested." *Electrical World* 88 (1926): 671.

———. "2,000,000 Volt Research Facilitated at Stanford University." *Electrical World* 88 (1926): 1263–65.

Norberg, Arthur L. "The Origins of the Electronics Industry on the Pacific Coast." *Proceedings of the Institute of Electrical and Electronic Engineering* 64 (1976): 1319–21.

Peck, F. W. "Lightning—Part I." *General Electric Review* 32 (1929): 602–18.

Seidel, Robert W. "The Origins of Academic Physics Research in California: A Study of Interdisciplinary Dynamics in Institutional Growth." *Journal of College Science Teaching* 6 (1976): 10–24.

————. "Physics Research in California: The Rise of a Leading Sector in American Physics." Ph.D. diss., University of California, Berkeley, 1978.

————. "Accelerating Science: The Postwar Transformation of the Radiation Laboratory." *Historical Studies in the Physical Sciences* 13 (1983): 375–400.

————. "A Home for Big Science: The Atomic Energy Commission's Laboratory System." *Historical Studies in the Physical and Biological Sciences* 16 (1986): 135–75.

Smith, Norman. "The Origins of the Water Turbine." *Scientific American* 242, no. 1 (Jan. 1980): 146–47.

Sorenson, Royal W. "California Institute of Technology's Million-Volt Laboratory." *Journal of Electricity* 53 (1924): 242–45.

————. "Development and Characteristics of a 1,000,000-Volt Cascade Transformer at California Institute of Technology." *Journal of the American Institute of Electrical Engineers* 44 (1925): 373.

————. "Dedication of the New Ryan Laboratory." *Journal of Electricity* 57 (1926): 231.

Stone, R. S. "Neutron Therapy and Specific Ionization (Janeway Lecture)." *American Journal of Roentgenology and Radium Therapy* 59 (1948): 771–85.

Walton, E. T. S. "The Production of High-Speed Ions by Indirect Means." *Proceedings of the Cambridge Physical Society* 25 (1929): 469–81.

Weart, Spencer. "The Physics Business in America, 1900–1940: A Statistical Reconnaissance." In Nathan Reingold, ed., *The Sciences in the American Context*, pp. 295–358. Washington, D.C.: Smithsonian Institution Press, 1979.

Weinberg, Alvin. *Reflections on Big Science.* Cambridge, Mass.: MIT Press, 1967.

Wideröe, Rolf. "Über ein neues Prinzip zur Herstellung hoher Spannungen." *Archiv für Elektrotechnik* 21 (1928): 387–406.

Wilson, R. R. "Magnetic and Electrostatic Focusing in the Cyclotron." *Physical Review* 53 (1938): 408–20.

CHAPTER 2

Controlling the Monster: Stanford and the Growth of Physics Research, 1935-1962

Peter Galison, Bruce Hevly, and Rebecca Lowen

T here is a kind of collective myth about the evolution of physics research in the mid-twentieth century. It characterizes the 1930's as an Edenic period of individual, independent research. World War II, according to the story, interrupted the physicists' work, the nature of which was completely transformed in the postwar years by the creation of federally sponsored laboratories. Although radical changes certainly occurred in mid-century, this simplistic periodization is inadequate on at least two counts. First, the breaks and continuities of this story do not hold up to historical scrutiny. And second, this narrative is incomplete. Concerned primarily with the institutional growth of physics illustrated by a tenfold increase in federal research and development funding during World War II, it fails to connect this institutional growth to the physicists' reactions to their changing environment and to changes in the intellectual content of their discipline.

Focusing on Stanford University, we propose a new way to understand the reformulation of physics research in the mid-twentieth century. We argue first that during the 1930's, Stanford's physicists, on their own initiative, undertook organized, applied research; late in the decade they established ties with the Sperry Gyroscope Company that persisted into World War II. After Pearl Harbor, the Stanford physicists changed the location and style of their work as required by the war. It was during these war years, while exposed to new ways of organizing research and new sources of funding, that the physicists—along with Stanford's administration—redefined their aims and opportunities and began planning in earnest for the postwar period. The significant break thus occurred in the early war years and not in the months following V-J Day. A new era began in 1954 with the physicists' proposal for a multibillion-electron-volt linear accelerator; it was characterized by extended debates over this project (dubbed "M" for monster), which evolved into the Stanford Linear Accelerator Center (SLAC).

In studying these three stages (1935–41, 1941–54, 1954–62), we concentrate on the physicists' concern over the *control* of the research. In our view, this is the underlying issue at stake in the debates of each of these periods: who controls the disposition of apparatus, the direction of research, the disclosure of scientific information, the research personnel, and the style of research? These questions simultaneously engage sponsorship and institutional structure on one hand and the changing conception of physical research on the other.

Physics research at Stanford expanded in stages, each one marked by the physicists' exploitation of new resources. These opportunities, in turn, placed constraints upon the nature of that research. And, at each stage, the expansion of physics created tension and, at times, conflict at the boundaries between department, university, government, and the quasi-autonomous research programs. If we pay special attention to some of these disputes, it is not because we want to underline contentiousness. Rather, it is because these conflicts signaled substantial changes occurring in the research enterprise and different views of how research should be conducted. Only by tracing the genealogy of the character of research can the evolution of large-scale research in modern physics be understood.

Knowledge for Innovation and Litigation, 1935–1941

During the 1920's and 1930's the Stanford physics department aspired to become one of the leading research centers in the West. Its efforts to achieve this goal under chairman David Locke Webster involved first an organized attempt at large-scale research and, when that failed, a concentration on applied research eventually supported by the Sperry Gyroscope Company. In 1936, Assistant Professor William W. Hansen invented the rhumbatron, a conducting metal chamber producing a standing oscillatory electric field able to accelerate electrons. The invention, which had possible commercial as well as scientific applications, confronted the department with a host of new problems associated with patentable knowledge. Sperry's support, attracted by a later invention, the klystron (a vacuum tube that can produce, amplify, and detect microwaves), answered these needs. Yet the relationship with

Sperry also imposed constraints that influenced the practice of physics at Stanford before World War II.

Webster came to Stanford in 1920 at the age of 32, having previously taught at Harvard, Michigan, and MIT. Stanford's president, Ray Lyman Wilbur, charged him with transforming the physics department after the retirement of its first generation of professors, whose teaching was outmoded and who did little research.[1] An experimentalist specializing in X-ray research and its application to the frontiers of atomic physics, Webster built up groups in his specialty and in ultraviolet spectroscopy, two areas he believed gave Stanford access to all of the atom outside of the nucleus.[2] Frustrated at times by Stanford's lack of resources compared to those of the University of California and later to Caltech's, he hoped that a prudent investment in atomic research would attract prestige, foundation support, and more prominent faculty members from the East.

Both of the powers in California physics had flourished in part by linking foundation support with large, highly visible research facilities and the interests of West Coast industrialists.[3] Webster hoped to compete with his California rivals by imitating their success in large-scale research, though on a slightly more modest scale. In fact, Webster's willingness to organize and regiment his faculty in a common endeavor would become a hallmark of his style as department chairman. In 1935 he began to plan a huge (70- to 100-foot, three- to four-million-electron-volt, $100,000) X-ray tube, a device intended to extend the X-ray program into nuclear physics. As originally conceived, the huge tube would rely for power on the giant transformers of the Ryan High-Voltage Laboratory, built for Stanford's electrical engineering department by California's electrical power industry. For over a year, members of the physics department worked under Webster's direction on designs and gathered information on costs and materials from contractors, duties uncongenial to some. But the project failed for lack of funds; neither the Rockefeller nor the Carnegie foundation could be convinced that the system might be useful for cancer research, which would have more readily justified its place in the foundations' programs[4] (see Fig. 2.1).

1 On the search for a physics department chairman and Wilbur's expectations, see Ray Lyman Wilbur Papers, Stanford University Archives, Box 43/Folder 2. See also Seidel, "Physics Research," pp. 106–8; Kirkpatrick, "David Locke Webster," pp. 377–81.

2 *Stanford University Bulletin*, Feb. 15, 1927, p. 211, Nov. 1929, pp. 34, 365; Kirkpatrick, "David Locke Webster," pp. 381–83; Seidel, "Physics Research," pp. 169–73, 191–94, 208–11.

3 Heilbron, Seidel, and Wheaton, *Lawrence and His Laboratory*, pp. 12–14, 24–26; Seidel, "Physics Research," pp. 7–8, 589–90, chapters 8 and 10; Kargon, "Birth Cries," pp. 310–18, "Temple to Science," pp. 15–19, *Rise of Robert Millikan*, pp. 91–121.

4 David Locke Webster Papers, Stanford University Archives, Box 1: "Super-Voltage X-Ray Project," vols. II and III; Kirkpatrick, "Autobiography," pp. 65–66, Stanford University Archives; *Stanford University Bulletin*, Dec. 31, 1935, p. 302, Dec. 31, 1936, p. 305; Seidel, "Physics Research," pp. 333–37. On power transmission research at Stanford's Ryan Laboratory, see Hughes, "Science Technology Interaction."

Fig. 2.1. Ryan High-Voltage Laboratory, ca. 1925. Photo courtesy Stanford Linear Accelerator Center and the U.S. Department of Energy.

After abandoning the 100-foot tube project in 1936, the physicists turned to Hansen's rhumbatron as a device that, through resonance effects, might accelerate electrons to produce X rays at little cost.[5] The tube project exposed department members to some of the drawbacks of team research, and also brought home the chronic shortage of research funds. The rhumbatron, as a patentable device, raised challenges to the traditional free exchange of scientific information. Industry, as well as scientists, was interested in the rhumbatron as the main element of a high-frequency resonant circuit. When inventor Lee De Forest asked if one of his engineers could see the new instrument, Hansen initially extended an invitation. But the university vetoed the visit, and a chagrined Hansen informed De Forest that "the university's patent attorneys ... feel that ... details should not be disclosed. ... I deeply regret this but there is nothing else I can do. The patent belongs to the university and I must follow the dictates of their attorneys."[6] As it became patentable—in legal terms, useful and "reduced to practice"—Hansen's research aroused Stanford's proprietary interest. Once realized, this transition from research as knowledge to research as property established the essential character of the klystron project.

Hansen had already provided the university with a list of ten possible applications of the rhumbatron, including physical and medical research, medical treatment, industrial x-raying, insect exterminating, and broadcasting.[7] Practical application of the physicists' work was realized with the invention of the klystron, the product of a collaboration between Russell and Sigurd Varian, Hansen, and Webster.

The Varian brothers, seeking at Sigurd's suggestion a source of microwaves for systems to aid aircraft navigation and detection, initially worked independently. In 1937, they came to Stanford, where Russell had studied for his bachelor's and master's degrees in physics and had worked as a research associate during 1934 and 1935. Building on Hansen's cavity resonator, Hansen and Russell Varian devised the klystron. Sigurd Varian, acting as

5 Webster to Post, June 14, 1949, William W. Hansen Papers, Stanford University Archives, Box 3/31; Hansen, "Emission and Absorption of Radiation," Sept. 21, 1933, Hansen Papers, Box 3/34. Of "Hansen's most ingenious and intriguing idea about the oscillating sphere," Caltech's Jesse DuMond wrote Webster, "that is a 'wow' if it will work." DuMond to Webster, Mar. 13, 1935, Webster Papers, Box 1. *Stanford University Bulletin*, Dec. 31, 1936, p. 305; Leslie and Hevly, "Steeple Building," p. 1170.

6 Hansen to DeForest Laboratories, Mar. 12, 1937, Hansen Papers, Box 1. Hansen's description of the rhumbatron, submitted to the *Journal of Applied Physics* in July 1937, was at first withheld from publication at Stanford's request in order to avoid "adverse effect on commercial developments." It finally appeared in the number for October 1938. See Hansen, "A Type of Electrical Resonator," p. 654.

7 Hansen to Erwin, Sept. 23, 1936, Hansen Papers, Box 1/3. Hansen listed four potentially patentable devices in a memo for his records and pursued patents on two in addition to Stanford's patent on the rhumbatron. "Memorandum: W. W. Hansen, January 22, 1937," Hansen Papers, Box 1/3.

machinist, turned the designs into working models; Webster contributed a mathematical theory explaining the klystron's effects. Stanford provided laboratory space and $100 for materials in return for a share of any future royalties accruing from a workable device.[8] In August 1937, one of Russell's proposals for a microwave resonator—two resonating chambers connected by a drift tube, in which the accelerated electrons from the first chamber bunched up and then were "caught" by the second chamber to produce a powerful high-frequency signal—became hardware on Sigurd's bench and worked. The excited crew adjourned to Webster's house for celebratory beers, and the next morning the department chairman called a meeting to discuss patenting and promoting the klystron.[9] Stanford's administration, short of funds and unsure of how to pursue and protect a patentable device, was unable to provide the physicists with the help they needed.[10]

Sperry stepped in, agreeing in April 1938 to provide a percentage of royalties to the inventors and the university, as well as research funds for developing the klystron, in return for a license to manufacture the device. Stanford's physicists were not pulled away from pure research by Sperry; they were as interested as Sperry in developing the klystron for blind landing systems and radar, both of which were under development by government and industry.[11] Webster and Sigurd Varian, both experienced pilots, worried that

8 Ginzton, "The $100 Idea"; Leslie and Hevly, "Steeple Building," pp. 1170–71. Russell Varian roomed with Hansen in 1934 and 1935, and discussed the supervoltage X-ray project and Hansen's efforts to accelerate electrons by means of resonating chambers; D. Varian, *Inventor and Pilot*, pp. 151–64, 173–80. See also "Statement of W. W. Hansen," Hansen Papers, Box 4/45, and for Webster's development of klystron theory, see Webster, "Cathode Ray Bunching," and "Klystron Generators."

9 R. and S. Varian, "A High Frequency Amplifier"; D. Varian, *Inventor and Pilot*, p. 187.

10 The university had been developing a patent policy in response to Iodobismitol, a drug created in the medical school and patented by Stanford, as well as Hansen's rhumbatron. See *Stanford University Bulletin*, Dec. 31, 1937, pp. 7–8. Both Hansen and Webster had been interested observers of this process, and neither was satisfied with the results; Webster's objections are in Webster to Wilbur, Dec. 7, 1937, Louis Terman Papers, Stanford University Archives, Box 18.

11 For the Stanford–Sperry agreement (Apr. 27, 1938), see F. E. Terman Papers, Stanford University Archives, Series 1, Box 8/14. Hansen and Webster had contacted the military and the Civil Aeronautics Authority about applications of the klystron to aircraft detection and blind landing before cooperation with Sperry began. See, for example, Hansen to Gordon Duvall, Oct. 13, 1937, Hansen Papers, Box 1/5.

Whereas large industrial concerns in America most often recruited scientists to work in corporate laboratories, sponsored research on campus was not uncommon in the 1920's and 1930's, especially in electrical engineering and chemistry departments. As in nineteenth-century Germany, such relationships "required a certain amount of circumspection to secure such cooperation without offending academic dignity and propriety" (Beer, "German Chemical Dye Industry," p. 65). When research managers at Du Pont discovered in 1925 that a Notre Dame chemistry professor had discovered a promising catalyst for synthetic rubber production, the company quickly secured a "gentlemen's agreement" in which Du

aerial warfare would become a global threat, having spread already from Spain to China; their concern lent a special urgency to the work.[12] The physicists did have reservations over Sperry's insistence on keeping the results of the work secret, but they were soon resolved when Webster secured the university's assurance that applied work would be considered of "equal importance with pure scientific research" in evaluating the physicists for promotion.[13] With a satisfactory resolution of the secrecy issue, generous funds for an interesting project, and a sponsor to help protect their invention and bring it to the market, the physicists' relationship with Sperry seemed off to a good start.

But almost immediately, Webster clashed with the company's representatives over the selection of new staff members, control of laboratory facilities, and the direction of research. Sperry had agreed to pay for as many as eight research assistants at Stanford.[14] In June 1938, Sperry's director of research, Hugh Willis, sent three engineers to work in Webster's laboratory. The chairman was upset, partly because both he and Russell Varian felt the men were "nearly useless because of a lack of research instinct," but mainly because Willis, "as a member of an independent organization, had no authority to appoint any man to our staff." But, "in the interest of good cooperation," Webster decided not to make an issue over which group—Stanford's physicists or Sperry—should have responsibility for hiring the staff.[15]

Six months later, after the physicists had developed several working klystron models, Webster again found himself in conflict with Sperry. Concerned that competition from General Electric and Westinghouse was "going to be quite severe," Sperry decided to begin klystron production and, with Webster's concurrence, established a production shop in the physics laboratory.[16] A rift opened when Sperry "demanded that [Webster] establish the separate organi-

---

Pont handled the legal work and provided a graduate chemistry fellowship in return for an option on the patented process. In 1928, when the chemist, a Jesuit priest, balked at accepting an annual $1000 consulting fee, his superiors convinced him to establish a relationship with Du Pont for the good of the university. By 1934, a further agreement assigned all inventions by Notre Dame's instructors and fellows in organic chemistry to Du Pont. (Smith, "Ten-Year Invention," p. 38; see also Wise, "Ionists in Industry," and Servos, "Industrial Relations.")

12 Russell Varian to Webster, June 17, 1939, Russell and Sigurd Varian Papers, Stanford University Archives, Box 22. Sigurd Varian had been a senior pilot for Pan American; Webster had been a research pilot and aeronautical engineer for the Air Corps during World War I, an Air Corps reserve officer in the 1920's, and an active private pilot from the mid-1930's on.

13 Webster, memo for files, Apr. 27, 1938, Webster Papers (addendum), Box 1.

14 Hansen to H. Hugh Jackson, Sept. 8, 1938, Hansen Papers, Box 1/9.

15 Webster, memo to file, June 14, 1939, Webster Papers (addendum), Box 1. Russell Varian to Webster, June 17, 1939, Varian Papers, Box 22.

16 Hugh Willis to Hansen, Jan. 10, 1939, Hansen Papers, Box 1/10.

zation within our building under Cooke [a Sperry engineer]."[17] Webster was willing to allow the production of klystron tubes in the physics building, but he did not intend to cede to Sperry direct control of any activity, whether research or production, conducted on campus. Hansen reported that Webster told Sperry that "they could do their engineering elsewhere," and the company soon set up a production facility in the nearby town of San Carlos.[18] Although the incident was resolved to Webster's satisfaction, it marked the turning point in his attitude toward research sponsored by Sperry; his suspicions were aroused, and he was no longer interested in compromising with the company. As Webster explained, "All these quarrels would be unimportant except as straws showing which way the wind blows."[19] Common to all these "quarrels" was the question of who controlled research based on campus but supported by Sperry.

The groups on campus and at San Carlos were soon feuding over which one had primary responsibility for research. Sperry's Willis was planning to hire a research staff for the supposed production facility. Moreover, both Hansen and Sigurd Varian were aware of rumors that Willis, according to Hansen's letter to Russell, wanted "to cut out the research [at Stanford], Sig, and, as soon as possible, you."[20] Webster and Russell Varian decided to appeal directly to Sperry's president.[21] The result, as Russell Varian gloated, was "defeat of Willis's plans to either shove us into a secondary position or shove us out." Sperry acknowledged the Stanford physicists' primacy with respect to research, Webster reported, leaving "the Stanford Klystron Laboratory completely available for fundamental research in this field." The physicists agreed to work to "reestablish mutual confidence" between their group and the Sperry engineers in San Carlos.[22]

Webster's hopes for a truce with Sperry proved short-lived, however. Since the project's inception, the company had felt free to intervene in the laboratory and direct research along particular lines, choosing, for example, one klystron configuration and closing off research on another. Webster, the product of a mercantile Boston home, accepted this as the investor's right—especially when

17 Webster memo, June 14, 1939, Webster Papers (addendum), Box 1.
18 Hansen to John Woodyard, Mar. 10, 1939, Hansen Papers, Box 1/10.
19 Webster memo, June 14, 1939, Webster Papers (addendum), Box 1.
20 Hansen to Russell Varian, June 15, 1939, Varian Papers, Box 9; see also Hansen to Russell Varian, July 7, 1939, Varian Papers, Box 9, and Sigurd to Russell, n.d., Varian Papers, Box 19. According to Sigurd, Willis had said, " 'All you have to do is design them [the klystrons] right; a lot of research isn't necessary'!! Wow." Russell Varian to Sigurd, July 18, 1939, Varian Papers, Box 18. According to Russell, he took "the initiative in stating the case" against Willis.
21 Webster memo, June 14, 1939, Webster Papers (addendum), Box 1; and Hansen to Webster, July 12, 1939, Hansen Papers, Box 1/12.
22 Webster to Wilbur, Mar. 2, 1939 (also reporting a successful test of the blind landing system at MIT), Webster Papers (addendum), Box 1. Russell Varian to Hansen, July 1939, Hansen Papers, Box 2/14.

the company sided with him and Russell Varian during a disagreement with Hansen over two possible klystron designs.

In consultation with Sperry's management, Webster and Russell Varian agreed "to push toward shorter waves as soon and as fast as we can" by working on the hollow-beam klystron, a design promising speedy development. Webster gave two reasons for taking the quickest path: "for a reduction to practice at shorter waves before anyone else does, and also because it is known to too many people who will try it if we don't."[23] Here the patent situation, a concern now shared by Stanford and Sperry, clearly determined the direction of klystron research. Hansen, however, argued for work on a novel klystron model, the radial shooter, the development of which would be more difficult, but its final form more elegant.[24] Webster and Sperry prevailed. As Webster told Hansen, the technical merits of either design mattered little; Sperry's interest "alone ought to decide the question." "After all," he concluded, "it is the Sperry Company's money that pays for the research."[25]

While Webster readily acknowledged and accepted the idea that Sperry, as the provider of research funds, should direct the physicists' work, he was unable to tolerate Sperry's increasing emphasis on securing the company's patent position rather than on developing the klystron itself. In late 1939 Sperry restricted the Stanford physicists to problems identified by the company, with the aim of strengthening the patent structure.[26] Rather than working to make the actual device more reliable or applicable to systems being developed for blind landing and aircraft detection, Webster's most creative physicists now "retired to their office to claim all other ideas, good, bad, and unproved, which they could think of to patent."[27] This type of knowledge was useful only to lawyers in filing patent interferences or as leverage in developing patent pools with other companies. Hansen's reaction was much the same as Webster's had been to Sperry's choice of the hollow-beam over the radial-shooter configuration. "Sperry may be damphools," he told Webster. "I think they are. But it's their money so we have to do it their way or not at all."[28] The fundamental issue here was not whether the physicists would do applied, rather than pure, research. Rather, it was whether the physicists would occupy their time producing knowledge for litigation rather than for innovation.

In their research at Stanford on the large X-ray tube, the rhumbatron, and the klystron, the physicists had participated in organized and directed research, worked on applied as opposed to pure physics, and accepted restrictions on the free exchange of information—all before Sperry began to support

23 Webster to Sigurd Varian, July 20, 1939, Varian Papers, Box 11.

24 Woodyard, "Amplification and Modulation," pp. 121–23.

25 Webster to Hansen, July 27, 1939, and Hansen to Webster, July 22, 1939, Hansen Papers, Box 1/12.

26 Hansen to Webster, Oct. 23, 1939, Hansen Papers, Box 2/14.

27 Webster to Norris Bradbury, Mar. 10, 1943, Webster Papers, Box 10.

28 Hansen to Webster, Oct. 23, 1939, Hansen Papers, Box 2/14.

their work. Sperry's initial support brought substantial benefits to the physicists, enabling them to develop the klystron in time to contribute to the war effort and to begin to understand and exploit the microwave spectrum. Indeed, microwave techniques would become the centerpiece of Stanford's postwar research program. But these opportunities were balanced by the constraint of Sperry's influence over the direction and character of research, which troubled Hansen and the Varians and finally alienated Webster. Webster resigned from the project in December 1939, formally citing eye problems but convinced, according to notes he made of his conversation with Stanford's president, that "science and patents don't mix any more than oil and water."[29] A year later the rest of the group, still at work for Sperry on the klystron and its applications for the war already raging in Europe and Asia, left campus for first-hand experiences with industry and government. From their war service would come new possibilities for supporting physics research at Stanford.

The Turn to Federal Support, 1941–1954

World War II drew most of Stanford's physicists away from Palo Alto and set the stage for a new period of research sponsorship in the postwar period. Influenced by their experiences in wartime laboratories at Los Alamos, MIT, Aberdeen, and Harvard, the physicists began shaping their plans for postwar research.[30] They conceived new strategies for organizing their department, identified the government as a potential source for funding and hardware, and perceived new possibilities for the development of klystron technology and its application to scientific research. With klystron royalties earned from the Sperry partnership, the physicists planned to establish a new, partially autonomous microwave laboratory within the Stanford physics department. The lab would rely heavily on federal support, which seemed to promise substantial amounts for operating costs without the problems associated with patent-oriented industrial sponsorship. Indeed, federal money was a crucial element in making Stanford a leading center for physics research after the war, finally fulfilling Webster's prewar goal. The limitations imposed by government sponsorship, however, emerged shortly after the lab was completed in 1949. By 1950, the Stanford physicists became concerned that government support, like industrial sponsorship, also imposed control, in ways both obvious and subtle, over the way their work was organized, institutionally and intellectually.

Although most of the prewar microwave group—including the Varians, Hansen, and Edward Ginzton, an electrical engineering Ph.D. from Stanford—worked together during the war, other Stanford physicists followed

29 Webster memo to files, Dec. 15, 1939. As he put it, somewhat more pointedly, in his autobiography, "A patent is a legal analog of sticky fly paper: it attracts some of the lowest forms of life." Webster, "Reminiscences," p. 111, Webster Papers (addendum), Box 1.

30 Galison, "Physics Between War and Peace"; Leslie, "Playing the Education Game," pp. 61–69.

different paths. Webster left microwave physics and its applications. An Army Air Service pilot/development engineer in World War I, Webster believed most of his efforts in that war had been wasted; he sought involvement during World War II in a project with immediate applications. After a series of National Defense Research Council and civilian jobs—including one as an instructor at an Army radar school, where he applied for a patent on a magnetron-powered linear accelerator—Webster ended up at Aberdeen Proving Ground, developing rockets for combat.[31] Norris Bradbury, a Naval Reservist, was assigned to active duty and sent first to the Naval Ordnance Laboratory and then to Los Alamos, where he eventually succeeded J. Robert Oppenheimer as director in 1946.[32] Felix Bloch worked for the Manhattan Project, first using the Stanford cyclotron and then serving at Los Alamos for a few months in 1943; he left New Mexico to join Stanford electrical engineering professor Frederick Terman and a group of Stanford engineers at Harvard's Radio Research Laboratory.[33] Most of the klystron group went to work for Sperry Gyroscope Company on Long Island. The team would return to Stanford augmented by Marvin Chodorow, an electrical engineer who came to Sperry during the war via the company's relationship with MIT.[34]

While scattered about the country, the group held what Bloch referred to as a "department meeting in letters" to debate their postwar future. At the center of their discussions was the question of how to use the money generated by the royalties from Sperry's wartime klystron sales. University policy stated that such funds went to the department responsible for the invention, except for amounts in excess of what could be usefully employed there. The physicists thus had to demonstrate that they indeed could made good use of the available funds. Webster wanted to fund fellowships for physics graduate students. He could see nothing good coming out of continuing the klystron research after the war, when it would be bereft of the prewar "pioneering crusading and military aspects that partially redeemed it" and devoted only to commercial ends. From Los Alamos, Bradbury seconded Webster's suggested use of the money for fellowships, but he believed that Hansen, as the one primarily responsible for the royalty money, had the ultimate right to determine how to spend it. Bloch and Hansen, in consultation with department chairman *pro tem* Paul Kirkpatrick at Stanford and Terman in Cambridge, orchestrated the campaign to create a Stanford Microwave Laboratory.[35]

31 On Webster's war work on submarine detection, radar, and rockets, see Webster Papers (addendum), Box 1.

32 Bradbury's departure on July 1, 1941, was reported in *Stanford University Bulletin*, Dec. 31, 1941, p. 363.

33 Leslie and Hevly, "Steeple Building," pp. 1173–74.

34 D. Varian, *Inventor and Pilot*, chapter 15.

35 Bloch to Webster, Mar. 23, 1943, and Webster to Bradbury, Mar. 16, 1943, both in Webster Papers, Box 10. Stanford's policy on distributing royalties on university-held patents was summarized in *Stanford University Bulletin*, Aug. 31, 1938, pp. 12–14. On the

Both Hansen and Kirkpatrick believed that physics would expand after the war, chiefly because of the enlarged opportunities physicists would find in industry.[36] The proposed microwave laboratory, then, would not only build on an area of prewar strength and perpetuate work being done during the war by members of the group, but would also make Stanford attractive to prospective students and sponsors after the war. With their own facilities and budget, Hansen and Ginzton pictured the Microwave Laboratory as a place where electrical engineers and physicists would work together on microwave physics and its applications: measurement and waveguide techniques, antenna and tube design, and, returning to the question that had brought Hansen to cavity resonators in 1935, the use of microwave power to accelerate electrons for use in experimental nuclear physics.[37]

Hansen, pondering the proposal he planned to submit to Stanford's president, revealed that, like Webster, he had some reservations about further involvement in industry-sponsored work:[38]

> Some help should be obtainable from the outside, e.g. Sperry.
> What can we sell them?
> Not our soul.
> Consulting.
> Students.
> Some research.
> Patents—new.
> Patent help.
> Scientific advertising.
> Terman thinks they will pay, and so do I, but how much and
> for what are questions.

As these ruminations suggest, the wartime debate over the Microwave Laboratory proposal was shaped by the group's experience with industrial sponsorship and its hazards. The participants knew that some federal support was possible after the war, but the greatest market for knowledge and students to be produced in such a laboratory seemed to be industry. Hansen's notes to himself ("What can we sell them? Not our soul") show that even those in favor

debate over the establishment of the Microwave Laboratory, see Leslie and Hevly, "Steeple Building," pp. 1174–76, and extensive correspondence held in the Hansen, Bloch, Webster, and F. E. Terman papers, Stanford University Archives.

36 Hansen to Kirkpatrick, Nov. 6, 1942, Felix Bloch Papers, Stanford University Archives, Box 5/20; Hansen, "Proposed Microwave Laboratory at Stanford," Nov. 17, 1943, Hansen Papers, Box 4/40; Kirkpatrick to Webster, May 26, 1944, Webster Papers, Box 10.

37 Hansen, "Proposed Microwave Laboratory at Stanford," Nov. 17, 1943, Hansen Papers, Box 4/40, and "Proposal for the Production of Super-Energy Electrons," n.d., Hansen Papers, Box 4/48.

38 Draft of Hansen to Tresidder, Sept. 27, 1944, Hansen Papers, Box 4/41.

of seeking sponsors who could support research beyond the reach of university budgets recognized that such arrangements always held the threat of outside control. For his part, Webster remained adamantly opposed, even hitching a cross-country bomber ride to Palo Alto to plead his case.[39] But the pro-laboratory side had convinced the university administration, and themselves, that they could maintain essential control. Webster was permanently replaced as chairman by Kirkpatrick.

Without even a building of their own but with $65,000 in the bank in 1946 (the department's budget for 1945–46 was $48,200), Hansen, Ginzton, and their students began to develop their program by building a linear accelerator that would use microwave power to accelerate electrons down a waveguide.[40] Their first six-foot model (the Mark I) demonstrated the waveguide principle and was powered by a magnetron, as was Webster's proposed design and a model proton accelerator being built by a group under John Clark Slater at MIT. But Hansen wanted to use klystrons for power to push the accelerator quickly to energy ranges he believed beyond the reach of the competing Betatron at the University of Illinois. Describing their proposed machine in a journal article, Ginzton and Hansen noted that to reach a billion electron volts a "considerable multiplicity" of magnetrons would be required, or they would have to introduce sources of higher power. "We have some hope," the klystron group modestly reported, "that such high power sources can be developed."[41]

The klystron stood in the center of the Stanford group's attention. With klystrons, the Hansen-Ginzton group could build both an accelerator and a microwave laboratory, providing an ideal transition into the postwar world. Their projects involved concrete tasks having ultimate, if vague, payoffs for nuclear physics, while offering the immediate satisfaction of solving hardware problems and learning more about microwaves. In addition, the linear accelerator (linac) soon attracted federal support. The U.S. government, through the Navy's Office of Research and Inventions (renamed the Office of Naval Research [ONR] in 1946), gave Stanford a $26,000 contract to develop a prototype linac. In addition to the money, the Navy agreed to provide several

39 Kirkpatrick to Hansen, Mar. 11, 1945, Hansen Papers, Box 4/41. As Kirkpatrick reported Webster's departure from administration, "It was a new thought to DL but he is now quite satisfied with it. . . . He is relieved to escape administration of a department which is to be deeply involved in researches which he regards as engineering and which he fears can only have evil influences." Webster's mission ran against a current that grew stronger through the 1940's and 1950's: "Although the universities enjoyed a seller's market, the internal pressures to sell were so strong that corporatively the academy retained no effective control." Forman, "Behind Quantum Electronics," p. 181.

40 Hansen, "Accelerating the Electron"; Ginzton, Hansen, and Kennedy, "A Linear Electron Accelerator"; Leslie and Hevly, "Steeple Building," p. 1177.

41 Hansen had said early on that if the electron accelerator could not improve on Kerst's device it was best to stay out of the project. Hansen to Webster, Feb. 4, 1943, Hansen Papers, Box 4/40. Quotations are from Ginzton, Hansen, and Kennedy, "A Linear Electron Accelerator," p. 107.

items from surplus radar stocks: an S-band spectrum analyzer, two standing wave meters, three synchroscopes, a modulator, a radar transmitter, and three S-band echo boxes and wavemeters.[42] Those who had spent the war at MIT and Sperry, or in radar shacks with the Pacific Fleet, were in familiar surroundings.[43]

Initially, federal support seemed to obviate many of the difficulties that had become associated with industrial sponsorship. But the constraints of the new relationship quickly manifested themselves, just as those associated with patent work had before the war. In 1947 Webster sent a proposal to the ONR for funding to continue his prewar work on the stripping of K-shell electrons from heavy atoms by electron bombardment. After department chairman Kirkpatrick joined Webster in consulting a confidential list of the Navy's research objectives, they both became "much less confident of the Navy's interest," as the K-shell research would not contribute to assuaging the "Navy's concern about nuclear structure." A meeting between Webster and ONR representatives confirmed these fears. "The . . . problem had no visible naval application," Webster reported, "and the Navy would have an awful time explaining any appropriation for it to a Congressman."[44] The physicists' projects, then, would have to pass a test of military relevance, even if a fairly liberal one.

Along with the problem of relevance came one of responsibility for the accelerator, a constraint that became clear upon Hansen's untimely death in May 1949, just over a year after ONR's support for a billion-volt machine (the Mark III) had been secured. Accelerators themselves had applications, for medical treatment and industrial radiography, for example.[45] But with Hansen gone, the Navy required, as a condition for further support, evidence from Stanford that a physicist of comparable stature would use the machine for research. "We now have a little concern about the future of the linear accelerator project," ONR representatives informed the deans of engineering and physical sciences at Stanford.[46]

> The Office of Naval Research would like to know whether Stanford is interested in continuing [the accelerator project]. . . . If the University wishes to carry through on

42 Task Order IV, Contract N6ori-106, June 12, 1946. W. W. Hansen Laboratory Papers, Stanford University Archives, Box 1.

43 Galison, "Physics Between War and Peace," pp. 69–81.

44 Kirkpatrick to Eurich, Mar. 20, 1947, and Webster, "Memo on Conference of Nov. 28, 1947," both in Webster Papers, Box 3.

45 For the immediate prospects that would "elicit the greatest interest from the various sponsoring agencies," based upon "the optimization of design for various purposes," see Karl Spangenberg to Terman, Sept. 28, 1949, W. W. Hansen Laboratories Papers, Box 10. For lists of specific interests in linear accelerators for applications on the part of the various Navy bureaus, see Fred L. Niemann, Office of Naval Research, to Ginzton, Apr. 12, 1951, and Niemann to Marvin Chodorow, Apr. 20, 1951, both in W. W. Hansen Laboratories Papers, Box 13.

46 Spangenberg to Terman, June 2, 1949, and Urner Liddel to Philip Leighton, June 7, 1949, Leonard Schiff Papers, Stanford University Archives, Box 14.

this million and a half dollar project [it] will require an implementation of staff from the standpoint of bolstering its leadership with men who combine scientific stature and experience. . . . It will probably be difficult to promote further funds unless something is done about the staff situation.

Funding for the accelerator now required proof that some of Stanford's physicists would tie their professional fate to using it.

Two other constraints, which can be mentioned only briefly here, also emerged. First, the presence of a semi-autonomous division within the physics department, with its own budget, research staff, and students, raised difficult questions about the department's control over its overall program of teaching and research. The situation was partly addressed in 1948 when the department chair was turned over to Leonard Schiff, who had joined the faculty the year before. Acknowledged for his ability to mediate between competing interests within the department, Schiff was able to smooth over disputes and unify the program.[47] Still, the problems of pedagogical and administrative autonomy remained unresolved. They would arise again with respect to the Mark III and SLAC.

Second, as the klystron itself became potentially more important for military electronics (for example, as a replacement for the magnetron in communications and high-power radar systems), the government began to regard aspects of its development as sensitive. It sought to control the spread of information about the device, just as Stanford and Sperry had felt it necessary to protect the original patent before the war. Ginzton, arguing that "our klystron, as it exists today, is not of practical importance to the Military Establishment," urged the Navy in May 1949 to resist restricting information about its development and limiting access to the Microwave Laboratory. Such arrangements, he argued, would be inimical to the traditions of science and the university, would not hinder anyone from copying Stanford's work, and would deprive the laboratory of the services of students who were not U.S. citizens.[48] A meeting on high-powered klystrons that August, sponsored by the Microwave Lab, the Joint Research and Development Board, and the ONR, and restricted to cleared personnel, brought a sharp letter of protest from Bloch. Although Bloch acknowledged that there might be "very exceptional and compelling reasons" for the university to compromise the principle of the free exchange of information, he argued that "research requiring such restrictions belongs primarily to institutions and laboratories where the principle of free research has been openly abandoned."[49] The meeting also brought an offer from the military of a contract to develop new klystron designs suitable for use in the field. Under this contract, klystrons were built to operate

47 Bloch, "Leonard Isaac Schiff," pp. 307–8.
48 Ginzton to Commanding Officer, ONR–San Francisco Branch (attention: Dr. W. Barkas), May 31, 1949, Schiff Papers, Box 14.
49 "F. B.," Sept. 21, 1949, Schiff Papers, Box 17/3. Bloch apparently intended to circulate this memo as a petition, but there is no evidence that he did so.

at higher frequencies (and so in more compact forms) and also to be sealed off and run independently of a laboratory vacuum pumping system, rather than as continuously pumped accelerator units.[50]

Before 1950, then, four kinds of constraints had emerged as a result of government sponsorship. Three of these were imposed directly by the government. The physicists' work had to bear some relationship to military interests; physicists also had to accept restrictions on the dissemination of sensitive information. And they had to demonstrate their commitment to making full use of the government-supported facilities, either by devoting their careers to the machinery or by hiring others who would. The fourth constraint arose from the traditional concerns of the physics department itself: sponsored projects such as the Microwave Lab or, later, SLAC could be constrained if the physicists asserted their departmental prerogatives.

First, on both the engineering side and the physics side of the Microwave Laboratory, the accelerator continued to be relevant to military interests. A two-part contract for the billion-volt machine made the development of a high-power pulsed klystron an explicit task of the project; supplementary military funds for klystron development to be carried out in conjunction with industry also supported the work. And the military's concern with nuclear structure continued. Robert Hofstadter, who arrived in 1950 and was able to begin research on the Mark II, a prototype section of the billion-volt machine, soon had an Armed Forces Special Weapons Project contract for nuclear structure research.[51]

In a second accommodation, the physics department was able to keep the Microwave Laboratory free of security restrictions largely by organizing the university's research program to accommodate classified research, shunting classified projects to the Electronic Research Laboratory and the Applied Electronics Laboratory in Electrical Engineering.[52] The personnel involved in

50 Spangenberg to Terman, Sept. 28, 1949, W. W. Hansen Laboratories Papers, Box 10/17. The Korean War and Project Lincoln both led to expanded support for development of the klystron and traveling wave tube at Stanford, as they did to the electronics field generally. See Leslie, "Playing the Education Game," pp. 69–80, and Forman, "Behind Quantum Electronics," pp. 159–73. Even before the war, Stanford's klystron team had recognized that developing a sealed-off tube would be necessary for extensive application in aircraft. Woodyard, "Amplification and Modulation." See also Sarbacher and Edson, *Hyper- and Ultrahigh Frequency Engineering.*

51 Microwave Laboratory, "Proposal to Expedite and Enlarge the Scope of Studies on Electron-Induced Showers in Various Materials," April 1953, and Hofstadter to Laslett, May 25, 1953, both in W. W. Hansen Laboratories Papers, Box 8/1. On specific funding for klystron development within the accelerator contracts, noting the fact that high-power klystrons were "essential" for long-range radar, see "Proposed Investigation of High-Power Pulsed Klystrons" and ONR Task Order IX to Contract N6onr-251, June 1, 1947, W. W. Hansen Laboratories Papers, Box 1.

52 See, for example, Susskind to Terman, n.d., W. W. Hansen Laboratories Papers, Box 11/11. On Terman's use of the electronics labs for classified research and their place in the growth of Stanford, see Leslie, "Playing the Education Game," pp. 68–72.

such projects did not change, but classified work was restricted to particular locations.

Third, the department was forced, by the presence of the government-sponsored accelerator, to commit faculty to high-energy physics. Most interesting is the department's response to the Navy's insistence that the linear accelerator, once completed, be well used by a leading physicist. After Hansen's death the military sponsors insisted that their "feeling of moral obligation" to fund the project's completion did "not extend to operating years."[53] ONR feared that Stanford's research talent in physics no longer matched the engineering proficiency in the Microwave Lab. Schiff quickly identified himself and Bloch as two of the Stanford physicists "who are expected to play an important part in connection with the development and research use of the linear electron accelerator."[54] He then set about completing a "Survey of Possible Experiments with Linear Electron Accelerators" that emphasized the strengths of linear electron accelerators over synchrotrons and betatrons.

Federal patronage after World War II presented physicists like Schiff with both constraints and opportunities. Already by 1945, in a survey of accelerator techniques, Schiff had realized that the availability of cheap and powerful surplus radar equipment would shape the choice of research tools.[55] At Stanford, such equipment was plentiful, and linear accelerator building had flourished precisely by exploiting the new technologies of waveguides and klystrons. Now the government's influence was felt a second time as Schiff sought to respond to the Navy's demand for a specific accelerator research program. His "Survey of Possible Experiments with Linear Electron Accelerators" emphasized the strengths of linear accelerators over competing devices and sought to bolster Stanford's position by demonstrating that even without Hansen, the physicists were well prepared to conduct a program of physical research.[56] Schiff proposed experiments centered on examination of the deviation of protons from a point-source scattering center, disintegration of heavy nuclei, and meson theories of nuclear structure—a program conforming to the ONR's interest in nuclear structure as determined by Webster and Kirkpatrick. But *writing* the experimental prospectus was for Schiff and Bloch only the first step; carrying it out would require devoting their careers to using the machine, a commitment both men were reluctant to undertake.

Therefore, Bloch proposed the unusual step of offering a job to a Berkeley faculty member, breaking a gentlemen's agreement against cross-bay poaching. W. H. K. Panofsky, disturbed by security restrictions on some activities at Berkeley and standing on principle against the state-required loyalty oath, was

53 F. V. L. Pindar, "Memo of Meetings—Feb. 13, 14 and 15, 1950," W. W. Hansen Laboratories Papers, Box 11.

54 Schiff to Terman and Ginzton, June 8, 1949, Schiff Papers, Box 14.

55 Schiff, "Production of Particle Energies."

56 Schiff, "Survey of Possible Experiments with Linear Electron Accelerators" (Microwave Lab Report no. 102), Webster's copy in Hansen Papers, Box 4/48; "Supervoltage X-ray Committee," Vol. 3, Webster Papers, Box 1; Bloch, "Leonard Isaac Schiff," pp. 303–4.

known to be on the verge of leaving his position. Bloch wrote to Schiff, "Do you think we should exploit the disintegration of U. C. to approach [Panofsky]. . . . He is really exceptionally good and wise and, I think, if he would come, he would do it only, knowing exactly what it implies."[57] With Panofsky as well as Hofstadter at hand to use the Mark III, Schiff and Bloch would be relieved of their responsibility for it. Thus, the physicists accommodated the requirements of government sponsorship, in ways that seemed to meet their own concerns as academics; in return, they hoped to reap the benefits of government support.

The ascension of the experimental physicists at the Microwave Lab also signaled a need for new projects to occupy the klystron engineers. By 1952, with the Mark III ready for action, Ginzton and Chodorow's part in the project had largely been completed. They no longer had a clear role at the Microwave Laboratory; they had neither the training nor the inclination to become nuclear physicists, although they hoped to go on designing new klystrons for larger accelerator systems. The completion of the Mark III and the addition of "two eminent nuclear physicists who are anxious to guide the use of the accelerator in nuclear physics research" not only seemed to assure funding from the ONR and Atomic Energy Commission (AEC) for nuclear research but also raised the need for new space to support the "klystron klan" and its further activities. Ginzton proposed that his group continue in a new location, under the name Microwave Laboratory, while the Mark III be turned over to the physicists and designated the High-Energy Physics Laboratory (HEPL). Both were to be under the aegis of the W. W. Hansen Laboratory of Physics. A glance at the amount of overhead generated for Stanford on klystron contracts, Ginzton suggested, showed that further investment in a new building would more than pay for itself[58] (see Fig. 2.2).

Continuing "as a bridge between Physics and Engineering," the klystron group saw new challenges ahead. "It is possible," Ginzton mused in April 1953, "that in the next few years a *much* larger accelerator than our billion volt may become of national interest."[59] Indeed, the new Microwave Laboratory had already negotiated a bid for a $150,000-to-$200,000 contract with the AEC to carry out design studies for the project; such a machine would require even more advanced microwave technology to be successful.[60] It would clearly provide great opportunities for Stanford's program—and would also impose different limitations on the physicists, strictures some of them would refuse to accept.

57 Bloch to Schiff, Sept. 2, [1950], Schiff Papers, Box 17/3.

58 Ginzton to Hilgard, "Subj: Reorganization of the Microwave Laboratory," and "Subj: The Future Activities of the Microwave Laboratory," Apr. 20, 1953; for a summary of costs to build the original Microwave Laboratory and its overhead earnings, see Ginzton and Pindar to Sterling, Jan. 8, 1952. All in Schiff Papers, Box 14.

59 Ginzton to Hilgard, "Subj: The Future Activities of the Microwave Laboratory," Apr. 20, 1953, p. 4, Schiff Papers, Box 14.

60 Ginzton to Hilgard, "Subj: Reorganization of the Microwave Laboratory," Apr. 20, 1953, p. 3, Schiff Papers, Box 14.

Fig. 2.2. Mark III Linear Electron Accelerator at Stanford's Microwave Laboratory. Photo courtesy Stanford Linear Accelerator Center and the U.S. Department of Energy.

Controlling the Monster

The opportunity to develop a larger linear accelerator appeared earlier than Ginzton had predicted in his letter to Stanford's administration. The principle of strong focusing had made possible the construction of synchro-cylotrons capable of reaching multibillion-electron-volt energies, and the AEC indicated in 1954 that it would be willing to fund such accelerators at a rate of one machine per year.[61] Despite Schiff's avowal in 1949 to university administrators concerned about demands on the university's budget and space that "it is not anticipated that [the Mark III] will be the first of a series of larger and larger machines," the physicists, by 1954, were hoping to take advantage of the AEC's largesse to construct a 25- to 50-billion-electron-volt linear accelerator.[62] The new, larger accelerator would provide Stanford's physicists with access to "a frontier of physics unapproachable by any other means now considered feasible," they explained to the university's president.[63] Again, the Stanford physicists believed that the unique aspects of linear electron accelerators, distinguishing them from machines being built or contemplated elsewhere, gave their proposal a solid claim for federal support. A linear electron accelerator would produce electron and gamma-ray beams of "considerable purity," with better performance than a circular electron accelerator, Schiff noted in a letter to the AEC. And the interactions of electrons and photons with nucleons were simple and well-understood compared to nucleon–nucleon interactions, making Stanford's machines well suited to nuclear structure research.[64]

But, in ways that the proponents of the accelerator did not anticipate, the project also created new sources of conflict, not only between the physicists and the AEC over responsibility for the facility's design and construction, but also among the physicists themselves. The magnitude of the proposed machine, dubbed "Project M," brought to the fore issues that had been smoldering during the early period of the Mark III's operation—how allocation of beam time should be determined, what the appropriate scale of research facilities should be, and what the rights and responsibilities of researchers not holding faculty appointments in the physics department should be.

In their initial presentation of the plan to build a larger accelerator,

---

61 Minutes of meeting of Ginzton, Hofstadter, Schiff, and Panofsky with the AEC's T. H. Johnson and G. A. Kolstad, Oct. 19, 1954, Schiff Papers, Box 14.

62 Schiff to Clarence Faust, acting president of Stanford, Jan. 18, 1949, Wallace Sterling Papers, Stanford University Archives, Box 24/Microwave Lab, 1948–50.

63 Ginzton, Hofstadter, Panofsky, and Schiff to Sterling, Oct. 8, 1954, Terman Papers, Box 2/18/7.

64 Schiff, "Fundamental Physics Aspects of a Multi-BeV Electron Linear Accelerator," attached to Schiff to William E. Wright, Nuclear Physics Branch, ONR, June 6, 1956, Schiff Papers, Box 14.

Ginzton, Hofstadter, Schiff, and Panofsky emphasized that it was in the multibillion-electron-volt range where "great progress" in high-energy physics would be made in the next two decades.[65] Although the Mark III had only recently come into operation and would be a useful research tool for many years to come, the physicists were anxious to "get our hat into the ring" and bid for AEC funds at a time when "many aggressive physicists scattered throughout the country" were "pressing . . . for development at their own institutions."[66] With Project M as a research tool of the physics department, but "self-supporting and separately administered," the physicists hoped to carry out studies of nucleon structure, measure production cross-sections of particles through various techniques, study the production of particle beams and their interactions, and test the limits of quantum electrodynamics.[67] The physicists hoped to build a *university* (not a national) facility, one that would avoid the security restrictions that they felt, and that Panofsky knew from experience, marred the atmosphere of the AEC-funded facilities at neighboring Berkeley.

The physicists' general enthusiasm for the proposed accelerator was not shared by Felix Bloch who, as acting director of CERN in 1954, was familiar with the complexities of administering a large accelerator.[68] The scale and expense of such a project would involve the physicists in "a fantastic [bureaucratic] and political rigamarole," leaving them little time for their own research, he warned Hofstadter in December 1954.[69] Bloch had other concerns as well, concerns shaped by the earlier conflicts involving the Microwave Lab. Bloch pointed out that the proposed facility would likely be "security-hunted," as the Microwave Lab almost had been.[70] He also raised questions about the relationship of Project M to the physics department and about the eventual use of the accelerator. "It was by no means trivial to prevent [the Mark III's] eating up the Physics Department," he reminded Hofstadter. With the multibillion-electron-volt accelerator located at Stanford, the physicists would face "nothing short of an ironclad commitment to use it—or better be used by it," just as the department had earlier been pressured by the Navy to

65 Ginzton, Hofstadter, Panofsky, and Schiff to Sterling, Oct. 8, 1954, Terman Papers, Box 2/18/7.

66 Schiff to Bloch, Dec. 22, 1954, Schiff Papers, Box 17; and Ginzton, Hofstadter, Panofsky, and Schiff to Sterling, Oct. 8, 1954, Terman Papers, Box 2/18/7.

67 Ginzton, Hofstadter, Panofsky, and Schiff to Sterling, Oct. 8, 1954, Terman Papers, Box 2/18/7; Ginzton and Panofsky to E. R. Piore, Chairman, Subcommittee on High-Energy Accelerators, President's Scientific Advisory Committee, Oct. 13, 1958, Schiff Papers, Box 14.

68 Bloch had had strong reservations about accepting the position at CERN and had resigned after fewer than three months, explaining that administrative duties had been heavier than he had expected and had demanded "an almost total sacrifice of [his] scientific work." See Hermann et al., *History of CERN*, vol. 1, pp. 265–72.

69 Bloch to Hofstadter, Dec. 8, 1954, Bloch Papers, Box 1/1/12.

70 Bloch to Hofstadter, Dec. 8, 1954, Bloch Papers, Box 1/1/12.

establish a full-scale research program using the Mark III. Given these likely constraints, Bloch was convinced that "to do physics on a large scale and yet in 'University style'" was impossible.[71]

By 1957, it was clear that the AEC had also come to the same conclusion. As the result of political pressure, the AEC determined that the proposed accelerator would be funded only if the facility were operated as a national lab available to non-Stanford physicists, with control over access to beam time placed in the hands of a committee of physicists from around the country.[72] While Panofsky and Schiff were willing to accept this constraint as unavoidable given the AEC's concerns that it not be accused of favoritism toward Stanford, Hofstadter's enthusiasm for the project waned considerably. "You know I have felt that Project M is starting in what I consider to be the 'wrong way,'" he wrote in September 1958 to Schiff from CERN, where he had a one-year appointment.[73] His unhappiness with the atmosphere at the Geneva facility, which he described as "that of an industrial laboratory," made him all the more certain that he did not "want anything to do with the gadget (M) the way it is going."[74]

Hofstadter had two main objections to organizing "M" as a national lab, both emanating from his experiences with the Mark III and reinforced by his stay at CERN. First, such an arrangement would mean he would not have unlimited access to the machine. For Hofstadter, part of the joy of academic physics was the boundless freedom it offered.[75] In Hofstadter's Princeton experiments (1947–49) on sodium iodide and its application to gamma-ray spectroscopy, he had worked on a table top. The scale of experimentation increased when Hofstadter came to Stanford in 1950 and began a long-term investigation into electron diffraction by the nucleus. In particular, by using the diffraction patterns of recoiling electrons to deduce the distribution of charge within individual protons and neutrons, Hofstadter demonstrated that nucleons could not be regarded as point scatterers—a result that brought him and electron-scattering research sudden prominence. But despite the augmented bulk of equipment, the apparatus remained under Hofstadter's imme-

71 Bloch to Hofstadter, Dec. 8, 1954, Bloch Papers, Box 1/1/12.

72 Between 1955 and 1957, the AEC and its General Advisory Committee (GAC) debated whether such large facilities belonged at universities or at national laboratories. In the spring of 1955, the AEC adopted as general policy the statement of Commissioner Libby that "we cannot build a 25-billion-volt machine at a university without ruining the university and we have rightfully decided we are not going to do this." By 1957, the AEC and GAC favored building the accelerator at Stanford but with the condition that it would become a national laboratory. See "Support of Accelerator Research," policy statement by AEC Commissioner Libby, Mar. 16, 1955, AEC 603/24, U.S. Department of Energy Archives (DOE)/AEC/Secretariat collection/Box 1305, and GAC minutes, 55th meeting, Sept. 30– Oct. 2, 1957, DOE/AEC/GAC collection.

73 Hofstadter to Schiff, Sept. 8, 1958, Schiff Papers, Box 3.

74 Hofstadter to Schiff, Sept. 8 and 28, 1958, Schiff Papers, Box 3.

75 Hofstadter, "Free Spirit in the Free University," commencement address given at City University of New York, June 13, 1962, Terman Papers, Box 3/31/4.

Fig. 2.3. Robert Hofstadter and magnetic spectrometer, Stanford High-Energy Physics Laboratory. This device was used in Hofstadter's electron-nucleon scattering experiments on the Mark III. Photo courtesy Stanford Linear Accelerator Center and the U.S. Department of Energy.

diate control. With the increasing size of the Mark III (and its staff), however, Hofstadter found his time on the machine limited, and he began to chafe under "laboratory arrangements [at HEPL that] do not give our electron-scattering group the amount of running time . . . that it feels would be desirable"[76] (see Fig. 2.3).

Second, Hofstadter feared that at SLAC, as at HEPL, centralized administration would mean "the lack of freedom in control of the research program."[77] He had strongly objected when Panofsky, to ease administrative burdens, had combined all of HEPL's government contracts; this centralized management, he argued, encroached on his independence as a scientist and "would be unthinkable" in other fields, such as low-temperature physics.[78] Panofsky, by contrast, argued that a certain degree of centralized control was needed to maintain the lab's basic structure and to protect the needs of younger faculty and nonfaculty researchers for beam time.[79]

The problems at HEPL were related to the growing scale of physics coupled to the ill-defined relationship between the lab and the physics department; it was a relationship that the physicists, when HEPL was established, had not anticipated as problematic. While the lab had a formal responsibility to the physics department, the position of physics department members using the Mark III relative to the staff of the lab had never been determined. This ambiguity had given Hofstadter some of the freedom he thought necessary for good research; in Panofsky's view, it had meant "a lack of democratic procedures" and a tyranny of the senior physics faculty over HEPL.[80] Through Schiff's mediation the physicists resolved the issue, creating a committee of senior physics faculty to set long-range policy for HEPL and opening up short-range decision-making, including the allocation of beam time, to all those using the Mark III.[81] To Hofstadter, the new arrangement was less than satisfactory; arguing that neither Project M nor the Mark III accorded him the

76 Albert Bowker, dean of the graduate division, to Terman, Oct. 13, 1960, Sterling Papers, Box B-5; Hofstadter to Schiff, Oct. 26, 1960, Schiff Papers, Box 14.

77 Hofstadter to Schiff, Oct. 26, 1960, Schiff Papers, Box 14.

78 Hofstadter to Schiff, Oct. 26, 1960, Schiff Papers, Box 14.

79 The question of directorship of HEPL generated considerable heat between Panofsky and Hofstadter and spawned extensive discussions about HEPL's administrative structure as well as its relationship to the department. See Panofsky to Hofstadter, Dec. 29, 1959, SLAC Archives/Director's Office (DO)/Hofstadter; Hofstadter to Panofsky, Jan. 8, 1959, SLAC/DO/Hofstadter; Hofstadter to Schiff, Jan. 9, 1959, Schiff Papers, Box 3; Panofsky to Hofstadter, Jan. 16, 1959, SLAC/DO/Hofstadter; Schiff to Hofstadter, Jan. 18, 1959, Schiff Papers, Box 3; Hofstadter to Panofsky, Jan. 26, 1959, SLAC/DO/Hofstadter; Hofstadter to Bloch, Feb. 5, 1959, Bloch Papers, Box 1/6/4; Schiff to Bloch, Mar. 12, 1960, Schiff Papers, Box 17; Panofsky to Schiff, Oct. 3, 1960, Schiff Papers, Box 14; Hofstadter to Schiff, Oct. 26, 1960, Schiff Papers, Box 14; and Schiff to Bloch, Drell, Hofstadter, and Panofsky, Oct. 27, 1960, Schiff Papers, Box 14.

80 Panofsky to Schiff, Oct. 3, 1960, Schiff Papers, Box 14.

81 Schiff to Bloch, Drell, Hofstadter, and Panofsky, Oct. 27, 1960, Schiff Papers, Box 14.

control over his research that he desired, he began seeking funds from ONR for another, 3- to 4-billion-electron-volt accelerator.[82]

Although both Hofstadter and Bloch registered unhappiness over the proposed two-mile accelerator, the other physicists began to plan ambitious experiments and to recruit physicists and technicians to join Project M. As an increasingly distinct corporate entity came into existence, strains between the constituents (Project M physicists, the department, Stanford, and the AEC) began to emerge. Disputes centered on three issues: control of the design and construction of SLAC, control of the research program, and the disposition between Stanford and SLAC of salary costs.

The AEC, concerned about the cost overruns that had become routine in the construction of multibillion-electron-volt accelerators, insisted on taking primary responsibility for the design and construction of the facility, with the exception of the accelerator itself[83] (see Figs. 2.4 and 2.5). Panofsky and the other physicists involved in planning SLAC adamantly opposed this, arguing, as Stanford's president explained to the AEC's general manager, that the entire facility, not just the accelerator itself, must be shaped by the scientists if it was to serve their research needs adequately.[84] The extended debates in Congress, and within the Bureau of the Budget, over appropriations for SLAC provided an opening for a resolution of this dispute. When funds were appropriated for only the first phase rather than the entire project, Panofsky proposed, with the AEC's agreement, that Stanford be responsible for design and construction on a "trial-run basis" for this phase of the project.[85]

Less easy to resolve to the physicists' satisfaction were their objections to certain AEC-proposed controls over the research program. The Commission planned to require the University to conform to all AEC security regulations,

---

82 Hofstadter to Jerome Fregeau, ONR, July 23, 1962, Schiff Papers, Box 14. Hofstadter, at one point in the conflict, also considered abandoning high-energy physics altogether. As he wrote to Bloch on Feb. 5, 1959, "I am searching for, and will continue to look for some other branch of physics that will take me away from big machine physics. . . . I don't care for the means by which such physics is now being done." Bloch Papers, Box 1/6/4.

83 John McCone, AEC chairman, to Sterling, Apr. 8, 1960, DOE/AEC/John McCone collection/Box 2276. Wrangling with the AEC was not new to the physicists; since their initial proposal in 1957, the AEC, along with the Joint Committee on Atomic Energy (JCAE), had raised questions about the feasibility of the proposed site and the reliability of the construction and cost estimates. Most irritating of all, the AEC and JCAE had raised questions about a possible conflict of interest in the designation of Ginzton as project director (Ginzton was the chairman of Varian, a likely supplier of klystrons for the accelerator) and had launched an investigation of the physicists' stockholdings and consulting activities. See also "Measures for Proceeding with the Proposed Stanford Accelerator," Report to the General Manager by the Director of Research, May 14, 1958, AEC 603/42, DOE/AEC/Secretariat/1305.

84 Sterling to A. R. Luedecke, AEC general manager, Feb. 26, 1960, Schiff Papers, Box 14.

85 Howard C. Brown, Jr., special assistant to the AEC chairman, memorandum for the files, May 20, 1960, USDOE/AEC/McCone collection, Box 2276.

Fig. 2.4. Construction of SLAC beam housing, October 28, 1963. Photo courtesy Stanford Linear Accelerator Center and the U.S. Department of Energy.

Fig. 2.5. Completed beamline at SLAC, June 1965. Photo courtesy Stanford Linear Accelerator Center and the U.S. Department of Energy.

and to stipulate that in times of national need, the AEC could determine SLAC's experimental program.[86] Panofsky, who "personally led the discussions in voicing the University's objections" to these provisions, struck a bargain with the Commission.[87] The AEC guaranteed free access to the lab by qualified visitors; Panofsky agreed to recognize "that the Commission in connection with its applied mission . . . may from time to time request the University to include certain additional programs in the schedule" of SLAC.

86 John C. Vinciguerra, director, AEC division of contracts, to Luedecke, Dec. 18, 1961, USDOE/AEC/McCone collection, Box 2276.
87 Vinciguerra to Luedecke, Dec. 18, 1961, USDOE/AEC/McCone collection, Box 2276.

These programs, however, would have to be "mutually acceptable" to Stanford and the AEC.[88] As in the earlier case of Sperry sponsorship of department research, the physicists found themselves accepting as unavoidable possible interference by an outside sponsor in their research program.

Panofsky and the other physicists now turned to the issue of hiring faculty for SLAC. Once again, Stanford's physicists found themselves at odds over the relationship between the department and an independent research facility, the delineation of which had not been dealt with during the planning stages of Project M. Their disagreement focused on joint appointments to the physics department and SLAC, which would allow SLAC faculty to teach advanced courses and direct thesis work, responsibilities that Panofsky and Sidney Drell felt were essential in attracting the best scientists to SLAC.[89] The suggestion was acceptable to others in the department on the condition that the entire physics faculty also expanded, to ensure that the department did not become top-heavy with high-energy physicists. But in response to the physicists' request for additional staff positions, Stanford's administration replied that the only possibility for expansion was with money from government contracts to fund the new positions. The physics department had always strongly resisted the practice of salary splitting, which was much encouraged by Provost Frederick Terman, fearing the inconsistent availability of "soft money."[90]

Though sympathizing with the department's stance, Panofsky, Drell, and others such as Dave Ritson and George Pake argued that "whatever objections in principle we have [to salary splitting], we have to admit at a certain time we have lost, we are powerless against Terman, and we are just hurting ourselves."[91] As the debates over the issue grew heated and as the majority of the department's physicists insisted that the best way to ensure "mutual respect and intellectual stimulation" between the department's physicists and those at SLAC was by having no formal links between the two groups, Drell and Panofsky resigned from the physics department to become faculty members of SLAC.[92] The department, under pressure from Stanford's administration, reluctantly agreed to a compromise that did not fully satisfy either side—

88 Panofsky to Schiff, Oct. 22, 1963, Schiff Papers, Box 14.

89 Drell to Panofsky, Mar. 3, 1962, SLAC/DO/Drell.

90 George Pake to Physics Professorial Group, Mar. 5, 1962, Schiff Papers, Box 17. The issue of salary splitting had arisen in 1959 when the physics department, short of teaching staff, appointed a research associate from HEPL to a one-year teaching assistantship in the department. According to Bloch, he was "not the only one who feels rather bad about the 'mixed' appointments." He was particularly concerned "lest it will be considered by the administration as a breach in our wall of principles through which Terman can hope to see his fond dreams of unprincipled opportunism come closer to fulfillment," Nov. 27, 1959, Schiff Papers, Box 17.

91 Drell to Panofsky, Mar. 3, 1962. See also Dave Ritson to Schiff, Feb. 27, 1962, Schiff Papers, Box 14; and Pake to Physics Professorial Group, Mar. 5, 1962.

92 Drell to Schiff, May 12, 1962, Schiff Papers, Box 17. Drell and Panofsky resigned from the department in May 1962.

SLAC faculty would be allowed, at the physics department's discretion, to teach courses and to supervise, in conjunction with a member of the physics department, graduate theses.[93]

At the outset of Project M, as with the microwave lab and with the Mark III, no one was completely sure what type of facility it would be, what its relationship to the physics department would be, or what constraints might be imposed on the project by its sponsor or by the university. These issues were resolved as the project progressed, but, as in the earlier periods, not to the satisfaction of all those involved. The benefits of outside sponsorship—funds otherwise unavailable for large facilities providing the opportunity to explore interesting physical phenomena—were inevitably accompanied by constraints and friction. In the earlier periods, the conflicts emerged in the relationship between the physicists and their sponsor, over security measures and the research program. By the late 1950's, establishing a satisfactory relationship with their sponsor had become, if not easier for the physicists, at least a more routine matter. But new and unanticipated conflicts—with the university and among the physicists themselves—had emerged. The process of shaping their department became not just a battle among the physicists but also one between the department and university administrators eager to exploit federal funds. The physicists also found themselves in conflict with each other, not only over their conceptions of the relationship between the research facilities and the department, but also over more philosophical issues, such as the physicists' relation to their equipment and their independence in pursuit of their research.

Conclusion

Each of the three stages of expansion that we have discussed promised new opportunities for the physicists. And each period was also accompanied by constraints that shaped the way physics was done and eventually led to a search for new ways of organizing research. Sometimes these constraints were explicit and evident; at other times, the limitations appeared only over time, the results of the subtle exigencies of the new organizational structures. Consider the several cycles of opportunities and their corresponding constraints.

Applied physics in the 1930's promised practical uses of the astonishing new microwave technology: aircraft navigation, radio communication, and medical applications. The physicists' developing interests raised problems beyond their experience. Sperry offered a solution to those problems insofar as it took over much of the legal intricacies associated with patent work and provided a much-needed infusion of funds for further research. Soon, however, the company began to compete with the physicists for control of the direction of the work and the personnel assigned to it, rights to the disclosure of proprietary information, and the prerogative to determine the distribution

93 Physics department memo on the relationship between SLAC and the department, May 23, 1962, Sterling Papers, Box B-5.

between innovation and litigation of the physicists' time. For some members of the department, most notably Webster, the loss of control to Sperry came to outweigh the new opportunities afforded by the company's resources.

With the entry of the United States into World War II, wary attitudes toward federal support began to change. The physicists' positive wartime experience in centralized, mission-directed laboratories at Los Alamos, MIT, Aberdeen, and Harvard served as guiding images of what might be possible after the war. Federal sponsorship began to seem an ideal solution to the constraints that appeared endemic to university–industrial relations. Therefore, during the war, the department, counting on government, as well as royalty, and industrial resources, began to plan a quasi-autonomous microwave laboratory. Again, the new source of support presented the physicists with new opportunities for research, and again, it constrained them in ways that became clear only as the institution took shape. Soon, for example, the Navy began to issue lists of acceptable research subjects; classification, not proprietary concerns, now came to limit the free dissemination of ideas.

Hansen and others debated how to draw upon these new opportunities, searching for the right product to "sell" the government, so long as it was "not our soul." But, and this is in many ways the crucial point, not all of the consequent constraints resulted from a Faustian pact such as Hansen's language implies. Some of the pressure to make accommodations arose from the bureaucratic structure itself. For example, how would teaching opportunities and responsibilities be parsed between the Microwave Laboratory and the department? How would resources be divided? Other constraints arose from the special kind of peer review that controlled ONR resources, as when the Navy pushed the Stanford microwave team to think beyond accelerator building and to devote additional staff to planning for physical experimentation using the accelerator.

As the Mark III neared completion in 1953, the enthusiasm for more accelerator building swept onward. But just as Webster had determined that the loss of control to industry had become too high a price for additional resources, now Bloch came to feel the same way about the next stage of expansion. Arguing that security restrictions and the scale of M would overwhelm the department and eliminate the "university style" of physics, Bloch resisted this next step. Meanwhile, the AEC argued on the opposite side—that the university was retaining too *much* control and that the government should have the right to determine the direction of research in times of national need. Later, as the project advanced to the next stage of planning, Hofstadter, who at first had been a proponent of M, became concerned that he would utterly lose control of his time on the machine as the facility came under the direction of a centralized program committee. Again paralleling concerns first raised in relation to Sperry and then in the context of the Microwave Laboratory, the department, the university's administration, and the sponsoring body clashed over the status of faculty positions dedicated to the new research entity.

Taken in isolation, the various disputes over salary splitting, time on the machine, proprietary secrets, military classification, teaching duties, and administrative autonomy may seem to be merely the ordinary business of academic politics. Viewed historically, it becomes clear that much more was at stake. These issues of control ultimately play a constitutive role in defining who is a physicist and what is the nature of physics research. Can the individual physicist determine the direction of research? Is he or she answerable to a centralized research facility? Where are the boundaries of authority between individual, department, university, and research sponsor? Is patent defense a part of the job? Does the government have the right to redirect the research of the laboratory? These questions continued to be debated in the decades following the establishment of SLAC, but at Stanford their formulation in the periods 1935–41, 1941–54, and 1954–62 changed forever the physicists' role in modern research.

Acknowledgments

For support of part of this research, the authors are grateful to SLAC both for permission to use archival materials and for financial support. We would especially like to thank William Kirk and Burton Richter for their help. We would like to acknowledge the Stanford University archives, in particular Roxanne Nilan, who assisted us with many inquiries, and we are grateful for permission to reference material from this collection. For support of this research, one of us, Peter Galison, wishes to acknowledge NSF grant (No. DIR 8911508).

References Cited

Beer, John Joseph. "The Emergence of the German Chemical Dye Industry." *Illinois Studies in the Social Sciences* 44 (1959).

Bloch, Felix. "Leonard Isaac Schiff." *National Academy of Science Biographical Memoirs* 54 (1983): 301–23.

Forman, Paul. "Behind Quantum Electronics." *Historical Studies in the Physical and Biological Sciences* 18 (1987): 149–229.

Galison, Peter. "Bubble Chambers and the Experimental Workplace." In Peter Achinstein and Owen Hannaway, eds., *Observation, Experiment, and Hypothesis in Modern Physical Science.* Cambridge, Mass.: MIT Press, 1985.

———. *How Experiments End.* Chicago: University of Chicago Press, 1987.

———. "Physics Between War and Peace." In E. Mendelsohn and M. R. Smith, eds., *Science, Technology, and the Military.* Sociology of the Sciences Yearbook, 1988. Dordrecht: Kluwer Academic Publishers, 1988.

Ginzton, Edward L. "The $100 Idea." *IEEE Spectrum* 12 (1975): 30–39.

Ginzton, Edward L., William W. Hansen, and W. R. Kennedy. "A Linear Electron Accelerator." *Review of Scientific Instruments* 19 (1948): 89–108.

Hansen, William W. "A Type of Electrical Resonator." *Journal of Applied Physics* 9 (1938): 654–63.

————. "Accelerating the Electron." *ONR Research Reviews,* Aug. 15, 1948.

Heilbron, J. L., Robert W. Seidel, and Bruce R. Wheaton. *Lawrence and His Laboratory: Nuclear Science at Berkeley, 1931–1961.* Berkeley: Office for History of Science and Technology, 1981.

Hermann, Armin, John Krige, Ulrike Mersits, and Dominique Pestre. *History of CERN,* Vol. 1, *Launching the European Organization for Nuclear Research.* Amsterdam: North Holland, 1987.

Hughes, Thomas P. "The Science Technology Interaction: The Case of High-Voltage Power Transmission Systems." *Technology and Culture* 17 (1976): 646–62.

Kargon, Robert H. "Temple to Science: Cooperative Research and the Birth of the California Institute of Technology." *Historical Studies in the Physical Sciences* 8 (1977): 3–31.

————. "Birth Cries of the Elements: Theory and Experiment Along Millikan's Route to Cosmic Rays." In H. Woolf, ed., *The Analytic Spirit.* Ithaca, N.Y.: Cornell University Press, 1981.

————. *The Rise of Robert Millikan: Portrait of a Life in American Science.* Ithaca, N.Y.: Cornell University Press, 1982.

Kirkpatrick, Paul. "David Locke Webster II." *National Academy of Sciences Biographical Memoirs* 53 (1982): 367–400.

Leslie, Stuart W. "Playing the Education Game to Win: The Military and Interdisciplinary Research at Stanford." *Historical Studies in the Physical and Biological Sciences* 18 (1987): 55–88.

Leslie, Stuart W., and Bruce Hevly. "Steeple Building at Stanford: Electrical Engineering, Physics, and Microwave Research." *IEEE Proceedings* 73 (1985): 1169–80.

Sarbacher, Robert I., and William A. Edson. *Hyper- and Ultrahigh Frequency Engineering.* New York: Wiley, 1943.

Schiff, L. I. "Production of Particle Energies Beyond 200 MeV." *Review of Scientific Instruments* 17 (1946): 6–14.

Seidel, Robert W. "Physics Research in California: The Rise of a Leading Sector in American Physics." Ph.D. diss., University of California, Berkeley, 1978.

Servos, John W. "The Industrial Relations of Science: Chemical Engineering at MIT, 1900–1939." *Isis* 71 (1980): 531–49.

Smith, John K. "The Ten-Year Invention: Neoprene and Du Pont Research, 1930–1939." *Technology and Culture* 26 (1985): 34–55.

Varian, Dorothy. *The Inventor and the Pilot.* Palo Alto, Calif.: Pacific Books, 1983.

Varian, R., and S. F. Varian. "A High Frequency Amplifier and Oscillator." *Journal of Applied Physics* 10 (1939): 140, 321.

Webster, David L. "Cathode Ray Bunching." *Journal of Applied Physics* 10 (1939): 501–8.

————. "Klystron Generators." *Journal of Applied Physics* 10 (1939): 864–72.

Wise, George. "Ionists in Industry: Physical Chemistry at General Electric, 1900–1915." *Isis* 74 (1983): 7–21.

Woodyard, John R. "Amplification and Modulation at High Frequencies by Electron Velocity Control." Ph.D. diss., Stanford University, 1940.

CHAPTER 3

Some Thoughts on the Early History of CERN

Dominique Pestre and John Krige

T he history of the first decade and a half of the life of CERN, the European Organization for Nuclear Research, has now been written.[1] For some six years we have immersed ourselves in the social, political, and institutional, as well as the scientific and technical, aspects of the organization's birth and development. Now, in this chapter, we step back a little and focus attention on two major themes that have emerged from our work. We have chosen them for their methodological interest, and because they help to bring out how the situation at CERN, an intergovernmental laboratory built from scratch,[2] differed from that in "comparable" American high-energy physics laboratories.

1 The results have been published in Hermann et al., *History of CERN*, vols. 1 and 2. Our chapters in these books are based on papers we have found in the CERN archives and some national archives and are extensively documented. In the interests of efficiency we shall thus not refer to primary source material in what follows, preferring simply to indicate the chapters in these two volumes where further details may be found.

2 There is an extensive and growing literature on the development of big science facilities in the United States. Besides other chapters in this book, see Leslie, "Playing the Education Game," for Stanford; Heilbron, Seidel, and Wheaton, *Lawrence and His Laboratory*, and Seidel, "Accelerating Science," for Berkeley; Hoddeson, "KEK and Fermilab," and Westfall, "The First 'Truly National Laboratory'" for Fermilab. For studies of similar

Physicists, Politicians, and State Bureaucracies in Europe and at CERN

The How and the Why of the Birth of CERN

To develop the points we want to make on this issue, we need first to give a thumbnail sketch of the main events and personalities involved in the launching of CERN.[3]

Toward the end of 1949 several persons associated with nuclear matters in Europe began to think seriously about the possibilities for multinational cooperation in this area. The most important of the first initiatives was that taken by Raoul Dautry, Administrator-General of the French Commissariat à l'Energie Atomique (CEA). At a European Cultural Conference in Switzerland in December 1949, he had a resolution passed recommending that studies be undertaken for the creation of a European institute for nuclear science "directed toward applications in everyday life." Six months later Isidor I. Rabi, inspired in part by the launch of the Brookhaven National Laboratory, put a resolution to the annual conference of UNESCO in Florence, which he attended as a member of the American delegation. Rabi invited the states who so wished to create one or more regional European laboratories, including one in nuclear science. The resolution was adopted by UNESCO's General Assembly on June 7, 1950.

Two small groups took up these proposals in the following months. One comprised a handful of specialists in classical nuclear physics (people such as Lew Kowarski in France and Peter Preisswerk in Switzerland) and in cosmic rays (most notably Edoardo Amaldi in Italy and Pierre Auger in France). The other group was composed of three important administrators of science— Raoul Dautry, Gustavo Colonnetti (president of the Italian Consiglio Nazionale delle Ricerche), and Jean Willems (director of the Belgian Fonds National de la Recherche Scientifique). In December 1950 a first gathering of scientists and administrators organized by Auger—also the director of UNESCO's Department of Exact and Natural Sciences—and Dautry proposed that the biggest accelerator in the world (i.e., about 6 billion electron volts, so just bigger than the Bevatron) be constructed. A reactor was ruled out for political reasons, notably the problems posed by military and industrial applications.

In May, October, and November of the following year (1951), Auger, along with a number of scientific consultants, further refined the project advocated in Geneva. In December 1951 their recommendations were submit-

---

developments in Japan, see Hoddeson, "KEK and Fermilab," and Traweek, Chapter 4, this volume.

   3 This section is based on Hermann et al., *History of CERN*, vol. 1, chapters 2–8 and 14. See also Pestre and Krige, "La naissance du CERN."

ted to a European intergovernmental conference officially called by UNESCO but in fact orchestrated by Auger himself. After lengthy discussions that reflected serious differences of opinion among the scientists attending, the conference proposed that a temporary organization be established. It was endowed with $200,000 and given eighteen months to present potential member-states with worked-out technical, organizational, and financial plans. The formal agreement embodying these proposals was signed on February 15, 1952, by all nations represented, except the United Kingdom. Early in May, with the $200,000 guaranteed, and five signatures ratified, the agreement entered into force.

The provisional CERN Council held its first meeting on May 5, 1952. The technical groups to design the accelerators and plan the laboratory were set up. In October Geneva was adopted as the site for the laboratory, and construction of a 25- to 30-billion-electron-volt proton synchrotron embodying the new alternating gradient principle recently announced at Brookhaven was decided on. This meant that a research and development effort—with its associated risks—was needed, and that the machine would take some five or six years to build. In January 1953 the British government was represented officially in the Council for the first time, and the discussion of the text of the convention establishing the permanent organization began in earnest. On July 1, 1953, this convention was signed by eight of the eleven member-states of the provisional CERN and by the United Kingdom. It entered officially into force fifteen months later, and on October 7, 1954, the "permanent" CERN Council met for the first time.

Now that we have some idea of the circumstances surrounding the birth of CERN, we want to discuss critically one of the more conventional ways in which its creation has been explained. Against the tendency to limit the account to a static analysis in terms of sociopolitical forces (the European movement, the military, etc.), we would stress that, if one really wants to understand what happened, it is crucial to follow *also* the events as they unfolded, to recompose the exact historical process leading to the CERN we know.[4] Of course it is important, in historical work, not to restrict oneself to the narrative dimension, to the ways in which individual actors relate concretely to one another—but neither must one ignore this dimension and focus only on more global aspects and large-scale explanations. A balance between the two must be found, a balance that is not the same always and everywhere and depends very much on the subject under study. Our conclusion is that, in the *particular* case of CERN's creation, the former dimension was the more

4 The importance of studying the minutiae of the process of decision making was brought home to us by Allison, *Essence of Decision,* and other works by the same school, and reinforced by Rudwick, *The Great Devonian Controversy.* For a more extensive bibliography, see Pestre, "Les décisions de très gros équipements."

decisive, that an analysis in terms of *process* provides the key to understanding. The basic reason for this is that no historical "necessity" imbued the birth of CERN, that this laboratory "might not have been" or might have emerged with a very different shape from the one it has.

As a working hypothesis the assumption of a degree of inevitability may be defensible if one were to write the history of the atomic energy establishments created in the scientifically advanced European countries in 1945 and 1946, bodies like France's CEA or Britain's Harwell. As Gilpin, Salomon, and others have emphasized, with the explosion of the bomb, science, and nuclear science in particular, moved from the periphery to the center of the political process. The governments of major powers had little choice but to develop their own atomic energy programs if they wished to retain their influence. In the case of CERN, however, there was less compulsion, and the situation was far more fluid, indeterminate, and subject to the day-to-day course of events. Here it is more valuable to accept that there were coincidental elements in the creation of the organization, that "chance" also played a role in the precise definition of what became CERN. Thus the obligation to lose nothing of the concrete process through which events gradually evolved.[5]

The opposite of what we believe should be done is illustrated by the way in which the "founders" of CERN, writing in the 1960's and 1970's, described the birth of the organization.[6] Seeking to explain the existence of CERN—or, more precisely, why it *could not but exist*—they identified two main historical forces. The first was that of the politicians then favoring collaborative European bodies like the European Economic Community; the second was that of the nuclear physicists who held that no single European state had either the financial or human resources needed to build the big laboratories that were the key to the future of physics. At the intersection of these two historical forces we find CERN, a *European* laboratory devoted to fundamental *particle physics*, a field sharing in the glamour of nuclear science but free of the nuclear "problem"—applications, particularly military.

The fascination of this kind of explanation is clear: above all, it seems to grasp immediately the essence of the matter. And though we are the first to admit that it is of some considerable value, we make two radical objections to it, all the same. First, it appeals to a statics of forces indifferent to the actual course of events and sees CERN simply as the "inevitable" resultant. Second, it is retrospective because it tends to consider the result (CERN in 1954) as

5 The references are to Gilpin, *American Scientists and Nuclear Weapons Policy*, and Salomon, *Science et politique*. The relative absence of "necessity" in the birth of the international organization that is CERN has been brought out in our conclusion to Hermann et al., *History of CERN*, vol. 1, chapter 14, while Krige, "The Installation of High-Energy Accelerators in Britain" illustrated the contrasting "inevitability" in the launch of a new national accelerator building project immediately after the war.

6 Typically, Kowarski, "New Forms of Organization."

having been the conscious goal of all from the start, as if the outcome were the simple, logical, and necessary response to an immutable and unambiguously posed question: how to equip *Europe* with a *prestigious* collaborative institute in *fundamental* nuclear physics. As it turns out, this is factually wrong and leads to unacceptable simplifications in the description of what actually happened. Let us merely say that the scientific community was neither united nor clearly "aware" of where its "best" interests lay. For Niels Bohr, James Chadwick, and Hendrik Kramers, for example, it was not obvious that the construction of the most powerful accelerator in the world was either necessary or desirable. The European spirit was neither as widespread nor as decisive as the story would lead us to believe—it counted for little if anything in Britain, for example. And many states hesitated about getting involved in a business whose long-term development was difficult to foresee and which they did not control.[7]

The problem with this kind of explanation, then, is that it "forgets" that it is dealing with a specific historical process and that, in the very particular case of CERN, the main actors enjoyed a large degree of autonomy with respect to the scientific establishment *and* to the state bureaucracies of the day. This was possible because at the end of the 1940's most European countries had neither a clearly formulated policy for science nor organs of state in charge of such questions. Individuals were thus left "free" to act as champions of "products" that they then managed to "sell" to key people in their government. Although each state's attitudes differed, particularly with the passage of time, they shared one characteristic: the states as such played a relatively passive role or, more precisely, were kept at arm's length from the process of CERN's creation, in a reactive position, and were not given any real chance to take the initiative. Power remained effectively in the hands of a group of people who were at once influential at home and free to act from personal conviction without having to wait for an official mandate. In a sense—and here we touch on a decisive conjuncture that forbids us to argue simply in terms of big forces explaining the (necessary) how of CERN—this facility was fortunate in being the *first* postwar European collaborative scientific venture. A decade later, when scientists connected with CERN tried to pull it off again, by setting up comparable bodies for space research, they encountered a stronger resistance by most of the states—and they found it far more difficult to control "their" project.

Was There Not an "Intimate Embrace" of Science and the Military Behind the Birth of CERN?

One of the major contemporary themes in American historiography of science is the importance of the role played by the military in the postwar

7 The opposition to "Auger's" project by leading members of the European scientific establishment has been studied in depth by Pestre in Hermann et al., *History of CERN*, vol. 1, chapters 5 and 6. The situation in Britain is described at length by Krige in Hermann et al., *History of CERN*, vol. 1, chapters 12 and 13.

development of fundamental research in the United States.[8] That granted, it is only natural to wonder whether a similar situation did not prevail on the other side of the Atlantic, whether, as Pickering has put it, "the wartime embrace of science and the military was not dissolved in peace" in Europe as in America. Put differently, and against the line of argument we have just developed, the American situation may lead one to suspect that there was, in fact, at least one major sociopolitical force that imbued the birth of CERN with "necessity," namely, the military.

Now there is no doubt that the military in Europe were *kept informed* of the launching of CERN, and were "aware" of the strategic importance of nuclear science. At the same time all the evidence suggests that rather than showing a strong interest in the laboratory, the "European" military—the military establishments in France, Britain, Italy, and so on—were relatively *indifferent* to it. If they were willing to let it be set up, it was because this laboratory was in no way one of their priorities. Perhaps it could serve as a training ground for a pool of unique expertise that could be useful elsewhere— as the scientists pushing the project reminded their governments—but this was not enough to convince the military to play an active part, a direct role, in the process leading to the creation of CERN.

At the most general level this attitude is not surprising, and seems to be consistent with our overall thesis. All the same, granted the importance of this question, we need to go a little further than this. Let us begin by asking why governments were apparently ready to finance the project laid before them by some of their advisors. The answers: foreign policy (to build Europe), to make up a gap in science and technology (the Continent vis-à-vis Great Britain and the United States), to help put a country back on the international map (this was the case for Germany)—*and* because CERN, an *international* organization, did not disturb the major European political–military equilibrium. Because CERN was to be *restricted* to doing fundamental research, no expert (even among the military) believed that CERN would meaningfully affect *national* interest (military interests included).

One objection that can be made to this line of reasoning is that the military and industrial interests of science, and of basic nuclear research in particular, were sometimes put forward to stimulate a positive attitude toward CERN. We know that some physicists (Werner Heisenberg, Francis Perrin), as well as certain high state officials (Gustavo Colonnetti in Italy, Sir Ben Lockspeiser in Britain), did this on some occasions.[9] Such arguments, however, never ap-

8 Some recent studies are those of Kevles, Chapter 12, this volume, Leslie, "Playing the Education Game," Pickering, "Pragmatism in Particle Physics," Sapolsky, "Military Support for Academic Research," Schweber, "Some Reflections on the History of Particle Physics," and "The Empiricist Temper Regnant," and the whole edition of *Historical Studies in the Physical and Biological Sciences* edited by Seidel. The quotation in the following sentence is from Pickering's review of Hermann et al., vol. 1.

9 This is discussed in a little more depth in Hermann et al., *History of CERN*, vol. 1, chapter 14, section 9. In this volume there is the reproduction of a letter from Gustavo

pealed to benefits that might flow directly from CERN, and were put forward at a time when it was more or less uncritically assumed that fundamental research "automatically" produced useful technology. In other words, these arguments seem always to have been advanced within the vague if classical political framework of "who knows what might come out of basic science." And because they were used infrequently and unsystematically, we believe that they were of secondary importance, just a tactic, and not a particularly central one at that, used to sell the project.

It might then be argued that we are naive, that we have been the unwitting victims of a kind of conspiracy of silence: if there is little reference to military importance in the correspondence or in the minutes of top-level meetings inside governments, it does not prove that the military were not extremely interested. It simply shows that they were prudent, or that the matter was so evident to all that it was left unsaid. We make three observations in reply to this. First, when the military did speak in interministerial meetings—as they sometimes did—they said quite explicitly that they were not opposed to the CERN project *because* they expected no spin-offs from its research. When they did hope for useful results, even if only in the long term, they asked for the projects to remain *national* (such as Harwell's high-intensity linear accelerator). Second, at no time and among none of the member-states did the military show any desire to "control" the laboratory even a little, leaving the departments of foreign affairs (in France, for example) or the departments responsible for basic civil research (such as the Department of Scientific and Industrial Research [DSIR] in Great Britain) to take charge of the matter. Finally, the military never considered paying a penny, even under the cover of another national institution. We add one more argument. Because CERN was to be *multinational,* involving countries as diverse as neutral Switzerland, the United Kingdom, and Yugoslavia (in the context of the Korean War!), its protagonists, as well as the governments, tried their best to "de-ideologize" the project, to disconnect it from everything that could be of military interest. In fact, it was precisely by "depoliticizing" CERN—so carefully avoiding any interactions with the military—that the Council could win the support of the member-states while retaining the freedom it wanted. After all, CERN would only do "pure" science for the benefit of everybody.

To conclude this point on the creation of CERN, we want to insist again on the originality of our case. Unlike America's Lawrence Radiation Laboratory or France's CEA, CERN was not a body that grew *organically* out of the

---

Colonnetti to Alcide de Gasperi, the President of the Italian Council of Ministers, arguing that Italy should join CERN and stressing the importance of the need to "mobilize science and scientists for national defense." Colonnetti also argued that the money channeled to (all sectors of) science through the main civil research council, the Consiglio Nazionale delle Ricerche, should be considered "as an integral part of defense expenditure."

national soil, in an "intimate embrace" with national and military interests. On the contrary, it was an *unnatural, multinational* creation, endowed with a very special shape, the product of a unique gestation process, during which nothing necessitated that it come into being and in which the military played virtually no role at all. In brief, we are inclined to maintain the uniqueness of CERN with respect to equivalent national laboratories in the United States *and* in Europe.

The Council and the Member-States in the 1950's and 1960's

CERN is of interest to those who like to explore the enduring relationships between states and big science laboratories for two reasons. First, we are dealing not with a simple relation between one political and one scientific network but, because of CERN's multinationality, with the interactions between many such networks. Second, among the many examples of communal laboratories in Europe, CERN is almost always regarded as the most obvious success, the one that has found the right recipe, the right balance in its dealings with national governments.

What characterized the "CERN system" during this period was the existence of a central group, composed equally of scientists and "political" personalities, the CERN Council.[10] This body was at once extremely powerful and blessed with a large degree of autonomy from state authorities. Formally located between the national state bureaucracies, which paid for CERN and gave its members their "directives," and the CERN Director-General, whom it appointed but who was the real master of the laboratory, the Council knew how to make itself the central pivot of CERN's policy. Though legally comprising delegates appointed by the national governments, it appears in fact to have been a body not administratively constituted from above. At its core lay a group of virtually immovable men who rotated the powerful posts among themselves. Consisting essentially of personalities who played a leading role in CERN's birth in 1951 and 1952, this group enjoyed a kind of historical legitimacy that the states never challenged—except once in 1961 when the United Kingdom tried and failed. Welded together through a struggle that had lasted for years, determined to see their child prodigy succeed completely, they became known as the "founding fathers."

Aware of the balance of forces between countries and within each country, careful not to offend anyone, this group always tried to achieve unanimity in the Council, thereby aiming to give governments as little opportunity as possible to intervene directly, or to complain. However, they always carefully avoided having this search for consensus become a formal institutional procedure; the rules for making decisions in the Council never required unanim-

10 On this notion of CERN system, see Pestre in Hermann et al., *History of CERN,* vol. 2, chapter 7, especially section 1.3.

ity, even for the adoption of the budget. In this way the historical core managed to maintain a real feeling of unity and adventure in the body of the Council—and ensured that no one state alone could block the functioning of the organization (one or two "recalcitrant" governments could always be outvoted). In other words, the Council was not only the organ representing the states and responsible for *controlling* CERN, but also the body expected to *advise* the same states on matters concerning CERN and high-energy physics. And it saw its meetings as providing an opportunity for collective reflection and elaboration, particularly on how best to plead for the development of the organization before the national authorities.

Underpinned by this wish for cohesion, and by the desire to see CERN grow as best it might, this group thus kept on with the original adventure into which it had been launched at the very beginning of the 1950's, keeping the states at their distance, but for the "greater good" of each government. Because it operated in a field considered prestigious, high-energy physics, and exemplified stable collaboration and technical efficacy, it raised little opposition in the member-states. The support of the more determined governments dragged along the more hesitant ones, the situation varying according to the hazards of international politics, changing economic circumstances, and the evolution of domestic policies for science.

This very brief summary calls for one important refinement. United as it was around its shared roots and the determination to see "its" laboratory succeed, the Council always worked very closely with the European high-energy physics establishment. Around 1962 and 1963 this mixed group of diplomats and influential scientists conceived the project of integrating CERN more obviously into a European "pyramid" of institutions and laboratories whose development could be achieved only collectively, in planned harmony of one with the other. There was a tactical dimension to this wish to associate all European laboratories with CERN's work; it amounted to having everyone accept CERN's place at the apex of the European accelerator pyramid and it avoided making enemies of those who had paid for CERN. Given a place apart, outside any direct competition for money, CERN had a unique and specific task all the same: to be as good as the best American institutions. In 1963 this way of seeing things was ratified during the first meetings held by the European Committee for Future Accelerators (ECFA).[11]

Having considerable influence over their national authorities, and increasingly enjoying the support of the European high-energy physics establishment, the members of the CERN Council were able to ensure that the pursuit of national interests, insofar as it had any importance at all, generally tended to reinforce the development of CERN rather than to stifle it. This is not to say that one can look to CERN as a model for multinational collaboration. On the contrary, the specificity of the case, the circumstances surrounding its birth,

11 For more details on the role of ECFA, see Pestre in Hermann et al., *History of CERN,* vol. 2, chapter 12, notably sections 4 and 5.

and the unique nature of its research facility in Europe indicate that the species could not—and would not—be reproduced easily. The member-states that have lived with the "CERN system" for over three decades now would not allow it.

The Structure of the European High-Energy Physics Community and Its Effects on Research

Learning to Do "Big Physics"

In the early 1960's the Europeans had to learn to work together in this organization created out of nothing, this CERN without a past, without history, without tradition—but endowed with basic equipment more or less as good as the best across the Atlantic. The result was what they themselves saw as a difficulty to adapt to a scale of experimentation two or three orders of magnitude greater than what they were used to. What they remembered were the big discoveries they let slip through their fingers to the benefit of America's Brookhaven National Laboratory. It was there that the existence of two neutrinos was confirmed experimentally in 1962, where the Ω^- particle predicted by the new SU(3) classification was identified the following year, where substantial evidence for the violation of charge conjugation and parity invariance (CP) was acquired in 1964. The clear initial superiority of Brookhaven in the production of important scientific results, followed by a more comparable performance after 1964, was confirmed by two British researchers a few years ago using the Science Citation Index (SCI) and counting the articles cited more than 30 or 100 times in the four years after their publication.[12] More interesting for our purposes, however, is that Irvine and Martin took the opportunity of their study to ask about 200 American and European physicists the reason for this initial "gap" between CERN and Brookhaven. In the physicists' view four kinds of factors were involved (see Fig. 3.1).

1. CERN's management erred in planning the equipment needed to exploit the accelerator. Already spoken of at CERN in 1961, this *unpreparedness* came down to a lack of magnets, quadrupole lenses, and separators to build secondary beams, and a delay in the building of big detectors, primarily, but not only, bubble chambers.

2. Not only were qualified experimentalists far fewer in Europe than in the United States, they *lacked experience* and had difficulty elaborating a research program focused on the most important physics questions. In 1962 CERN's research director, Gilberto Bernardini, gave this reason as the most important for CERN's trailing behind its American rivals.[13]

3. There were the effects of CERN being *multinational,* effects particularly

12 The findings were presented by Martin and Irvine, "CERN's Position in World High-Energy Physics," and Irvine and Martin, "Scientific Performance of the CERN Accelerators."

13 See CERN Council minutes, June 13, 1962, pp. 14–19.

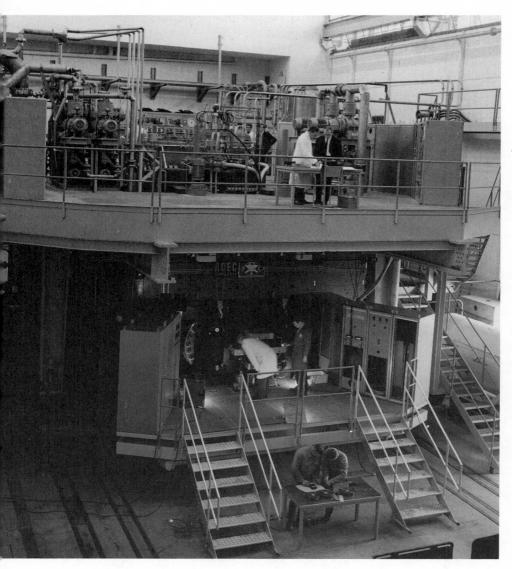

Fig. 3.1. The CERN 2-meter hydrogen bubble chamber, with its surrounding installation, December 1964. Photo courtesy PHOTO CERN.

noticeable in the "cheap proton" policy—have the maximum possible number of experimental groups working around the machine—and the structure of the committees responsible for settling experimental priorities. Cumbersome and slow, CERN's decision making was compared to that at Brookhaven, which was felt to be much more supple and quick because it was concentrated in a few hands, those of Maurice Goldhaber, the director, in particular. While more "cautious" and "democratic," the CERN system was also seen as less efficient than the more "autocratic" procedure at Brookhaven.

4. Finally, *cultural differences* between Americans and Europeans were mentioned, the former being described as more bold and speculative in their approach, the latter as more conservative, more likely to proceed gradually. This was supposedly revealed in the tendency at Geneva to "overdesign" equipment, to design equipment more reliable in the medium to long term at the price of making it available to experimentalists that much later. (The converse of this difference is that the Europeans always produced more systematic and refined results—as Irvine and Martin confirmed.) In the accounts given by American physicists, these last two themes were seen to reflect differences in "style." In contrast to the Europeans, the Americans described themselves as knowing how to get around organizational restraints, as more quick to adapt and to turn a mistake to their advantage, as more capable of grasping the essentials of what has to be done and to ignore "junky" research—in short to be more alert and clever than their European colleagues in what is, above all, a high-pressure race to be the first to make big discoveries.

If we confine ourselves to impressionistic evidence—and accept of course that all that really matters is the race for a Nobel Prize—these accounts can seem convincing. In essence they seek to explain the difference in the production of a few results that the community deems to be decisive by identifying a number of "gaps" between the United States and Europe. The difficulty, however, is that such very global arguments tend to explain "too much," that when confronted closely with concrete cases they appear sometimes true, sometimes false, and sometimes quite irrelevant. Accordingly, to show what we mean, we consider in turn, and in some detail, the exact problems the experimentalists at CERN had to confront in the early 1960's.

Let us begin by looking at the question of the standard equipment necessary for the installation of secondary beams. Since there is no ideal stance from which one can judge the preparations that CERN "ought" to have made, the best alternative is to compare CERN and Brookhaven. First, CERN does not seem to have been later than Brookhaven in placing its first order for magnets and quadrupole lenses. CERN's order was not quantitatively smaller, but it was far less varied (magnets of the same length, relatively fewer quadrupoles, etc.). Second, CERN apparently did not place its second order as quickly as did Brookhaven, nor in the second did CERN rectify the limitations of the first. In seeking to explain these developments we have been led to conclude that no one of sufficient authority at CERN placed a high priority on the design of beams, no one dedicated himself to keeping up with developments in this field, no one thought design of "standard" beams sufficiently important to be preferred over more noble tasks such as building bubble chambers or more sophisticated equipment. At Brookhaven, on the contrary, the secondary beam problem was studied in detail from 1959 onward. If there is an equipment gap to be found here, it is associated with an underestimation of the importance of the problem, with the fact that no one at CERN saw the implantation of "everyday" equipment of this type as being a particularly important job. It was rather neglected in the distribution of key tasks in the organization.[14]

As for less standard beam material, such as electrostatic particle separators, it is interesting that both CERN and BNL initially planned to build similar devices (10-meter tanks), and at about the same time. CERN's separators, however, were ready much later than Brookhaven's, seriously impeding the bubble chamber program until early in 1962. The problem here was twofold. On one hand, starting from nothing, major research and development had to be undertaken in Europe; Brookhaven, for its part, relied on its experience and decided to build smaller devices (about 5 meters long) modeled on those in use at the Cosmotron. This does not tell the whole story, however, because the Europeans *chose* (be it consciously or not) to construct sophisticated, multipurpose separators that took far longer to build than the conventional ones ordered at Brookhaven.[15] This brings to mind the general argument that the Europeans tended to overdesign their apparatus. The trouble with such a formulation is that it obscures differences more fundamental, more at the root of the specific problem we are trying to illuminate here, namely, that in Europe the gap between physicists and engineers was still great, and this gap was inscribed in the structure of the laboratory and its power relations. This gap made it possible for the engineers and builders at CERN to act with considerable autonomy once a task had been given to them, and it allowed them to indulge a tendency to seek technological perfection. It also allowed them to be relatively insensitive to the demands of the physicists for whom big discoveries often meant acting quickly, for whom having an "imperfect" piece of equipment ready at the right moment was often more important than having a "perfect" one ready when the dust of the battle had settled. This clearly happened in the case of electrostatic separators for secondary beams at CERN: the engineering division building them did so at its own pace, without really worrying about physics[16] (see Fig. 3.2).

14 See Krige in Hermann et al., *History of CERN*, vol. 2, chapter 9.
15 *Ibid.*
16 On the institutional reality of these differences, see Pestre in Hermann et al., *History of CERN*, vol. 2, chapter 7, section 2; on the autonomy of "engineers," see the debate about the intersecting storage rings and the 300-GeV PS discussed by Pestre in Hermann et al., *History of CERN*, vol. 2, chapter 12, sections 3 and 6.

Fig. 3.2. European "perfectionism" vs. American "pragmatism." This is one of three giant, very sophisticated electrostatic separators built by CERN in the early 1960's to purify secondary particle beams. Brookhaven initially had similar grandiose plans, but opted for a simpler, more conventional device. CERN's decision meant that the laboratory was late to exploit the potential of its new proton synchrotron when it first worked, although in the years to follow it built some of the best separated beams in the world. Photo courtesy PHOTO CERN.

Before coming back to the differences between physicists and engineers in Europe, we continue with our analysis of the precise problems facing European scientists from 1960 to 1962. Now we want to focus on big detectors, and to try to understand why there was a notable time lag between CERN and BNL—not to speak of Berkeley—in the operation of big bubble and spark chambers. Our impression is that we need to introduce another element here: the fact that European *physicists,* understood in the narrow sense of the term, were not leaders in the field of experimental high-energy physics in the 1950's and 1960's, and that, as a result, they were not the brains behind new instruments *directly connected to the art of experimentation.* At that time at CERN the development of *new* kinds of detectors did not spring from ideas generated by local practice but was generally based on the importation of concepts born and tried out elsewhere. This dependence had two kinds of effects. Unlike a group that innovates, betting on its idea and doing a lot of preliminary research and development before being able to show that its equipment works and is qualitatively superior to other devices, groups not at the heart of the initial research tend to wait and see if the idea is worthwhile.[17] In the case of bubble and spark chambers, the first reaction was to keep an eye on developments, and the decision to "take the plunge" was made only when the advantages of the devices were there for all to see. This is not an indication of a hesitant "nature" or of a systematic propensity to be conservative, but merely an attitude to be expected from *any* group—be it European or American— that is not at the heart of the action. This process leads one, moreover, when the decision is taken to enter the field, to position oneself with regard to the leader(s) and their latest choices and to skip the intermediate stage: this often seems to be the only way to avoid always having obsolete equipment. On the other hand, it accentuates "backwardness" in the short to medium term because the most advanced equipment takes longer to build. These considerations were clearly at work at CERN when it was decided to build a 2-meter hydrogen bubble chamber, the key argument being that Europe's *central* laboratory could not afford to have equipment inferior to what the Americans were building. As a result CERN was without its own big hydrogen bubble chamber in the first years after the proton synchrotron (PS) worked.[18]

Finally let us consider big and sophisticated equipment, which is a response to needs that can be formulated well in advance and are less directly linked to the development of experimentation. We are thinking here of things like radio frequency (RF) separators, whose principles were known but required several years of research and development, or of the neutrino horn invented by Simon

17 See Krige in Hermann et al., *History of CERN,* vol. 2, chapter 9, and Krige and Pestre, "CERN's First Large Bubble Chambers."

18 Krige and Pestre, "CERN's First Large Bubble Chambers," and Pestre in Hermann et al., *History of CERN,* vol. 2, chapter 8, section 6.

van der Meer. Here the Europeans were often leaders and revealed a considerable capacity to imagine and to innovate. We find the same thing in the design and construction of accelerators such as the 28-billion-electron-volt PS, a novel machine based on the newly discovered strong-focusing principle, which the Europeans unhesitatingly chose to build before the Americans had launched their program. The concept of the intersecting storage rings, advocated at CERN from 1960 to 1965, was a response to an innovative drive of a similar kind.[19] In such cases the image of Europeans as more conservative and less innovative than Americans does not fit. Employed indiscriminately, and without specifying to whom it is supposed to apply, the distinction stops one from seeing the more important differences we have already identified. In fact, one must distinguish between instances in which physicists strictly speaking were decisive, in which instrumental developments were associated directly with the art of detection and rooted in physics questions; and cases in which, by contrast, the aim was rather to solve research and development problems, to develop and to improve radically devices whose features were already glimpsed, even if vaguely. In the latter the Europeans do not seem to have been backward at all. On the contrary, they might be considered too bold, too innovative—indeed unwilling—to devote themselves to projects, like standard beam transport equipment, that did not seem to pose a sufficient technical challenge.

American and European Physicists

We have now arrived at the heart of the matter. What happened in the United States between the 1930's and the 1960's—a phenomenon from which the Europeans were largely excluded—was the emergence of a profound symbiosis previously unknown in basic science, a fusion of "pure" science, technology, and engineering. It was the emergence of a new practice, a new way of doing physics, the emergence of a new kind of researcher who can be described at once as *physicist,* in touch with the evolution of the discipline and its key theoretical and experimental issues, as *conceiver of apparatus and engineer,* knowledgeable and innovative in the most advanced techniques (like electronics at that time) and able to put them to good use, and *entrepreneur,* capable of raising large sums of money, of getting people with different expertise together, of mobilizing technical resources. The most successful examples of such men were to be found around Ernest O. Lawrence, who was one of the first to orient his group in this direction. It was men like Luis W. Alvarez, E. Lofgren, Edwin M. McMillan, Wolfgang Panofsky, and Robert R.

19 For the PS, see Krige in Hermann et al., *History of CERN*, vol. 1, chapter 8, section 5; for the intersecting storage rings, see Pestre in Hermann et al., *History of CERN*, vol. 2, chapter 12, section 3.

Wilson, for example, who became the masters of the new physics and who imposed their rhythm on world science.[20]

What characterized them was a pragmatic and utilitarian approach notable for its clear stress on "getting numbers out," an approach preferring results and practical efficacy to means and aesthetic harmony. The approach was rooted in "an educational philosophy that emphasize[d] the empirical, the experimental practice" (Schweber), and was kept alive by the institutional arrangements in American universities that encouraged theoreticians, experimentalists, and apparatus builders to work together.[21] Then there was the experience of the war, which meant lavish financial and technical means, multidisciplinarity, and the linking of people with different educational backgrounds. The war gave Americans an imperative to succeed at whatever cost by using all the technical and industrial resources available. This reinforced the "full-blooded empiricists," the "radical pragmatists," the people for whom all was permissible methodologically, who preferred a heuristic emphasizing improvisation and risk. In physics this stimulated phenomenological approaches and discouraged "a sustained focus and effort on fundamental theory" (Schweber); in practice it brought the engineering side of laboratory work to the fore, notably in the demand for industrially available material to be used in new and interesting ways.[22] Subsequently, once these methods had proved their indisputable efficacy, there was the added bonus of the Cold War and the growing importance of applied research. The American system for supporting science—notably by the Department of Defense and its famous summer schools—as well as the plethora of unexpected and exciting experimental results generated with the new means at hand, consecrated this technical approach to treating problems, far and away the most efficient means for imposing structure and order on a field dragged forward by experimental and technological practices. As a result, fifteen years after the war, the gulf between the United States and Europe was impressively wide.[23]

By contrast, European physicists in the years 1945–60 appear above all as the heirs to a tradition that continued to attach great importance to "pure" science and kept "applied" science separate. It kept fundamental theory, some-

20 For this section, see Holton, "Les hommes de science," Schweber, "Some Reflections on the History of Particle Physics" and "The Empiricist Temper Regnant," the special edition of *Historical Studies in the Physical and Biological Sciences* edited by Seidel, and autobiographical works such as Alvarez, "Recent Developments in Particle Physics," and York, *Making Weapons Talking Peace*. Remarks of the same kind could be made about entrepreneur-engineers like Vannevar Bush or Frederick Terman at Stanford.

21 This is directly inspired by Schweber's remarks on American theoretical physics in "Some Reflections on the History of Particle Physics."

22 This is also inspired by Holton, "Les hommes de science."

23 Among many works, see Godement, "Aux sources du modèle scientifique américain," Kevles, Chapter 12, this volume, and the issue of *Historical Studies in the Physical and Biological Sciences* edited by Seidel.

thing refined, apart from experimental phenomenology, still regarded as of lesser importance in the elaboration of knowledge. Without the stimulus of a war effort European physicists did not become apparatus builders *before all else,* and—even in Britain[24]—remained people for whom the building of big and sophisticated equipment did not derive directly from their expertise. Being experimentalists in the classical sense of the word, they did not become managers immediately able to handle the new scale of activity demanded by big science. An experiment—and even if nuances are needed depending on whether we are talking of electronic detectors or track chambers—remained something one did in the short term, on a human scale, something that was not in itself a permanent race to use equipment constantly having to be changed. In short, experimenting remained primarily the *practice of an art,* secondarily the *mastery of techniques.*[25]

It is for this reason that the engineers who worked around European physicists enjoyed so much autonomy. Indispensable by virtue of the size of certain undertakings, they were put in charge of "all big equipment," and this often led them to become the "real bosses" of the laboratory. In effect, the physicists had to go through them, and only they were ready to manage centers employing one or two thousand people and in which investments were made on a five- or ten-year basis. Kept, by contrast, on the periphery of physics proper—because, after all, that was not their main preoccupation—they remained detached from the urgency of research and the needs growing from it. Excellent at designing equipment whose goals were clearly defined, they could not imagine, starting from an experimental practice they did not have, the new detectors invented by the Americans. Capable of being the first to install a 28-billion-electron-volt PS embodying a new focusing principle, they were not in a position to "invent," to "think of," to "have the idea for" a bubble or spark chamber. Standing back from day-to-day experimental practice—and constrained by certain cultural and educational traditions peculiar to Europe—they tended to prefer technology *per se,* to be "pure" technicians, to refuse boring and unimaginative tasks, to demand the license to explore new avenues, to work on challenging projects. For want of an interface, since no Alvarez or Panofsky existed in Europe, a hiatus was always possible. And more: since this intellectual and professional difference was inscribed in the organization's structure, the phenomenon was amplified, perpetuated, and rigidified.[26]

Now that we have identified the crux of the problem, the core of the

24 For example, see Hoch, "Crystallization of a Strategic Alliance."

25 Victor Weisskopf was well aware of the situation when he gave his first speech at CERN as Director-General (after having spent a year there already). It was reported by Pestre in Hermann et al., *History of CERN,* vol. 2, chapter 7, section 2.4.3.

26 The story of the decision to build the intersecting storage rings conveys much of this feeling—see, for example, Pestre, "Les décisions de très gros équipements."

difference between CERN and the equivalent American laboratories, we are in a position to consider a last argument used to account for the "delays" or the "setbacks" at CERN in the years 1960–65, namely the multinational character of the body, which was said to weigh on and to impede the functioning of its experimental program (the question of the experimental committees) and to allow physicists to perform many experiments of little interest at the expense of giving priority to decisive experiments of lasting significance (the so-called "cheap proton" policy).[27]

We have already alluded to the fact that, because of its *multinationality,* rules and regulations have always been more formalized at CERN than at "ordinary" laboratories. There is, however, an ambiguity in the expression "CERN as multinational laboratory." It conceals two notions that are not distinguished, the fact that CERN brings together several sovereign *states,* and the fact that it is a *central* laboratory for a polycentric physics community (that it is, one might say, a laboratory shared by various groups, similar to Brookhaven). In the early years the first aspect was dominant; CERN was a new business, the wishes of its various member-states did not yet converge, and the relationships between CERN and the national physics communities were somewhat formal. Once *concrete* experimental work got under way around the PS, however, and once it was officially accepted (in 1961 and 1962) that budgets should grow as a matter of policy, there was a radical shift, and the second aspect became prominent. This is clear from the increased autonomy that the executive enjoyed with respect to the Council and the Scientific Policy Committee (SPC)—the latter no longer intervened in the organization of the experimental work after 1961, and we find *very* few "nationalistic" complaints by them regarding the choice of experiments made by the laboratory's directors—and by the fact that the problem became the more general one of the relationship between CERN scientific *staff* and the *visitors-users.* What CERN had to deal with, then, was not what one might imagine—rivalries between national groups that had to be managed by a complex system of experimental committees—but the rapid emergence of a problem common a few years later to *all* big science laboratories, notably the American national laboratories when faced by a user rebellion (Brookhaven in 1964, for example) or trying to spell out how to manage the 200-billion-electron-volt accelerator then being designed near Chicago.[28]

27 Martin and Irvine, "CERN's Position in World High-Energy Physics," and Irvine and Martin, "Scientific Performance of the CERN Accelerators," reporting the opinions of many physicists.

28 See Westfall, "The First 'Truly National Laboratory': The Birth of Fermilab." The point had already been raised during the planning of the Stanford linear accelerator when a number of still unresolved issues—"how allocation of beam time should be determined," "the rights and responsibilities of researchers not holding physics department faculty appointments"—rose to the surface in 1954. See Galison, Hevly, and Lowen, Chapter 2, this volume.

One might object that, even if CERN's multi*nationality* was not responsible for its experiments committee system, this system was very cumbersome all the same and introduced rigidities into the laboratory's functioning. Highly decentralized, comprising three committees specialized in different detection techniques, track chamber, emulsion, electronic, it suffocated rapid adaptations to changing circumstances and impeded the implementation of a central policy concerned above all with crucial experiments.[29] This conclusion, too, would be too hasty, however, and actually would *invert* cause and consequence. Our impression is that the committee system *reflected* the conditions prevailing in the European physics community, that it took the form it did because at the time there were no physicists in Europe having the aura of an Alvarez or a Maurice Goldhaber, because it allowed a community not always that sure of itself to reduce the risks inherent in any autocratic system of management. In this sense it was not so much the source of an overly "prudent" experimental program as a structural counterpart of the situation of European physicists at the time, be they from CERN or from national laboratories, namely, of not yet quite knowing how best to use equipment of the scale of that in Geneva. If the CERN of the years 1960–65 appeared to be a "big photocopier" reproducing and improving novel work done elsewhere,[30] it was because the European *physicists* were learning how to experiment, were learning new ways of doing things with which their American colleagues had been familiar for almost two decades. Their "conservatism" and their "prudence" on the one hand, "the heaviness of their decision-making system" on the other, were thus merely two manifestations of the gap between the two practices, two manifestations of the apprenticeship the Europeans were serving—in the absence of a master, and by a method of trial and error.

29 See Pestre in Hermann et al., *History of CERN*, vol. 2, chapter 8, section 4.

30 The phrase was Pierre Germain's in an interview with Dominique Pestre held on November 14, 1988 (along with Gordon Munday and Peter Standley). Germain was the director of CERN's PS division in the 1960's.

References Cited

Allison, G. T. *Essence of Decision: Explaining the Cuban Missile Crisis.* Boston: Little, Brown & Co., 1971.

Alvarez, Luis W. "Recent Developments in Particle Physics." Nobel Lecture, Dec. 11, 1968. In *Nobel Lectures in Physics, 1963–1970*, pp. 241–90. New York: Elsevier, 1972.

Gilpin, Robert. *American Scientists and Nuclear Weapons Policy.* Princeton: Princeton University Press, 1962.

Godement, Roger. "Aux sources du modèle scientifique américain." *La Pensée* 201 (Oct. 1978): 33–69; 203 (Feb. 1979): 95–122; 204 (Apr. 1979): 86–110.

Heilbron, John, Robert W. Seidel, and Bruce R. Wheaton. *Lawrence and His Laboratory: Nuclear Science at Berkeley, 1931–1961.* Berkeley: Office for History of Science and Technology, 1981.

Hermann, Armin, John Krige, Ulrike Mersits, and Dominique Pestre. *History of CERN,* Vol. 1, *Launching the European Organization for Nuclear Research.* Amsterdam: North Holland, 1987.

———. *History of CERN,* Vol. 2, *Building and Running the Laboratory.* Amsterdam: North Holland, 1990.

Hoch, Paul. "Crystallization of a Strategic Alliance: Big Physics and the Military in the 1940s." In *Program, Papers, and Abstracts for the Joint Conference of the BSHS and the HSS,* pp. 366–74. Manchester, Eng., July 11–15, 1988.

Hoddeson, Lillian. "Establishing KEK in Japan and Fermilab in the U.S.: Internationalism, Nationalism and High Energy Accelerators." *Social Studies of Science* 13 (1983): 1–48.

Holton, Gérard. "Les hommes de science ont-ils besoin d'une philosophie." *Le Débat* 35 (1985): 116–38.

Irvine, John, and Ben R. Martin. "CERN: Past Performance and Future Prospects. II. The Scientific Performance of the CERN Accelerators." *Research Policy* 13 (1984): 247–84.

Kowarski, Lew. "New Forms of Organization in Physical Research After 1945." In C. Weiner, ed., *Rendiconti della Scuola Internazionale di Fisica Enrico Fermi, LVII Corso,* pp. 370–401. New York: Academic Press, 1977.

Krige, John. "The Installation of High-Energy Accelerators in Britain After the War: Big Equipment but not 'Big Science.' " In M. De Maria, M. Grilli, and F. Sebastiani, eds., *The Restructuring of the Physical Sciences in Europe and the United States,* pp. 488–501. Singapore: World Scientific, 1989.

Krige, John, and Dominique Pestre. "The Choice of CERN's First Large Bubble Chambers for the Proton Synchrotron." *Historical Studies in the Physical and Biological Sciences* 16 (1986): 255–79.

Leslie, Stuart W. "Playing the Education Game to Win: The Military and Interdisciplinary Research at Stanford." *Historical Studies in the Physical and Biological Sciences* 18 (1987): 55–88.

Martin, Ben R., and John Irvine. "CERN: Past Performance and Future Prospects. I. CERN's Position in World High-Energy Physics." *Research Policy* 13 (1984): 183–210.

Pestre, Dominique. "Comment se prennent les décisions de très gros équipements dans les laboratoires de 'science lourde' contemporains: Un récit suivi de commentaires." *Revue de Synthèse* 4 (1988): 97–130.

———. "The Creation of CERN in the Early 50s: Chance or Necessity?" In M. De Maria, M. Grilli, and F. Sebastiani, eds., *The Restructuring of the Physical Sciences in Europe and the United States,* pp. 477–87. Singapore: World Scientific, 1989.

Pestre, Dominique, and John Krige. "La naissance du CERN, le comment et le pourquoi." *Relations Internationales* 46 (Summer 1986): 209–26.

Pickering, Andrew. "Pragmatism in Particle Physics: Scientific and Military Interests in the Postwar United States." Paper presented at the History of Science Society Annual Meeting, Bloomington, Ind., Oct. 31–Nov. 3, 1985.

———. Review of Hermann et al., *History of CERN,* vol. 1. *Times Higher Educational Supplement* 19 (Apr. 8, 1988).

Rudwick, Martin J. S. *The Great Devonian Controversy.* Chicago: University of Chicago Press, 1985.

Salomon, Jean-Jacques. *Science et politique*. Paris: Seuil, 1970.

Sapolsky, Harvey M. "Military Support for Academic Research in the United States." Paper prepared for the joint meeting of the U.S. and British History of Science societies, Manchester, Eng., July 1988.

Schweber, Silvan S. "Some Reflections on the History of Particle Physics in the 1950s." In *Pions to Quarks*. Proceedings of the International Symposium on Particle Physics in the 1950's, Fermi National Accelerator Laboratory, May 1–4, 1985.

———. "The Empiricist Temper Regnant: Theoretical Physics in the United States, 1920–1950." *Historical Studies in the Physical and Biological Sciences* 17 (1986): 55–98.

Seidel, Robert W. "Accelerating Science: The Postwar Transformation of the Lawrence Radiation Laboratory." *Historical Studies in the Physical Sciences* 13 (1983): 375–400.

———, ed. *Historical Studies in the Physical and Biological Sciences* 18, part 1, 1987.

Westfall, Catherine. "The First 'Truly National Laboratory': The Birth of Fermilab." Ph.D. diss., Michigan State University, 1988.

York, Herbert F. *Making Weapons Talking Peace*. New York: Basic Books, 1987.

CHAPTER 4

Big Science and Colonialist Discourse: Building High-Energy Physics in Japan

Sharon Traweek

Are there cultural differences in the production of big science? My answer to this question is yes, in many ways. TRISTAN at KEK, a new high-energy physics facility at Tsukuba, a new science city in Japan, provides a fine opportunity to explore this issue: it is a "cultural laboratory" mixing high-energy physicists not only from throughout Japan, but also from Canada, China, England, France, Germany, India, Israel, Korea, the Philippines, Switzerland, and the United States. I did fieldwork there as an anthropologist from April 1986 to July 1987, continuing the participant—observation research I have conducted among high-energy physicists since 1972. How, I wanted to learn, did the physicists of Tsukuba see themselves in relation to the community of scientists in Japan and to the world community of high-energy physicists? How were they seen by these two groups? How do the new science city and KEK fit into the usual practices of research and education in Japan? How do high-energy physicists work with the nuclear and accelerator physicists at the now multidisciplinary KEK? Put differently, I wanted to know the representations the Japanese physicists were making of themselves and their relations with colleagues in other places and other branches of physics, how they were being represented by those colleagues, and how all this was being strategically negotiated and renegotiated in the everyday activities of getting the resources to do physics in ways it had never been done in Japan: "world-class" experimental high-energy physics. Specifically, I wanted to see if cultural differences among Japanese and between Japanese and Americans shaped laboratory practices, both between groups and within groups. After exploring differences within Japan, in later sections of this chapter I turn to important differences (and similarities) between the American and Japanese high-energy physicists' leadership styles, decision making, funding, research organization, gender relations, and succession practices. In these ways an anthropological approach can show not only how diverse a phenomenon "big science" is, but also how its practices are culturally embedded.

I am not a specialist in Japan studies; I see myself as part of a group of about 100 anthropologists and sociologists doing ethnography of science and technology communities. Some of us are concentrating on understanding how these communities constitute and maintain themselves as coherent communities and how they construct the artifacts they call knowledge; this means studying how they recruit and socialize new members, the life-career stages of the initiated, the community's boundary maintenance procedures, the sustenance (funding) practices, the different modes of constructing the equipment and ideas that hold the community's attention, the strategies for acquiring the resources (recruits, funding, network, reputation, etc.) to construct authoritative equipment and ideas, the disputing process for evaluating competing authoritative knowledge claims, and the strategic uses of oral and written modes of communication, as well as the shared ground on which the community stands, tacitly agreeing not to contest.

My analytic approach to this material is closest to what is called symbolic or, more recently, interpretive anthropology, which emphasizes the range of meanings any group of actors constructs to explain, debate, justify, and enable their actions to themselves and others with whom they fully expect to have sustained interactions and by whom they want very much to be understood, although they may not want to reach agreement. Interpretive anthropologists, like the other practitioners of what are usually called "critical cultural studies" (including sociologists, literary critics, critical legal studies researchers, art historians, philosophers, economists, classicists, and historians), attend to patterned communicative practices, such as oral and written discourse or any other "social text" (such as a poem, an article, a detector, or a conference) in which both the form and content convey significant meaning to members of the community. Consequently, "strategic discursive practices" and "representations" are key words in our analytic lexicon. For many years now researchers have been concerned with how relations of power are enacted, accomplished through discursive practices and representations, hence the interest in how communities construct "differences" within themselves and between themselves and others. My work on the international high-energy physics community and big science is a part of this analytic discussion.

In this chapter I begin by discussing the relationship between "big science," "infrastructures" for science and technology, and the emergence of national scientific communities. I then set out to describe how some scientists, Japanese high-energy physicists, try to constitute themselves as a coherent group, how they engage in the practice of doing physics and organizing research, how they try to construct and make use of an "infrastructure" of science and technology in Japan, the strategies they are employing to establish big science in Japan, and how some of them are trying to deploy these accumulating skills and resources to take a larger, more powerful role in the international high-energy physics community. This is a story of outsiders trying to become insiders, the senses they make of themselves, the ways they try to transform themselves, the judgments of those they are trying to join, and the comments of the new outsiders, those physicists with less power, money, status, and equipment than the Japanese but enough to step into the margins of the story.

Center and Periphery

In the mid-1970's Lew Kowarski, one of the key figures in the development of CERN, argued that big science is born of wartime emergency and survives on national and multinational prestige, interdisciplinary efficiency, military-like hierarchies, autocratic leaders, committees, and money. Kowarski only saw two forms of big science practice: the national and the international, and he thought those were converging; he believed that all big science organizations are successful for the same reasons: sharply defined and ambitious objectives, "mixing scientific competence with administrative competence," "participation of respected and strong personalities," and political realism. Kowarski added that all big science labs have the same problems: the proportion of "pure scientists" at these labs dwindles as the new hired hands, administrators, clerks, technicians, and librarians, proliferate; fewer "sacrificially-minded people" are attracted to work in these now affluent sciences; big, caste-stratified teams have no recognized intellectual "master"; and there is a preference for leaders who "play safe." He reminded us that Alvin Weinberg saw three problems with big science: too many publications, too much money, and too much administration, and that Sir John Adams predicted the end of funding increases, which occurred about 1970.

Kowarski then challenged us to imagine "new democratic forms of management" for big science and concluded his address on the organization of postwar physics with a curious aside about cultural differences and big science: big science performs runs yielding measurements and not experiments yielding discovery; "America's vocation seems to be to perform less precise, less reliable measurements, and to make rather more discoveries." Kowarski characterized the United States as a "rather anarchic country . . . [where] all sorts of tendencies . . . clash, and [where] there is no uniform direction, no *Gleichschaltung*, to use the European word." He suggested that it was for these reasons that Americans might discover democratic big science. He seemed to be arguing that cultural differences could eradicate the evils of big science and preserve its virtues.[1]

A fascinating leitmotif in Kowarski's address concerned the relation between big science and public opinion. Certainly big science requires a big audience; Donna Haraway and Bernard Schiele, among others, have shown how this audience is produced and seduced by scientists.[2] The role of this awed audience for science is not to judge the value of the projects of scientists and engineers; its functions are to approve, fund, and to provide recruits, and as Kowarski said, it is essential to big science.

I want to turn from this excluded but necessary other audience for big science to the audience of practitioners, those who are authorized to judge between experiments and runs, between discoveries and measurements. If one gazes at this audience for only a moment, one does not see a collection of equal scientists. Instead, they are ranked, not only individually, but also by nationality. They are nearer and farther from "the action," nearer and farther from stage center.[3] Scientists say that the differential right to judge (or act) in their arena is determined solely by merit; they also argue that scientists are much more likely to be meritorious if they are from Europe or North America (and male). It is this discourse on center and margin, core and periphery, among scientists that concerns me in this chapter. I am interested how this "colonialist discourse" might be reenacted in the organization of large laboratories and research groups, in the daily production of scientists and scientific knowledge.[4] The discourse of dominant and subordinate nations and peoples, I find, is reinscribed in scientific discourse by all its speakers, even the included others, those scientists from subordinated or marginalized nations, regions, and peoples.[5]

In conventional histories of science it is accepted that national scientific communities emerged in a specific order: Italy, Northern Europe, England, Scotland, France, United States, Canada, Soviet Union, Israel, now Japan and Australia, perhaps to be followed soon by India, Brazil, Korea, and Saudi Arabia.[6] A national scientific community is said to have emerged when it

1 Kowarski, "New Forms of Organization in Physical Research After 1945."

2 Haraway, *Primate Visions;* Schiele, "Les enjeux caches," pp. 157–85, "Vulgarisation et television"; Schiele, Perraton, and Boucher, *Ciel, Une Expo!.*

3 On hierarchies and status in high-energy physics, see Traweek, *Beamtimes and Lifetimes,* pp. 106–25.

4 There is an extensive literature on colonialist discourse; some crucial references include, in my opinion, Said, *Orientalism;* Bhabha, "Of Mimicry and Man" and "The Other Question"; Minh-ha, "Of Other Peoples"; "Canons"; "Writing, Race, and Difference," and Group for the Critical Study of Colonial Discourse, *Inscriptions.*

5 On marginalization in the international scientific community, see Restivo and Vanderpool, *Comparative Studies in Science and Society.*

6 For this notion of the sequential emergence of national scientific communities, see Ben-David, *The Scientist's Role in Society,* and Price, *Science Since Babylon.*

displays a fully developed "infrastructure" for science. An infrastructure in-cludes (1) sustained funding for education and research at all levels, from elementary schools to national laboratories, (2) a certain proportion of the country's gross national product (GNP) allocated regularly for scientific work, (3) a certain proportion of the country's population engaged in scientific work, and (4) scientists engaging in a high level of information exchange and docu-mentation about their work.[7] Unquantifiable, but much more significant, is the unqualified acceptance of a country's researchers' observations and anal-ysis by a core country's scientists. For example, it was not until the 1930's that identifications of botanical specimens by American scientists were accepted without question by European scientists.[8] Southeast Asian scientists are only now beginning to acquire that status. Calvin Morrill of Harvard has shown how American scientists routinely challenge the observations of their Brazilian colleagues in Brazil, even if those scientists were trained in the United States.[9]

What the accounts of big science ignore is the necessity for the infrastruc-ture. What the accounts of infrastructure have ignored is not only the neces-sary public audience, but also the necessarily large GNP. Obviously, big science can only be supported by very rich countries. Scientists in rich coun-tries know this and consequently they are suspicious about the quality of scientific work done in poor countries; similarly, those who do big science are suspicious about the quality of little science.

An Anthropologist Among the Physicists at Tsukuba

I decided to observe scientists working in Japan, a nation that, having acquired the large GNP, is now quite rapidly producing the large public audience for science, and beginning to build the coveted infrastructure for an indigenous scientific community. Japan is a country in which only very re-cently did it become possible for ambitious scientists who want international recognition to be able to spend their entire careers working at home, doing research in Japanese (although they must still write in English). More impor-tant, they need not always travel abroad to meet other established scientists because their peers now come to Japan, not only to speak and advise, but to

7 There is an extensive literature on the necessary and sufficient conditions for the development of scientific and technological national communities and on the science policies most efficacious in establishing these conditions. Some works relevant to the situation in Japan include Gerstenfeld, *Science Policy Perspectives;* Bartocha and Okamura, *Transform-ing Scientific Ideas;* Strauss, "Organization of Research."

8 On the changing status of national research communities of biologists in the 1930's, see Abir-Am, "The Discourse of Physical Power," and "Beyond Deterministic Sociology and Apologetic History."

9 Calvin Morrill, History of Science, Harvard University, personal communication at the Annual Meeting of the Society for the Social Study of Science, Worcester Polytechnic Institute, Worcester, Mass., Nov. 1987.

listen and collaborate as well. Only in the 1980's has it been possible to do big science in Japan. By studying one of the first sustained international collaborations in big scientific research based in Japan using state-of-the-art equipment built in Japan, I hoped to overhear how these diverse scientists renegotiated their dominant and subordinate status in their daily research practices.

I expected that the colonialist discourse in science would be most articulate at a new laboratory outside Europe and North America where hitherto subordinated scientists were trying to change their status. For this they need not only high GNP, a willing audience, and an infrastructure, they also need the acceptance of the Euro-American dominant scientists. I also knew that many of the foreign scientists, especially the younger ones, already assumed that Japan was "on the map," and they fully expected that working at KEK would be no different from working at SLAC or Fermilab or CERN.

Working together closely at only a few sites in the world generates a very intimate community out of a collection of scientists from many nations, as I have argued at length elsewhere.[10] While the physicists themselves often believe that their shared commitment to physics research and their shared knowledge ought to eliminate any cultural differences among them, of course such differences persist and create complications. For example, some Japanese physicists said to me that they tend to think of their American colleagues as rather lazy and careless; some Americans said the same about Japanese. Some Japanese said American physicists act like children; some Americans said Japanese male physicists act like women. Some Japanese physicists said Americans thought like people from a third-world country; some Americans called Japan a backward country. Some Japanese called Koreans devious; Americans said Koreans are "like us." And so on. The question is how much this sort of discourse affects laboratory organization and research practices.

In April 1986 I returned to Tsukuba (pronounced "tscubah" by locals, "tsookoobah" by Tokyoites, and "scuba" by foreigners), Japan's new "science city," where 42 new national state-of-the-art research laboratories and a new university have been built over the last twenty years.[11] (The Japanese government is now busy building another "science city" in the southwest of Japan between Kyoto and Nara.) Tsukuba's planners might claim kinship with Novosibirsk in the Soviet Union; the founders of Tsukuba University apparently had the University of California at San Diego in mind at the outset; the designers of KEK certainly took both Fermilab and Hideki Yukawa's Research Institute for Fundamental Physics at Kyoto as institutional models.[12] In spite of these consciously selected antecedents, Tsukuba is quite distinctive and disturbing to many people in Japan; it breaks with some Japanese traditions in

10 Traweek, *Beamtimes and Lifetimes.*
11 On the establishment of Tsukuba Science City, see Birnbaum, "Japan Builds a Science City."
12 Hoddeson, "KEK and Fermilab."

science and engineering, in work, and in education. It is also a very new town in a largely agricultural district and an economically distressed one at that; most Japanese seem nowadays to prefer the huge, established cities, especially Tokyo, about two and a half hours to the southwest by public transportation. To Tokyoites the name of the prefecture in which Tsukuba is located, Ibaraki, means quintessential hick. Certainly there are many frustrations and difficulties there for both the Japanese newcomers and the visiting foreigners. Americans would call it a "frontier town."

I stayed at Tsukuba until July 1987, going almost daily to KEK (pronounced kay-ee-kay), the National Laboratory for High-Energy Physics (Ko-Enerugie Butsurigaku Kenkyusho), and watching an international collaboration of scientists prepare equipment of their own design for an experiment to be conducted at KEK's new colliding-beam facility, called TRISTAN, which for a time is the most powerful in the world.[13] TRISTAN is the first "world-class" facility for research in high-energy physics built outside North America and Europe; its operating budget in 1985–86 was 13.6 billion yen. Three separate groups of experimental high-energy physicists, called VENUS, TOPAZ, and AMY, were spending years and tens of billions of yen to have their experiments ready when TRISTAN became fully operational in the summer of 1987.[14]

The first facility at the one-by-two-kilometer KEK site had been completed in 1976 with a capital budget of 13 billion yen; it includes a proton linear accelerator that now injects a 40-million-electron-volt beam into a booster synchrotron, which in turn injects 500-million-electron-volt beams into a 12-billion-electron-volt proton synchrotron (PS). A 5-milliampere beam is utilized in the neutron-scattering experimental facility (KENS) and a 10-milliampere beam in the pulsed muon facility (BOOM). Research at the PS now is primarily, although not exclusively, in solid-state physics and medical physics; users include scientists from KEK, other Japanese national laboratories, and Japanese universities, as well as from the University of California, Los Angeles, the Max Planck Institute, and the Beijing Institute for High-Energy Physics. Research began at the PS in 1977 with an internal target beam for counter experiments and a fast extracted beam for bubble chamber experiments; many physicists associated with these original PS experiments are now working at TRISTAN.

Construction on a 2.5-billion-electron-volt electron synchrotron radiation facility, including an injector linear accelerator, was begun in 1978; the Photon Factory was completed in 1982 at a cost of 20 billion yen. Some of the physicists who maintain, operate, and modify this facility were trained in particle physics, but experiments there focus on medical research and mate-

13 TRISTAN Project Group, *TRISTAN Electron-Positron Colliding Beam Project.*
14 KEK National Laboratory for High-Energy Physics, AMY, TOPAZ, and VENUS collaborations.

rials science. Photon Factory users include scientists from other national laboratories, universities, and private companies, such as NTT (Nippon Telegram and Telephone), Hitachi, and NEC (Nippon Electric Company).

In April 1981 the TRISTAN project was funded and construction began in November. TRISTAN is an acronym for Transposable Ring Intersecting STorage Accelerator in Nippon; the project report for 1987, published on the occasion of the dedication ceremony for TRISTAN on April 7, states that the project was named TRISTAN "after the passionate story of . . . Wagner's opera, with the love and dreams for our science research, particularly for hunting quarks in Nippon."[15] The TRISTAN complex consists of (1) the 400-meter-long electron linear accelerator (LINAC) feeding electrons at 2.5 billion electron volts to the Photon Factory (for which it was originally built) and feeding electrons and positrons at the same energy into (2) an accumulation ring (AR) 377 meters in circumference, which accelerates 10-milliampere beams up to 8 billion electron volts and then injects them into (3) the main ring 3 kilometers in circumference, which accelerates the beams to between 25 and 30 billion electron volts. There are four experimental halls, one at each positron–electron collision point, where luminosities of about 1×10^{30} cm^{-2} sec^{-1} are achieved.[16]

The four halls are named Tsukuba (in the direction of Tsukuba Mountain, the main geological feature of the region), Nikko (in the direction of Nikko, a famous mountain resort area a few hundred kilometers to the northwest), Fuji (in the direction of Mount Fuji far to the southwest beyond Tokyo), and Oho (toward the nearby village of Oho). The names of the first three would be immediately recognizable to all Japanese; the fourth would not. The international collaboration is based in the fourth hall, Oho, a name known only to locals. The foreigners told me they chose it, deliberately; they also have considered using the logo of a local used car dealer for their experiment. The logo is of a swashbuckling pirate. This sort of defiant identification with underdogs amuses the foreigners at the lab; the Japanese are less likely to joke about the underdog role. Their identification is not ironic.

For the first experimental runs at TRISTAN four projects were approved by the Program Advisory Committee. One, approved in 1985, is named SHIP, an acronym of Search for Highly Ionizing Particles; it is also called Nikko-maru after the experimental hall where it is located and after the Japanese word for ship. SHIP is a small, inexpensive, passive detector designed to make some use of an otherwise uncompleted experimental hall; at the center of Nikko-maru is a set of solid-state track detectors (made in both Japan and the U.S.), sensitive to highly ionizing particles, which are processed after a year of exposure. The experiment is designed to test various theories that predict the

15 TRISTAN Project Group, *TRISTAN Electron-Positron Colliding Beam Project*, p. 1.

16 *Ibid.*, pp. 2–6, 45–59.

existence of monopoles in the energy region available at TRISTAN.[17] The SHIP collaboration is quite small, composed of a handful of physicists from five institutions: KEK, the Japanese Institute for Space and Astronautical Science, Gifu University, Harvard, and the University of California at Berkeley.

The Nikko-maru leader, an assistant professor at Harvard, is a Japanese-American whose parents were born and educated as physicists in Japan. She is one of a handful of women physicists affiliated with KEK (only one is Japanese). Her manner and way of speaking are thoroughly American—open, engaging, direct—she also speaks Japanese fluently. Her collaboration is an example of international scientific collaboration not infrequently conducted in Japan: passive equipment, requiring no complex design, modification, or operation, generating data that are analyzed after the experiment is finished by the diverse members of the collaboration at their home institutions. In economic terms one might call it a "joint venture," requiring detailed bilingual negotiations, but no extended interaction among the members.

The Nikko-maru leader's father is a theoretical physicist, professor at an American university, and frequent visitor to KEK. His collaborations at KEK are typical of the sort encouraged by the Japan Society for the Promotion of Science for many years: using funds allotted to bring foreign scientists to Japan to support visits by Japanese nationals who have been abroad more than ten years. Such individuals can speak to the concerns of Japanese scientists better than can other visitors who do not know Japanese or how the Japanese scientific community works; they can also communicate the concerns of foreign scientific communities in terms the Japan-based scientists might find comprehensible.

Like the other two large detectors, the TOPAZ detector at Tsukuba Hall is designed for precise particle identification. It has five main components: an inner drift chamber (IDC), a time-projection chamber (TPC), and time-of-flight counters (TOF). These are arranged concentrically within a thin 1.2-tesla superconducting solenoid magnet surrounded and capped by calorimeters (BCL and ECL) and drift chambers. Outside all this are iron slabs and muon drift chambers (MDC). As is customary in very large collaborations, each component of this detector is the responsibility of a different group within the TOPAZ collaboration, which includes scientists from KEK, the University of Tokyo, the Institute for Nuclear Study, Tokyo University of Agriculture and Technology, Nagoya University, Nara Women's University, and Osaka City University, as well as Lawrence Berkeley Laboratory, which does not have representatives based at KEK.[18]

Many at KEK regarded this collaboration as being organized in the most

17 *Ibid.*, p. 143, and KEK National Laboratory for High-Energy Physics, *Annual Report, 1985*, pp. 38–39.

18 KEK National Laboratory for High-Energy Physics, AMY, TOPAZ, and VENUS collaborations.

traditionally Japanese manner. For example, when the TRISTAN beam was first available for experimental use, TOPAZ did not make use of it because all members of the collaboration did not agree that the detector was completely ready. I was told that certain components of the detector were not completely debugged; if particle tracks could not be definitively identified because of that defective component, the responsible group would lose face publicly. All the Japanese in the collaboration understood the problem; the foreigners at the lab were flabbergasted that "majority rule" did not prevail within the group and that the TRISTAN directors did not force TOPAZ to do the run. Also, they simply could not understand why physicists would not use an available beam. The repatriated Japanese agreed but said they understood the TOPAZ decision.

The Discourse of Regional Differences

At Fuji Hall the VENUS detector also has inner and central tracking chambers, time-of-flight counters, a thin 0.75-tesla superconducting solenoid magnet, barrel and end-cap drift chambers and calorimeters, and muon detectors; VENUS is an acronym for VErsatile Nihep and Universities Spectrometer.[19] The collaboration is composed of scientists from Fukui University, Hiroshima University, KEK, Kobe University, Kyoto University, Osaka University, Tokyo University of Agriculture and Technology, Tohoku University, Tohoku Gakuin University, Tokyo Metropolitan University, University of Tsukuba, and Wakayama Medical College; these groups are listed alphabetically in their proposal, a common procedure in Europe and North America, but unusual in Japan, where groups usually are listed in the order of their institution's status. That VENUS is a tightly run collaboration is visible even in the cabinet holding the members' hard hats where all the hats are assigned, numbered, and lodged in proper order. That it is also a prosperous collaboration is noticeable everywhere at Fuji Hall, even in its lobby where there is a sophisticated display of detector components; when the associate director shows the lab to important visitors, Fuji is the only experimental hall he shows.

To a Japanese it would be immediately significant that VENUS includes Kyoto and Osaka Universities whereas TOPAZ includes Tokyo University. The primary division in Japanese culture and politics is between the Kanto region where Tokyo is located and the Kansai region where Osaka and Kyoto are. For example, since Tsukuba Science City has been built in Kanto, it is nearly inevitable that the next such community will be built in Kansai; it is also nearly inevitable that the first would have been built in the Kanto area. Tokyo represents the establishment, Osaka and Kyoto represent the most significant opposition. Every national organization in Japan must have represen-

19 *Ibid.*

tation from at least these two parts of Japan, and KEK is no exception. When I first visited KEK in 1976 as the PS was nearing completion, I was told that the theory and counter groups were Tokyo-dominated, the beam-channel group was Kyoto-dominated, and the bubble-chamber group was dominated by Tohoku University.[20] It appears to me that this division into spheres of influence has been replicated in the new facilities at TRISTAN: the highest ranking university in TOPAZ is the University of Tokyo, and among the institutions represented in VENUS those with the highest status are the universities of Osaka, Kyoto, and Tohoku. The liaison between Kansai and Tohoku is surprising.

Sendai, to the far northeast of Tokyo and where Tohoku University is located, is the center of perhaps the next most politically and culturally significant region in Japan, after Kansai and Kanto. Sendai was nearly leveled by American bombs at the end of World War II; now the city looks almost American with its broad avenues and grid street plan. People from both Kansai and Kanto regard the Tohoku area as very conservative and traditional. I have heard the leadership style of the physics department there described as "feudal" and "American": to Japanese both words mean leading "by force of personality" in an authoritarian manner, like Sendai's Lord Date and General MacArthur (sometimes called Shogun MacArthur in Japan). The department has a long history of collaboration on international bubble-chamber experiments; it does sophisticated computer-based data analysis in Japan for experiments conducted elsewhere. The retiring leader has had enough influence in the government to get funding for extensive capital spending on computers and a building to house them.

The Japanese national government has recently completed long-range planning for regional economic development, international economic cooperation, and science and technology policy. The Tohoku area has been selected for massive regional development based on science and technology; Tohoku University and the University of California will be partners in establishing joint programs in international business and international relations with an emphasis on science and technology policies as they relate to business and diplomacy.[21] The Shinkansen (what foreigners call the "bullet train") tracks finally reached Sendai a few years ago, signaling the beginning of this new era of planned development. Some Tohoku people are pleased with the resources these changes will bring to the region; others are less pleased with being brought into Tokyo's orbit, something the shoguns never quite accomplished with Lord Date. I surmise that Tohoku University's alliance with Kyoto and

20 KEK National Laboratory for High-Energy Physics, *Annual Report, 1976*, pp. 38–39.

21 Atsushi Shimokobe, President, National Institute for Research Advancement (NIRA), presentation on the past, current, and future programs of NIRA, International House of Japan, May 1987.

Osaka universities in VENUS is an effort to maintain a degree of independence from Tokyo University in future developments at KEK.

The differences between VENUS and TOPAZ mirror very important cultural differences between Kansai and Kanto, differences obvious even in apparently superficial matters, such as the way sushi is made, the way people talk and move and dress, even the size of tatami mats, the basic unit of measurement in people's houses. Tokyoites would joke that it makes sense that VENUS looks orderly, efficient, and prosperous: they think Kansai people are overly concerned with commerce. Kansai people would not be surprised that the VENUS collaboration was ready to take advantage of the opportunity offered by the TRISTAN beam and that TOPAZ was not; they see themselves as practical and entrepreneurial and Tokyoites as overly preoccupied with their own status. The Kansai region has suffered major economic setbacks in the past two decades with the government's policy shift toward information industries, located primarily in the Kanto area. (Some believe the Kansai economic decline began earlier, with government centralization policies.) Now the Kansai region is trying to build strength in information industries and information sciences. The new science city to be built between Kyoto and Nara is a part of this plan for regional recovery. In this context the Kansai–Tohoku alliance in VENUS seems opportune, given the Tohoku group's strength in data analysis.

The other two major institutional members of the VENUS collaboration, the universities of Hiroshima and Tsukuba, are also surprising additions. Ten years ago one would have found a rather stable five-part configuration in the Japanese high-energy physics community: Tokyo University, considered by outsiders to be conservative, establishment, and elitist, with strong ties to the government and the ruling Liberal-Democratic Party; Kyoto, Nagoya, and Hiroshima, as seen by outsiders, shared an anti-establishment stance shaped by the Japanese Communist Party and voted as a bloc in the Japan Physical Society; a cluster of non-establishment, non-Communists; a collection of powerful, eminent senior physicists with their own domains, such as Yukawa and his Research Institute for Fundamental Physics at Kyoto; and finally the traditionalists, exemplified by Tohoku University. Each of these five factions was identified with different physics questions, addressed with different kinds of equipment; for example, counters at Tokyo, bubble-chamber analysis at Tohoku, cosmic-ray physics at Nagoya and Hiroshima, and so on. The Ministry of Education also funded these groups in rather stable proportions, according to my informants ten years ago. The establishment of KEK challenged this arrangement; for a time the old configuration appeared to be reconstructed within KEK, but, as I have written elsewhere, the situation was unstable. In anthropological terms the community's ecology changed and its social structure changed with it: the changes in world political relations in the last twenty years, Japan's emerging status as a rich country, the economic realignment of regions within Japan, the radically expanded infrastructure for science and technology in Japan, and the return to Japan of a cohort of expatriated scientists have all contributed to the transformation of the community. The TOPAZ and VENUS collaborations are examples of that transformation: Tokyo and Nagoya linked in TOPAZ and the universities peripheral to them are aligned in VENUS.

At any rate, the VENUS detector was the first to be rolled into a collision region (September 1986) and the first to identify large-angle Bhabha scattering (November 19, 1986, four days before the AMY detector was rolled into its collision region). That same month TOPAZ had just completed assembling its detector; not yet in the beam line, it was used to collect cosmic ray data, an ironic display of Tokyo being in third place in this local race to the beam line.[22]

Kokusaika and Nihonjinron

This local discourse on regional differences extends to the subject of international relations. Kokusaika is the Japanese word for the very widely discussed and volatile issue of how Japan ought to participate in global society. It is understood that Japan's recently acquired status as an economically wealthy and powerful country brings with it both the right and the responsibility to act in global political, intellectual, and cultural arenas. The newspaper images of Prime Minister Yasuhiro Nakasone standing alongside Ronald Reagan, Margaret Thatcher, François Mitterrand, and the rest at economic summit meetings were an arresting display to the Japanese people of these rights and responsibilities. Japanese people were fascinated and disturbed by Nakasone's capacity to shake hands comfortably, laugh, and deal with "westerners" (our ethnocentric label—the Japanese word is, politely, gaikokujin, outsider) in their style, right down to the chummy Ron–Yasu banter. To begin to understand the Japanese public's consternation, imagine the consequences in the United States if Reagan had behaved in a convincingly Japanese manner during Nakasone's visit to Washington to discuss trade issues.

The current government position on kokusaika is that Japanese people ought to participate in global society in ways that are consistent with being Japanese; they believe the first stage is to define Japanese-ness, nihonjinron in Japanese. (Anthropologists and historians of traditional Japanese society consequently are exceedingly well funded, compared to their colleagues in other countries.) There is a vast, widely read public and academic literature on these interrelated topics of kokusaika and nihonjinron.[23] Its popularity is in part a measure of how controversial the subject of international relations now is in Japan. I have already suggested that there are, of course, different versions in

22 TRISTAN Project Group, TRISTAN Electron-Positron Colliding Beam Project. On instabilities at KEK, see Traweek, Beamtimes and Lifetimes, pp. 131–42.

23 For a commentary on the history of nihonjinron and the rather more sophisticated nihonbunkaron in Japanese history, see Harootunian, Things Seen and Unseen.

Japan of Japanese-ness, underneath the 125-year-old image of homogeneity propagated by the central government. In the current debate it is not surprising that these different, sometimes regional versions of Japanese-ness correspond to different Japanese strategies for acting globally.

Kokusaika and *nihonjinron* are also hot topics in the scientific community, both for individuals and for groups. Since the end of World War II the best young Japanese scientists were expected to go abroad for two or three years at the end of graduate school to work on projects at well-known laboratories and universities in North America and Europe, and then return to Japan and spend the rest of their careers working in Japan with other Japanese. It has been thought important not to acquire foreign mannerisms and ways of thinking during these sojourns; it has been considered bad form to speak foreign languages too fluently or to read foreign languages for pleasure: I have heard people criticized for reading so much "sideways" print. Everyone discusses whether to marry before his trip abroad: will the wife (I never heard of a woman student being selected for this opportunity) keep the physicist "Japanese" while abroad, or will the wife get contaminated with "western" ways, making the physicist even more "foreign" when he returns to Japan.

Another strategy has been to invite scientists to Japan from countries poorer than Japan. Universities in the southwest of Japan, from Osaka and Kyoto in Kansai to Hiroshima and Kyushu, tended to emphasize this strategy. It is interesting to note that cosmic-ray physics and nuclear physics are very strong in this part of Japan; the former has, until recently, been very inexpensive, and the latter has long had easily identifiable industrial and commercial applications and hence support from private industry. As cosmic-ray physicists have come to use very expensive equipment, they too have forged close relations with private industry. Private industry then encourages the government to fund these fields as a way of funding what in the United States would be called research and development. At the same time Japanese cosmic-ray and nuclear physicists have long maintained close collaborative relations with foreign scientists: they did not need the government to endorse and finance these hitherto very inexpensive "little science" collaborations.

Another position on international scientific relations has been that Japanese research groups should collaborate with foreign groups on experiments conducted abroad and do a portion of the experiment's data analysis in Japan; this path is followed at those universities, including Tokyo, Nagoya, and Tohoku, that have long enjoyed higher levels of government funding. Scientists in this position seemed to me to wear their foreign experiences both more comfortably and more lightly than their colleagues who had arranged to be abroad for shorter periods of time. They do not mind speaking foreign languages in front of other Japanese and they openly display their fondness for certain foreign foods or certain foreign arts, especially "western" classical music. They enact a sort of connoisseurship of foreign high culture, a posture of power not unknown in many other countries, including the United States; it is certainly not the same as acting or thinking in foreign ways. These scientists still wield their power in Japanese ways, apparently more concerned with their status in the Japanese scientific community than in the international arena.

Finally, a distinct minority of Japanese scientists have spent most of their careers abroad, having arranged for themselves work in the countries where they were sent as postdoctoral research associates; the others consider this career path selfish, since one never brings the knowledge home. These scientists are disturbing for another reason: they know how to act and think in ways their colleagues label foreign (even if foreigners might find their actions and thoughts rather more Japanese). Japanese who have spent many years as expatriates, if they return to Japan to work, have to develop strategies for coping with the deep cultural suspicion in Japan with which they, and their families, will always be treated. Such people are said to "no longer have Japanese souls." It is generally agreed that an adult can live abroad up to three or four years and still have a Japanese soul, but not as long as seven or eight years; the intervening years are problematic. Everyone agrees that spending the high-school years abroad leaves an indelible mark; some Japanese expatriates choose to return to Japan as their children reach adolescence for this reason.

Some work very hard at erasing all traces of their experience abroad. I heard of one such man who was searching for a wife; rather than wanting a woman who also had lived abroad and could identify with and share his experience, he wanted a woman who had never traveled outside Japan. He felt that such a wife could teach him how to be Japanese again and would compensate for his residual foreign ways. Other former expatriates choose not to erase or conceal their foreign habits. Some want to irritate, to insist on their ways being acknowledged, if not accepted. Most want their hard-won foreign skills to be recognized as useful and important in Japan; they want to be a resource, not a problem. Ten years ago this would have been exceedingly fanciful; in the midst of the current debate on *kokusaika* and *nihonjinron* it is more plausible, but this is a path requiring extraordinary personal courage, because one will face powerful prejudices, daily. I must mention that such people can be extraordinarily effective too: they know both the usual Japanese ways of doing things and other ways as well; if astute, they can make use of their expanded strategic repertoire.

Particles, Nuclei, and Power

Scientists who have followed each of these career strategies are now working together at KEK, but with very different scripts for the future of KEK, for the future of big science in Japan, and for the future of Japanese high-energy physicists in the international arena. Some think experiments at KEK ought to be run by Japanese scientists in a "Japanese" manner, like TOPAZ; others prefer to continue their collaborations abroad and use KEK primarily for teaching purposes, rather like the Institute for Nuclear Study, perhaps inviting scientists from all over Asia as a sort of Japanese Fulbright program; several want to continue upgrading KEK, encouraging scientists from all over the world to submit proposals for experiments, and raising the status of KEK to the level of SLAC, Fermilab, DESY, and CERN. This third group is especially pleased to have the AMY collaboration at KEK. There is a fourth position, held by a few: that the nuclear physicists who dominate the Japan Physical Society (and hence all Japanese physics funding) want to expel the high-energy physicists from KEK and turn TRISTAN into a super photon factory, an electron synchrotron radiation facility.

For American high-energy physicists it is incomprehensible that nuclear physicists might be determining the future of American high-energy physics facilities. In America the high-energy physicists decide when they will share facilities with nuclear physicists and when they will bestow upon the nuclear physicists facilities no longer considered state-of-the-art in high-energy physics. The politics of decision making around Argonne National Laboratory has often been given to me as an example of the difference in status between high-energy physicists and nuclear physicists and engineers in America. In Japan nuclear physicists have more power than do high-energy physicists; it is crucial to understand this in order to understand the politics of big physics in Japan. In Japan the nuclear physicists control the Japan Physical Society, which in turn has traditionally controlled the funding for all physics research and education in Japan, establishing priorities and funding levels before budgets are submitted to the Ministry of Education (abbreviated, familiarly, as *Monbusho*), which until recently funded all academic research in Japan. The American Physical Society has no such function; each subfield's funding is organized rather differently. Of course, HEPAP (the High-Energy Physics Advisory Panel) operates within its domain much as the Japan Physical Society does in its. Nevertheless, HEPAP competes with solid-state physics funding proposals, nuclear physics proposals, and so on at the Department of Energy, National Science Foundation, and so forth, not within the American Physical Society. As we all know, American high-energy physicists have been much more adroit at the politics of funding in Washington than have other physicists. Not so in Japan, but that is beginning to change.

A few Japanese high-energy physicists believe that the Japanese high-energy physics community ought to be willing to accept the nuclear physicists taking over KEK on the condition that the budget for high-energy physics experiments to be conducted abroad is expanded massively; they would use this money to become major players in design and operation of whatever machine comes after the superconducting supercollider (SSC). (As those of us who follow the high-energy physics community know, as soon as one facility is funded, the next one is being discussed, and certainly the post-SSC machine is being discussed.) Some believe that the founders of KEK may have trouble accepting the shift in KEK's mission; others say that the founders are realistic and will accept a transition as long as both high-energy physics and KEK remain well funded. (The assumption is that they want KEK to remain well funded because their names are too much connected to KEK to not lose face if it were to decline in status.)

Realizing that they may need leverage outside the Japan Physical Society in order to negotiate effectively with the nuclear physicists, some high-energy physicists in this fourth group have established informal communications with agencies other than *Monbusho*. They turned to the Science and Technology Agency, the Finance Ministry, and the Foreign Ministry, in particular. *Monbusho* is known to be rather irritated with the emergence of national laboratories beyond the control of universities, since its own influence is through the universities. The development of national science and technology policies, whether as a part of regional development, national prestige, or diplomacy, has not been managed by *Monbusho*. In the Japanese government there is an unofficial status ranking among the ministries; this ranking affects from which university the ministry recruits most of its new members, how much funding the universities are allotted, how much influence they have in shaping national policies, and so on; *Monbusho* competes with other ministries when new projects with new funding, such as all the new science and technology projects, are being established. As these diverse agencies fight to control these new domains, some high-energy physicists have realized that their own point of view may be better served by escaping the influence of *Monbusho* and the Japan Physical Society.[24]

These are the strategies being discussed by physicists at KEK for how the Japanese high-energy physics community might enlarge its role in the international high-energy physics community. As I have tried to suggest, these strategies are embedded in a discourse about difference and power, a distinctively Japanese discourse about difference and power. I want to turn now to how the AMY collaboration at KEK affects the discourse about big science, both by Japanese and by the resident foreigners.

The AMY group is international, composed primarily of Japanese and Americans, with notable contingents from Korea and China; the Philippines, India, Israel, Switzerland, Germany, France, England, and Canada are also represented. Japanese physicists recruited the Indian; all the other foreigners were recruited by the Americans. Many of the Japanese had worked abroad for significant portions of their careers and returned to Japan to make a success of KEK, recruited by the lab's charismatic and forceful director. The

24 On the relation of Japanese government agencies and the national budget process, see Campbell, *Contemporary Japanese Budget Politics*, and Kyogoku, *The Political Dynamics of Japan*.

first Americans were from Rochester, disappointed by the closing of an accelerator at Cornell and eager to work at one of the new facilities under construction around the world; since TRISTAN was scheduled for completion first, they decided to submit a proposal there (as did one other group of foreigners, ultimately unsuccessful).

Why wasn't there a deluge of proposals from foreigners? I asked this question in the U.S. and was told often that no one believed the Japanese would really get TRISTAN operating at energies high enough and with adequate luminosities before the other labs. Some added that the complications of working in Japan would slow a foreign group. Some said it was too far to commute. Some said Japan was too far off the beaten track, that it was too important to be at the center of the action, which was not in Japan. The AMY organizers said that they had enough self-confidence to work away from the center for a while and that they would learn quickly how to be effective in Japan. They also believed they were taking a strategic risk with high possible gains: they were betting that the Japanese could do what they claimed on schedule, that the AMY group could do what it claimed on schedule, and that their only competitors to make the next group of discoveries in high-energy physics would be VENUS and TOPAZ. The youngest physicists in AMY were very anxious about these claims and risks: their careers would be determined by the results. A cynical American in AMY said that no one first rate would need to take all these risks.

Why did the leadership at KEK decide on the AMY proposal, even though the other group nominally had higher status in the international physics community? There are many parts to a full answer. One component is that the AMY proposal took maximum advantage of some constraints and opportunities in the configuration of TRISTAN beam characteristics and intersection regions. Another part, in my opinion, was the many-decades-old relationship between the Rochester physics department and Japanese physicists, many of whom were now leaders in their community. Some of them like to remember having enough Japanese at Rochester to field a baseball team. They feel indebted to Rochester and the Fulbright Program for launching their careers in physics. In Japan indebtedness creates obligations; more personally, it creates bonds of reciprocity, rather like what Americans mean when we say "I owe you one." In that context an agreement is not contractual, rather easily quitted if one so chooses; it is a commitment, abandoned at the cost of one's reputation and self-esteem. Japanese value people who are capable of honoring such commitments: some of the foreigners in AMY show that capacity, along with their willingness to take a risk.

I wrote earlier in this chapter that the Japanese not only needed high GNP, a willing audience, and a fully developed infrastructure to build big science in Japan, they also needed recognition from the dominant scientific communities. The presence of a foreign collaboration at TRISTAN contributed to that recognition and helped put TRISTAN "on the circuit." The fact that they were going about business almost as usual was clear to all visitors: obviously one could come to Japan and KEK, settle in, and do physics. The fact that AMY members continued attending all the major high-energy physics meetings showed that being at KEK did not remove one from "the action."

The Uses of Foreigners

The AMY collaboration also provided a daily, immediate display to the Japanese physicists at KEK of some foreign modes of doing research. The leaders of KEK thought that alone had educational value for young Japanese physicists, and they would not have to go to Hamburg, Geneva, Batavia, or Palo Alto to be confronted with this fact. The foreigners liked to build and modify equipment; they did not think equipment was necessarily better if it came from private industry. They asked for metal-working machines and were politely refused; they waited until some important governmental officials were being shown around, and then began operating some old, messy, noisy piece of equipment they had modified. The new machines appeared. The foreigners were not tidy and did not build tidy equipment: they never clipped the ends of cable ties, they built work tables out of scraps, their tubing and gauges looked like Rube Goldberg contraptions. It was quick and dirty and it worked. They were also proud of not expending money and time where they were not necessary. Senior foreign physicists came into Oho Hall saying they had checked the dumps outside the other halls and had found something useful, expressing shock at what some Japanese physicists were willing to throw away. Told they would have to requisition some essential, depleted supplies, they went to a local big hardware store called "Joyful Honda" and found some substitute. Some senior Japanese physicists were very eager to see the young Japanese physicists witness this resourcefulness and determination.

The presence of foreign ways of doing physics had other uses. Repatriated Japanese looked much less alien alongside real foreigners. Furthermore, the foreigners could be counted upon, unprompted, to express points of view that might be extremely awkward for any Japanese physicist, familiar with the issues I have described in this paper, to express. As TRISTAN came "on line," beam scheduling committees began to meet. Present at those committee meetings were representatives from AMY, TOPAZ, VENUS, TRISTAN, the LINAC, and the Photon Factory. Recall that the LINAC feeds beams to both the Photon Factory and TRISTAN and that the LINAC staff worked closely with the Photon Factory staff for several years before TRISTAN came on line. At these early meetings the Photon Factory was allotted the full LINAC beam for up to two-thirds of the time. The AMY foreigners were outraged and saw no reason to conceal their anger. Some announced that if this policy were allowed to continue, they would feel betrayed, and would leave KEK and

Japan. Some argued that no respectable lab would be run this way and if word "got out" that KEK was being run this way, KEK would be the laughingstock of the world scientific community. Because of the power of the nuclear physics community in Japan, it would have been difficult for a Japanese high-energy physicist to make these arguments; the foreigners spoke them with impunity. TRISTAN got more beamtime. Periodically, the Photon Factory would pre-empt TRISTAN without notice and these discussions would be repeated.

Later on, TRISTAN was shut down because the government had not extended the lab's funding for electrical power. Again the foreigners expressed shock that a country would build TRISTAN and then not provide adequate funding for its operation, a very long-standing problem for Japanese researchers. The foreigners began to joke about going into Tokyo and demonstrating against the government; by that time they were all aware of how conspicuous non-Asians are in Japan and how easy it would be for a group of big Caucasians to draw public attention to themselves. They were threatening to reach that audience for science directly. The funding for electrical power materialized. The foreigners at KEK had learned how to perform in the Japanese physics community's discourse about difference and power, and they had crucial roles to play in the Japanese debates about the practice of big science in Japan.

Decision Making and Leadership

The very difficulty the Americans had in learning to act effectively in the Japanese decision-making process evokes the differences between the ways physics is practiced in the two countries. These differences, some of which I would call cultural, pervade the activities of physicists, including relations within collaborations, laboratories, and departments, between high-energy physicists and nuclear physicists, and between physicists and government agencies. Most Japanese groups see themselves as much more democratic and less hierarchical than American groups. Japanese who have worked in the United States told me that they were quite surprised by the formality and structure that they found there, and wondered if that were the best environment for physics. In Japan groups often make their decisions by consensus, even if they sometimes find the process quite tedious. (I have heard that this model is most closely adhered to in the southwest of Japan and less so as one moves northeast, where a more traditional or "feudalistic" style is said to prevail. Ironically, this style, "governing by force of personality," is thought to be like the Americans', or at least like "Shogun MacArthur.") In Japan I found everyone actively discussing various matters of laboratory-wide concern before decisions were made. Everyone seemed to feel well informed. According to Japanese values, leaders always should consult with everyone in their groups, and the same values require that all members advise thoughtfully. The leader should decide on a policy consistent with good judgment and the health of the group; it is the responsibility of the group members to cooperate fully with the final decision if they believe this process has been respected, even if they disagree with the decision itself.

In the United States research group structures are hierarchical, even if the style is superficially informal. Decisions are made by the group leader, who then informs the group of how they are to be implemented; the group members may "drag their feet" if they seriously disagree. From conception and decision to implementation the total time seems to be the same in the United States and Japan. At an American laboratory when I asked the postdoctoral research associates what they thought of certain issues confronting the lab, almost all replied that they did not know what was going on. A few said these things were decided by the "old boys' club" (meaning the director, the associate directors, and the groups' leaders), adding that "they tell us what's happening only after they decide." Several asked me to discuss the matter with them, saying "you seem to be better informed than we are."

Competition is a fundamental tenet of American culture; it is very difficult for most Americans to imagine that competition has any negative implications or, conversely, that there could be any other motivation for performing with excellence. When competition is thought to be unfettered, as they presume it to be in the American particle physics community, organizational hierarchy is seen as a natural ranking of human talents, a meritocracy. Hence, the leader is seen as the best scientist and the most entitled to judge.

Another difference between the Japanese and American physicists concerns the extent to which the experimentalists are experienced working with different kinds of research equipment known as detectors. In Japan each university research group is very much identified with a specific kind of detector. This is generally due to the patterns of funding from the Japanese government and to the *koza* (chair) system in Japanese universities, which was adapted after the Meiji Restoration of 1868 from the German mode of academic organization. Each research group also tends to be identified with a certain orientation to national and international politics and with a specific group organizational style. Once students enter graduate school, they have, in effect, delimited the kinds of research they can do the rest of their careers, as well as their politics and their way of participating in collaborations. (In anthropological terms the groups are endogamous, practicing internal recruitment.) The new national research labs at Tsukuba are changing this, as are the chance to study and work abroad for long periods. In Japan, great emphasis is placed on purity. Blends, amalgamations, and mixtures are not valued at all; purity is associated with perfection, mixtures with mess. To be a product of one school of thought, or *iemoto*, is to display self-discipline and commitment; achievement and creativity can occur only in this context.

By contrast, in the United States young physicists often are encouraged to work on research issues very different from those they had done as students. Some groups have worked all together on a variety of detectors. Many senior prominent experimentalists seem to have deliberately set about working on a variety of machines before they propose the construction of a new detector on their own design; their diverse experience is thought to lend credence to their design choices. Americans value diversity highly, and consider mobility (exposing oneself to many approaches and influences) to be a sign of one's intellectual independence and creativity. In elite American universities taking a position in the department in which one is trained almost always is considered extremely bad judgment by both the student and the department faculty. It is presumed by others that the student could not be hired elsewhere and that the department could not attract any outside applicants. Anthropologically speaking, recruitment should be exogamous. The only respectable way to take a position in the department of one's training is to go to another school, establish an independent reputation, and then return: as everyone says, "you must go away to come back." To stay in one place is to value the security of habitual routines over the challenge of achievement, which is thought to come from displacement and discontinuities. In this view continuity and creativity are incompatible and independence is crucial to achievement and creativity. To Americans independence is also associated with self-discipline and intellectual commitment, just as Japanese feel these qualities are displayed by staying in one place.

In Japan one model for work groups is the *ie*. Generally speaking *ie* refers to an entire household, including its privileges and responsibilities in the network of households of which it is a part. It is the obligation of each member of the *ie* to maintain the household and its resources intact and pass them on to the next generation. In my opinion the organization of most particle physics research groups in Japan is consistent with this model of the *ie*.

In the United States a major model for work groups is not a large household but a sports team. That is, the leader is like a coach directing a team of football players, each of whom has specialized, distinctive skills. The coach is the only team member to understand the entire game process and the only one empowered to design the team's strategies and tactics. The membership and organization of the team survive only as long as the team is winning, accumulating a better record in competition with other teams. If the team loses, the owners will disband the team and assemble a new one, perhaps even relocating to a new city. Excellent athletes, in addition, are always being recruited by other teams, so the good players move from team to team. Any particular game may include, for instance, players and coaches who have worn the other team's uniform, and people on different teams may have once been teammates. Obviously, this process generates very strong professional loyalties and very weak institutional ties. I suggest that this team model is congruent with the organization of research groups in American particle physics. Of course, neither of these models, *ie* nor sports team, is inherently scientific.

Although the Japanese groups and networks are fixed and recruits to new positions must come from within and the Americans insist upon movement through groups, especially at the early stages of one's career, the Japanese community seems to tolerate much more diversity in leadership style and group organization than does the American. This may be the result of internal, endogamous recruitment: one need not adapt to other groups' styles because one rarely moves. The Americans move frequently and expect more similarity, perhaps in order to reduce the period of adjustment before one can work effectively. The Japanese social and intellectual ecology is quite diverse whereas the American is very homogeneous.

I would like my readers to understand that when I write "American" or "Japanese," I am using these terms as abstractions. No one person or group fits either pattern perfectly. Moreover, it is perhaps my most crucial point in this chapter that there is significant variation in the practice of physics within each country; in addition, both patterns I am describing in the last three sections of this chapter can be found in each country. For example, what I describe as the dominant "Japanese" style is also practiced in the United States, and the prevailing style in the United States most certainly is performed in Japan, too. The meaning, significance, and power of these styles, however, is different in each country.

Inheriting the Future

These two styles of leadership and decision making have very different implications for the next generation. In the American practice leaders find it quite difficult to bequeath the power and wealth that they have accumulated; Japanese leaders find it easy. Any research group leader has considerable wealth in the form of research equipment (detectors and targets) and software for data analysis, as well as his less tangible but perhaps even more significant reputation in the community. (I use the masculine pronoun in that last sentence not generically but specifically; although there are a very small number of high-energy physics research groups around the world led by women, I have not studied them; all my comments are about groups led by men.) His reputation is the power that the leader wields in the community as a whole, and is symbolized by his membership on lab program advisory committees and national policy advisory groups that determine what equipment will be built and what experiments will be accepted and by his control of a network cutting across labs and physics departments around the world. This determines the leader's access to scarce resources such as funding, accelerator beamtime, computer time, excellent young physicists, and even laboratory space.

In Japan this wealth is traditionally held by the *koza*, not just the person who happens to be the current leader, and that wealth will be passed on to those who become the next leaders of that *koza*. Because a Japanese group can "reproduce" itself in this fashion, its lifetime, like that of an *ie*, is dependent only upon the commitment of its old and new members. The lifetime of an American group, however, is ephemeral, lasting no longer than the leader's individual career, at the most. It even can be as short as the lifetime of a grant (one to three years), an experiment (three years or so, at least), or a detector (five to ten years). The American leader's wealth must be maintained assiduously; the process is difficult and very time-consuming. Like the group itself, the wealth is ephemeral and cannot be inherited. It must be reconstituted entirely in each generation. The implications of the differences between these two systems are massive. For example, cross-generational ties and peer relations are radically different in these two ecologies.

Japanese research groups, by way of summary, are very long-lived social structures, surviving beyond the lifetime of any member. Once selected to join, people usually remain in the same place the rest of their careers. Communication is strong within the group and weak between groups. In this pattern communication gaps between generations in the group should be small, but it is also very hard to incorporate newcomers, except as novices. These features lead to the development in depth of certain intellectual approaches and experimental techniques that are passed from one generation to the next. One very tangible manifestation of this is found in the way research equipment is designed and built, even in the quantity of spare parts that are purchased.

The strength of this pattern depends upon stable cross-generational ties. However, the very distinctive features of each generation of particle physicists to emerge since the 1930's have led to serious generational rifts. The generation that established the foundations of this internationally known Japanese research community are the retiring innovators, the men who have been its organization leaders throughout their careers. Members of the next generation, now in their forties and fifties, received much of their advanced education abroad and they often have continued to do collaborative research with their foreign colleagues. This group wants to work in Japan, and it is eager to establish truly international laboratories in Japan. The younger people in their twenties and thirties seem to have made use of their elders' international networks to take some training abroad, but fewer have the experience of either collaboration with foreigners or sustained work abroad. These generational differences are seen by the physicists as substantial, weakening communication and trust. This very much complicates the crucial process of succession.

By contrast, the American-style research team does not rely on strong cross-generational ties but on very good peer relations. As I wrote earlier, American teams are short-lived structures, and physicists are likely to work in several in the course of their careers, presumably learning many approaches and techniques. In the American practice communication is concentrated within one's generation, even across team boundaries. Gaps between generations, however, usually have been quite large.

While competition in Japan primarily has been between dominant *koza,* in the United States competition has been concentrated within generations, between individuals who are struggling to become research group leaders and laboratory directors. Although the American group leaders cannot bequeath their positions to their protégés, they do try to help their best students to get positions in other laboratories and universities; this in turn extends the group leader's own network and power base. However, these attempts are fought and often thwarted by members of the leader's own generation who are reluctant to see a shift in the existing balance of power. This system can function only as long as funding continues to increase, creating enough new positions for each powerful leader to establish a protégé in the newly formed research groups, preferably at newly formed laboratories. The recent declines in the rate of increase in science funding in the United States have undermined this system and intensified the competition between generations as well as between leaders in the same generation.

In the Japanese practice professors designate their successors and groups are perpetuated, but there are rarely any new groups. This arrangement is stable in a "steady-state" funding environment. In the American pattern the best, most ambitious scientists in each generation hope to establish their own new research group. This fission process is suitable for an environment of funding expansion. The problem is that the funding environment is now expanding in Japan and leveling off in the United States. The research organization structures and leadership styles are no longer appropriate in their new funding environments.

One solution could be to adopt each other's organizational structure and leadership style. As I have said, examples of both exist in each country: the coach/team approach is found in Japan, and the *sensei/iemoto* mode is not rare in the United States. It remains to be seen if each country's scientists will shift away from their dominant style to a less common model. Will "coaches" who have learned to locate players with highly developed skills and design strategies and to win every encounter with other teams now begin to build long-lived groups and designate successors? Will *sensei* accustomed to maintaining *ie* across generations and defining the boundaries among *iemoto* now begin to form ties with other *sensei* outside their traditional networks and encourage the new recruits to spend time working in various *iemoto?* Will they allow the next generation to name its own leaders and form its own groups?

Similarities: Gender, Minorities, and Talk

In this chapter I have emphasized the differences between (and within) the Japanese and American high-energy physics communities. Now I turn to some features that seem to pervade the entire community. The exclusion of women from both the *ie* lineage and team membership appears to be a significant similarity in the two types of groups.[25] However, it may become a major area of difference in just a few years. In both countries very few women physicists are now in the laboratories, but massive changes are very near for the American labs. For example, nearly 40% of the undergraduate science and engineering students at MIT are women; 20% of graduate students there are women, as are about 15% of the postdocs and about 10% of the faculty. These numbers are gradually increasing every year, although they are lower at MIT than at other comparably prestigious American universities, such as Stanford, where, for example, 50% of the undergraduates in engineering are women. Generally speaking, the higher the status of the university, the higher the proportion of women in science and engineering: marginal schools are almost entirely male. In my experience women in science and engineering usually have origins in much higher social classes than do their male colleagues; their sense of entitlement seems to help them to ignore (or not even hear) the rather class-based gender barbs from the men. They usually do not take academic positions because they see universities as much more conservative about hiring and promoting women than private industry or government.

The numbers of women (mostly Caucasian) in American science and engineering represent the gradual but cumulative effect of the 1964 Civil Rights Act's removal of restrictions on women in the workplace and schools. Until the middle 1960's the American academic world closely resembled the Japanese in its informal exclusion of women from any position of influence, particularly in science and engineering. Perhaps the 1986 equal-opportunity legislation in Japan will have an effect on the lives of Japanese girls now being born like that of the 1964 law on those born in the 1960's in the United States.

The 1964 Civil Rights Act has helped Caucasian women gain access to science and engineering communities, but it has not helped ethnic minorities. The demographic cohort from which scientists and engineers are conventionally drawn in the United States, working-class and lower-middle-class white men, has been drastically declining in the past few decades. Physics departments have compensated for the decline of this group by admitting foreign men, usually from Asia. The higher the status of the department, the higher the proportion of these foreign students: at the best places there are about 75% foreign students, few of whom stay in the U.S. after completing their postdocs (according to many, many studies). Japan is beginning to increase its population of foreign students in sciences and engineering, but the numbers are still very small. In both the United States and Japan the representation of ethnic minorities is infinitesimal. However, in the United States there is increasing concern about minority education in sciences and engineering,

25 I am addressing this subject in my "Strategic Practices of Women Scientists and Engineers in Japan," to be published in *Current Issues in Gender and Science*.

and new policies and programs are now being formulated; it is at least possible that in twenty years we will see minorities reaching women's current levels of participation. I heard no such talk or commitment among the Japanese concerning the inclusion of, for example, the substantial minority communities in Japan, such as Korean-Japanese, Chinese-Japanese, Burakumin, or Ainu. The two minority scientists I did meet in Japan spoke of pervasive and massive discrimination at every level of Japanese education and research.

Another crucial and fundamental feature of this international community of scientists is that "state-of-the-art" knowledge is transmitted orally, not in writing. High-energy physicists no longer consult scientific journals to study the latest developments in their field.[26] As soon as a paper is written and submitted to a journal, it is circulated to all the major laboratories and university departments in this field worldwide. In this form it is called a "preprint," which usually is available within several weeks of discovery or innovation. However, these high-energy physicists see their field as changing so rapidly that waiting to learn of interesting results, detector innovations, or new theoretical developments until they appear in writing is regarded as exceedingly unwise. What is being talked about is seen as the current more advanced knowledge. They do keep up with the preprints in order to know who is writing about what, but they prefer to talk to people to elicit what they want to know; it also is assumed that the whole story is rarely written and that crucial details are never written. Good experimentalists, in particular, write and talk physics, but they seem rarely to read physics.[27]

Conclusion

I hope that my description of the high-energy physics community's discourse on center and periphery, on dominance and subordination, on leadership and money, has convinced you that understanding this discourse is central to understanding the organization of high-energy physics in Japan. I have also tried to convey how recent and past discursive practices are now shaping the Japanese high-energy physics community's current strategies for establishing big science in Japan.

I hope too that my discussion of these practices leads to greater attention being paid to the specificity and variety of cultural practices in big science. We need to investigate Kowarski's claims, but especially his assumption that there are only two kinds of big science: national and multinational. We now know

26 For a fuller discussion of these issues, see my "Gossip in Science."

27 Earlier versions of these last three sections were first published in Japanese in *Chuokoron*, a quarterly journal on contemporary politics and public policies (Jan. 1987, pp. 143–56) and in my *Beamtimes and Lifetimes*, chapters three and four. These issues will be addressed more fully in my next book, *Physics in the Borderlands: Colonial Transgressions in Japanese Big Science.*

that the "convergence theory" of economic development is false and that there are many modes of economic development. We need to learn the varieties of big scientific research practices, if only to understand our own ecology better.

By describing some features of how the Japanese scientific community has developed in the past few decades, I hope to have raised your interest in the development of scientific communities outside North America and Europe. We have some rather vague, and perhaps peculiar, notions about the "rise of national scientific communities." We now have the opportunity to study the emergence of several national scientific communities into the international arena (Brazil, China, India, Korea, Saudi Arabia, and so on) and to study the consequences of there being many varieties of scientific and engineering practices.

References Cited

Abir-Am, Pnina. "The Discourse of Physical Power and Biological Knowledge in the 1930's: A Reappraisal of the Rockefeller Foundation's 'Policy' in Molecular Biology." *Social Studies of Science* 12 (1982): 341–82.

———. "Beyond Deterministic Sociology and Apologetic History: Reassessing the Impact of Research Policy upon New Scientific Disciplines (Reply to Fuerst, Bartels, Olby, and Yoxen)." *Social Studies of Science* 14 (1984): 252–63.

Bartocha, Bodo, and Sogo Okamura, eds. *Transforming Scientific Ideas into Innovations: Science Policies in the United States and Japan.* Tokyo: Japan Society for the Promotion of Science, 1985.

Ben-David, Joseph. *The Scientist's Role in Society: A Comparative Study.* Englewood Cliffs, N.J.: Prentice-Hall, 1971.

Bhabha, Homi. "The Other Question—The Stereotype and Colonial Discourse." *Screen,* no. 24 (Nov.–Dec. 1983).

———. "Of Mimicry and Man: The Ambiguity of Colonial Discourse." *October,* no. 28 (Spring 1984).

Birnbaum, Henry. "Japan Builds a Science City." *Physics Today,* Feb. 1975, pp. 42–48.

Campbell, John Creighton. *Contemporary Japanese Budget Politics.* Berkeley: University of California Press, 1977.

"Canons." *Critical Inquiry* 10, no. 1 (Sept. 1983).

Gerstenfeld, Arthur, ed. *Science Policy Perspectives: USA–Japan.* New York: Academic Press, 1982.

Group for the Critical Study of Colonial Discourse. *Inscriptions,* Issues 1–4. The History of Consciousness Program, University of California: Santa Cruz, 1986–88.

Haraway, Donna. *Primate Visions: Gender, Race and Nature in the World of Modern Science.* New York: Routledge, 1989.

Harootunian, H. D. *Things Seen and Unseen: Discourse and Ideology in Tokugawa Nativism.* Chicago: University of Chicago Press, 1988.

Hoddeson, Lillian. "Establishing KEK in Japan and Fermilab in the U.S.: Internationalism, Nationalism, and High Energy Accelerators," *Social Studies of Science,* April 1983, pp. 1–48.

KEK National Laboratory for High-Energy Physics. AMY Collaboration, *TRISTAN Proposal for Study of e+e− Interactions with a High-Luminosity High-Resolution Lepton Detector, November 1984;* TOPAZ Collaboration, *TRISTAN Proposal Study of e+e− Annihilation Phenomena by a Detector with Particle Identification, January 1983;* VENUS Collaboration, *Proposal for Study of e+e− Reactions with a Large-Aperture Spectrometer, January 31, 1983.* Tsukuba, Japan: KEK National Laboratory for High Energy Physics.

————. *Annual Report, 1976.* Tsukuba, Japan: KEK, 1977.

————. *Annual Report, 1985.* Tsukuba, Japan: KEK, 1986.

Kowarski, L. "New Forms of Organization in Physical Research After 1945." In Charles Weiner, ed., *History of Twentieth Century Physics,* pp. 370–401. New York: Academic Press, 1977.

Kyogoku, Jun-ichi. *The Political Dynamics of Japan.* Trans. Nobutaka Ike. Tokyo: University of Tokyo Press, 1987.

Minh-ha, Trinh T. "Of Other Peoples: Beyond the 'Salvage' Paradigm." In Hal Foster, ed., *Discussions in Contemporary Culture,* no. 1. pp. 138–42. Seattle: Bay Press for Dia Art Foundation, 1987.

Price, Derek de Solla. *Science Since Babylon.* New Haven: Yale University Press, 1961.

Restivo, Sal, and Christopher Vanderpool, eds. *Comparative Studies in Science and Society.* Columbus, Ohio: Charles E. Merrill, 1974.

Said, Edward. *Orientalism.* New York: Random House, 1979.

Schiele, Bernard. "Les enjeux caches de la vulgarisation scientifique." *Communication Information* 5, nos. 2–3. Quebec: Albert Saint-Martin, 1983.

————. "Vulgarisation et television." *Social Science Information/Information sur les sciences sociales* 25, no. 1 (1986): 189–206.

Schiele, Bernard, Charles Perraton, and Louise Boucher. *Ciel, Une Expo! Approche de L'Exposition Scientifique.* Paris: Expo Media 3, 1988.

Strauss, Monica M. "The Organization of Research in the Information Sciences: Case Studies in Japan and the U.S." M.A. thesis, Massachusetts Institute of Technology, 1986.

Traweek, Sharon. *Beamtimes and Lifetimes: The World of High Energy Physicists.* Cambridge, Mass.: Harvard University Press, 1988.

————. "Gossip in Science," submitted to *Language in Science.*

————. *Physics in the Borderlands: Colonial Transgressions in Japanese Big Science,* forthcoming.

————. "Strategic Practices of Women Scientists and Engineers in Japan." In Mary Frank Fox, ed., *Current Issues in Gender and Science.* University Park: Pennsylvania State University Press, forthcoming.

TRISTAN Project Group. *TRISTAN Electron-Positron Colliding Beam Project.* Tsukuba, Japan: KEK National Laboratory for High-Energy Physics, 1987.

"Writing, Race, and Difference." *Critical Inquiry* 12, no. 1 (Autumn 1985).

CHAPTER 5

SLAC and Big Science: Stanford University

W. K. H. Panofsky

Today, physics at Stanford University has evolved into a highly diverse activity, spreading over many departments and academic units. It spans a very large range in scale from traditional small laboratory experiments to the Stanford Linear Accelerator Center (SLAC) and the precessing gyroscope testing general relativity in space.

The progressive changes in physics have raised many profound issues relating to the role of Stanford University. Among these are the conflict, on the one hand, or symbiosis, on the other, between research and teaching; the extent to which large science enterprises permit the creative participation of graduate students and junior faculty; and the issue of proper recognition of the work of individuals when scientific papers require one page of a journal just to list the authors. Above all, we are facing tensions between the sponsor's quest for accountability, and even control, and the traditional academic freedoms to publish, to choose one's work, and to choose the academic staff within the university.

One must recognize that none of these issues is at all new and that in spite of all the changes that have taken place there remains a unifying spirit throughout the physics enterprise at Stanford. This spirit is an attempt to understand inanimate nature in its most fundamental aspects and to communicate this understanding to future generations.

Fig. 5.1. Panofsky adjusting target on Mark III Electron Accelerator, Stanford High-Energy Physics Laboratory, ca. 1955. Photo courtesy News Service, Stanford University.

SLAC did not represent a sudden transition to big science but was a step in an evolutionary pattern of growth that was initiated at Stanford during the Korean War. At that time a deliberate decision was made by Stanford Provost Frederick Terman in consonance with several faculty members including those of the physics department that the university should expand its involvement in government-supported scientific and technical activities. A primary motive for doing so at that time was the fear that during the Korean War the technical faculty would leave Stanford, following the pattern that occurred during World War II.

The evolution at Stanford from the Mark I to the Mark III and Mark II linear accelerators, initiated by Bill Hansen and continued under Ed Ginzton's leadership, is well documented. Because of the pressure of developing klystrons for applied purposes, largely military, the Microwave Lab and the High-Energy Physics Lab were separated but shared a common administrative structure called the Hansen Labs. The Microwave Lab dedicated its efforts primarily to high-powered microwave tubes, while the High-Energy Physics Lab's mission was the completion and exploitation of the Mark III and Mark II linear accelerators for nuclear and particle physics (see Fig. 5.1).

Mark II and particularly Mark III were not "small science." Budgets each year were in the multimillion-dollar range (when a million dollars was still a million dollars!). Professional operating technician crews were necessary, and the beam of the Mark III accelerator was shared among a multitude of users. With few exceptions these users were, however, "in-house," that is, Stanford faculty, students, and staff. Most of the work was done collaboratively, but these groups were small by today's standards in high-energy physics and in general a member of the Stanford faculty directed each collaboration. The lab was the responsibility of a director who was not necessarily a member of the regular faculty. He, in turn, was advised or controlled—it never was totally clear which—by a committee whose majority were members of the regular professoriate.

The Birth of SLAC

Mark III was a great success, leading to many important discoveries in particle physics including the Nobel Prize–winning work on the size and shape of the proton and neutron. This lent encouragement to studies that eventually culminated in a proposal for the construction of the two-mile linear accelerator, a laboratory that came to be called SLAC after some search for alternative acronyms.

The proposal to construct SLAC originated first from suggestions by Professor Robert Hofstadter, born from his desire to extend his Nobel Prize– winning studies on the structure of the proton and neutron to higher energies. Meetings were then held at my home and that of Professor Ginzton, leading subsequently to an informal study group encompassing most of the active staff members of the High-Energy Physics Laboratory and some members of the Microwave Laboratory. This group met informally "after hours," wrote extensive technical memoranda, and finally in April 1957 produced a proposal of about 100 pages. The civil engineering analysis that was part of the proposal was contributed by an outside corporation volunteering its services. It is interesting to compare this process with the vastly more extensive documentation now required to initiate a big-science construction project, illustrated by the superconducting supercollider (SSC). The studies leading to the SSC proposal involved up to 100 paid individuals, major experimental work on superconducting magnets carried out at three or four participating laboratories, innumerable reviews of cost and research and development, and the full-blown environmental impact statement process. The actual cost of writing the SSC proposal came close to a million dollars, in response to the government-required format.

The Stanford proposal to construct SLAC was submitted simultaneously to the Department of Defense, the National Science Foundation, and the Atomic Energy Commission. It would be impossible to conceive that an identical proposal could be submitted to three different government agencies today, since each agency requires its own detailed format for proposal submission. In contrast a single agency, the Department of Energy, issued a request for proposal to build the SSC and only one proponent—the Universities Research Association, Inc., then a consortium of 66 universities—responded. In summary, whereas in 1957 the SLAC proposal was a search for *support* of work to be directed by the proponents, in 1988 the SSC proposal was straitjacketed into the format of a government *acquisition,* with the work to be performed by the most qualified performer.

Let us return to the fate of the SLAC proposal. After many discussions and after review by an *ad hoc* panel appointed by the General Advisory Committee of the Atomic Energy Commission and the President's Science Advisory Committee (PSAC), President Eisenhower recommended that SLAC be given the "green light"; Congress authorized the project in 1961 after a one-year delay.

Some remarks on PSAC might be in order. That institution was created by President Eisenhower after Sputnik signaled that American science was not all it was expected to be. The work of PSAC was in essence divided into two categories: science in policy, and policy in science. The former dealt with providing informed scientific input to policy decisions in many areas of concern to the U.S. government. In the modern age hardly any field of governmental activity is unaffected by science, be it national defense, agriculture, foreign relations, health, or housing. It became clear that the president needed for his policy decisions scientific input that was not filtered through the programmatic or policy objectives of the various government departments and agencies.

The second category had to do with government support of science. Traditionally, a large number of government agencies support both basic and applied science. It is noteworthy that the one agency specifically created to support basic science, the National Science Foundation, actually provides funds for only about 20% of the total governmental contributions; the balance is supplied by the so-called mission agencies such as the Defense Department, what used to be the Department of Health, Education, and Welfare (in the health sciences), and the Atomic Energy Commission, now the Department of Energy (in nuclear and high-energy physics). While the role of PSAC in giving advice on "science in policy" has in retrospect been very successful, this cannot be said with equal conviction in respect to "policy in science." It is extremely difficult, if not impossible, for scientists active in a variety of disciplines to agree on scientific priorities when they are constituted into advisory bodies; this is perhaps neither unexpected or unhealthy. If major projects such as SLAC are under consideration, the most knowledgeable individuals are those directly affected by the discussions and therefore have to disqualify themselves from the deliberations. This is precisely what I did in respect to SLAC. In essence I served only as a witness before PSAC; in no way did I participate in its deliberations on whether the construction of SLAC should or should not be authorized.

Support of science by the federal government is an extremely complex and extensive undertaking. A presidential committee cannot possibly review even a small fraction of the proposals before government agencies, and it can hardly deal with the division of responsibility among different agencies. To do so would require a very large supporting staff and would essentially establish a group like PSAC as another layer in governmental bureaucracy, thereby impeding even further the speed of governmental decisions. Thus, as a practical matter, PSAC dealt only with some selected major decisions in this area, in particular when big-ticket items such as SLAC were involved.

Ground for SLAC was broken in 1962, five years after the proposal was submitted, and the first beam was generated in 1966. Thus the interval between proposal submission and the first beam was about nine years, divided roughly evenly between the political process of securing authorization and the physical process of building the machine. With the SSC as well, this proportion, but not the absolute time, is expected to be not too dissimilar.

A noteworthy fact about these time scales is that the construction time of "frontier" accelerators, from the electrostatic machines of the 1930's through SLAC and Fermilab of the 1960's, has hardly changed from the norm of four to six years, notwithstanding the increase in energy by five orders of magnitude. Somehow the effort brought to bear on constructing frontier high-energy accelerators has grown to make possible construction in the same period. In other words, the ratio of inertia to muscle needed to accomplish the task has remained roughly constant; the reader will recognize that this is the same reason why a flea and an elephant can jump roughly to the same height. Of course such a compression of construction time is desirable both from the point of view of efficiency and to accommodate both participation in construction and participation in research within one academic career.

SLAC and the Associated Community

A few additional relevant points in connection with the birth of SLAC are worth mentioning.

1. SLAC was the largest accelerator proposed at the time and remained the most expensive single installation in high-energy physics until the construction of the National Accelerator Laboratory, now Fermilab.

2. The community of physicists was not enthusiastic about the creation of SLAC. At the time of its creation the mainstream of high-energy physics used protons as the bombarding particle, and the wisdom of switching to the use of an electron beam with bad duty cycle was widely doubted. Yet because at the time of the SLAC proposal science budgets were growing at roughly 15% per year there was no feeling of competition or threat from the new facility to the programs of other sciences. The type of divisive debate that we are seeing today with respect to the SSC was absent.

3. Interestingly enough, although no other scientists opposed SLAC from fear that it might take priority over their own aspirations, there was opposition from one senior statesman of science. Professor Eugene Wigner testified before Congress that he opposed the construction of SLAC because it would usurp so much scientific and technical manpower that it would interfere with the military efforts of the United States. In retrospect concerns about insufficient manpower to carry out big science have been largely unfounded both with respect to SLAC and other projects. Big science projects such as SLAC themselves contribute greatly to the training of scientists and engineers.

It has been true throughout the history of particle physics that the number of proponents qualified for the experimental use of such facilities has exceeded available opportunities. It is largely for this reason that research groups tend to be larger than they really have to be. The only area where there is indeed a shortage of qualified performers is the construction and technology of accelerators, rather than the use of accelerators for physics. Qualified accelerator specialists have been and are now in great demand. A major reason for this is not so much the growth of new facilities for research but the burgeoning applications of accelerator technology to such areas as synchrotron radiation, cancer therapy, industrial radiography, and various defense-related problems.

The High-Energy Physics Lab was a facility of Stanford University, although it was operated outside the regular departmental framework. When SLAC was initiated there was a debate within the Stanford physics community whether SLAC should be operated like the High-Energy Physics Lab, described somewhat simplistically as an arm of the regular Stanford physics department, or should become more national in character. The decision was made and accepted by the government that SLAC should be a "national facility," meaning not quite a national laboratory. The meaning of this term evolved to signify that SLAC should be available equitably to scientists throughout the world, with judgment on priorities to be based on scientific merit and demonstrable ability to carry out the proposed program.

A committee structure was established for SLAC including a Scientific Policy Committee composed of scientists from outside Stanford, advising the president of the university and designed primarily to safeguard the rights of the outside users. The part of that committee's report dealing with the availability of SLAC's facilities to outside users was to be forwarded to the Atomic Energy Commission. The balance, being simply a program and management review, could in principle be kept privileged by Stanford's president, but this never occurred. Yet the line responsibility for running SLAC was strictly within Stanford. It devolved from the Stanford board of trustees to the president to the director to the line organization of the laboratory. This pattern is unique. Other high-energy physics laboratories in this country and abroad have become what Leon Lederman, the past director of Fermilab, has characterized as "truly national laboratories." This means that the legal responsibility for the laboratory is vested in a board composed of members from many universities or other entities. At the same time other large accelerators, notably that at Cornell, have remained proprietary.

With the benefit of hindsight I consider much of the debate about national laboratory, national facility, and even proprietary campus machines to be a tempest in a teapot, as long as the installations require a major professional presence for their design, maintenance, and operation. As a practical matter, the social interactions between the accelerator professionals, the inside users, and the outside participants are controlled much more by the state of the science and technical circumstances than they are by the formal arrangements for allocating use. The decision-making process, the mechanisms for review by outside committees, and the relationship to government oversight are all remarkably similar.

This conclusion that the decision-making process allocating research time is not greatly dependent on the nature of the official laboratory "constitution" does not mean that allocation of running time and other resources is without controversy. Possibly the most profound disagreements swirl around the question whether allocations are to be made *ad hominem* or on the demonstrable merit of each proposal. There always have been and will continue to be members of the scientific community with a not inconsiderable ego who feel that the "powers that be" should allocate facilities and running time to them on the basis of their reputation and past performance rather than on the merit of what they are proposing to do. During the history of SLAC and other laboratories several senior members of the scientific community have with-drawn their requests for running time in a huff, maintaining that they should not be subjected to the degrading level of review that the peer program committee reporting to the director generally exacts. Paradoxically, few members of the scientific community object to peer review of their proposals when such review groups advise government agencies. However, when such detailed accountability is due a laboratory director, or as far as that goes, a department head in a university, some senior members of the scientific community take offense. In other words, there is some objection in the academic community to detailed accountability to their immediate academic or scientific peers but much less objection if that accountability is focused on a more remote decision-making body.

When SLAC was created the matter of "national facility" vs. "proprietary physics department lab" was resolved by establishing SLAC as a national facility but having its own faculty. The need for a faculty was deemed necessary because traditionally the regular faculty members are the first-class citizens on a university campus, and therefore the use of the title was believed to be essential to attract the intellectual leadership so essential to the success of SLAC. In hindsight this decision proved to be amply justified by the results obtained. Yet the university paid a price for this choice in controversy. Moreover, the size of the faculty at SLAC was determined by the central university administration, and SLAC chose to accept such limits whether they did or did not match the needs of SLAC's program. Again the balance of values involved here might be resolved differently under different circumstances.

Then there is the relationship to the outside users. When SLAC was inaugurated, as mentioned above, the interest of the particle physics community at large was mainly focused on proton machines. Initially, therefore, the interest of outside users in spending a large amount of time and intellectual effort at SLAC was limited. For technical reasons associated with the characteristics of the SLAC electron beam, most experiments at SLAC were expected to be "facility centered," that is, to require the construction of large particle detectors that could then be used for a variety of experiments. Experiments in which a small user group assembles a single experiment from "building blocks" are rare and difficult at SLAC.

There are a variety of general technical reasons why SLAC's experiments are more likely to require large particle detectors. Experiments consist of recording the particles produced from primary collisions, registering in which direction the particles travel, determining their energy, and identifying their charge, mass, and possibly other characteristics. This task is accomplished by determining where particles go in space and in time, under the influence of external agents such as magnetic fields or interposed materials. For processes produced by SLAC's electron beam discrimination in time is very difficult, because the beam comes in bursts of less than one microsecond, repeated up to

360 times per second. Thus within the short time of the beam pulse it is very difficult, even with modern electronic devices, to untangle the time sequence of events. Thus all particles from the primary target must be first sorted out by direction and energy before their arrival can be timed; this takes complex equipment.

There are other technical reasons as well, increasing the complexity of detecting systems. SLAC's beam is very intense, but only a small fraction of the electrons produce events of interest. Thus the final detectors designed to tag the selected interesting phenomena have to be heavily shielded and separated from the primary target. Large and complex detectors are also a necessity for use with SLAC's colliding-beam storage rings; here the rates of interesting events are so slow that one cannot afford to throw anything away; thus the detectors have to surround the interaction point fully and identify each track as well as possible. Again this means complex detectors and associated facilities (see Fig. 5.2).

The design and construction of complex facilities requires the participation of first-rate particle physicists. However, in the initial absence of a strong outside interest, most of these instruments had to be built under the direction of SLAC faculty and staff, and this was done successfully. Thus the lab endured some criticism for allegedly "excluding" users from its program and thus not really living up to its charter as a "national facility." Yet again this was an unavoidable consequence of the technical situation with respect to electrons and the distribution of users' interests during the 1960's.

The situation changed dramatically when some of the techniques that had proven successful for proton accelerators were imported to SLAC. The most noted example is the transfer of the large 82-inch bubble chamber from Berkeley to SLAC. This device accumulates data in the form of pictorial images on film, which can be scanned at many university laboratories. The transfer of the instrument, together with the construction at SLAC of a special bubble chamber recording data at a high rate, suddenly transformed the laboratory to the world's most prolific producer of bubble-chamber film for a wide outside community. These examples illustrate that it is frequently a technical circumstance rather than an administrative fiat that controls the degree and kind of user participation.

A fundamental problem besetting all big-science high-energy physics facilities is the extent to which the lab should deviate from its primary goal of maximizing short-range physics output from its facilities in the interest of assuring the widest practical participation of university users. Frequently short-range productivity is impaired by the complexity and the realities of outside academic participation. Yet the very existence of high-energy physics depends in the long run on the creative input of university scientists and on the training of a new generation of students. Again, this is an issue that requires a middle course but should not be a source of major conflict.

Fig. 5.2. Panofsky at the SLAC beamline, March 1965. Photo courtesy Stanford Linear Accelerator Center and the U.S. Department of Energy.

All these controversies, quite prevalent earlier in the history of SLAC, have now largely run their course, and the practice of having a local program advisory committee advise the director is fully accepted. This practice has become a necessity if younger, less prominent proponents are to be permitted the opportunity to have their proposals considered on their merits. Large detectors have become the rule rather than the exception at all high-energy physics laboratories worldwide.

The Construction of Big Science Facilities and Academe

The advent of big science has raised a series of profound questions concerning the role of academic institutions in the management of big science laboratories. Dealing with these issues requires administrative inventiveness. Blind insistence on preserving academic practices no longer applicable is counterproductive, yet exclusive emphasis on administrative efficiency, financial accountability, etc., in disregard of academic values is even more destructive.

Academic institutions have become involved in big science laboratories as managers and operators of the facilities as well as through the participation of their faculties, students, and staff in the design and research work. But these roles involve challenges to traditional practices.

As the size of government-supported big science facilities has grown, the question of whether academic institutions are the proper agents to construct, manage, and operate such facilities keeps recurring. Superficially, construction of big science facilities has become a major undertaking akin to many space and military projects. Thus cost control is a prominent issue. Is it really appropriate to give contractual responsibility for the construction of such major multibillion-dollar installations as the SSC to academic institutions rather than to contract such construction out to "experienced industry" and then "turn the key over" to the "long-hairs and eggheads" to carry out their academic researches? This issue has substance. The construction of a laboratory like SLAC is indeed an activity quite dissimilar from the usual on-campus construction projects at a university. However, there are three main reasons militating against the "turn-key" approach where industry builds and academe uses:

1. The record of academic bodies, both individual universities and university consortia, in building big science installations costing nearly $1 billion within projected expenses, within schedule, and within advertised performance has been excellent. In fact, the record is much superior to that of projects for space, military systems, or commercial reactors.

2. Creation of a major accelerator or other big science facility involves a great deal more than constructing a major technical tool to within specified costs, schedule, and performance. Rather, what is involved is the creation of a vibrant institution that can support the research using the new facility, that can upgrade that facility as scientific needs change, and that provides the general infrastructure and intellectual atmosphere necessary for continued scientific vigor. This ambience must be created during the construction period.

3. In small science responsibility for carrying out a proposed project rests with the "principal investigator," who is a member of the academic staff of the university. He or she works with students and young research associates. If the principal investigator leaves or loses interest in the project, then the activity disappears. In contrast, when a university (or consortium of universities) proposes a big science activity the responsibility for both the construction of the facility and putting it to proper scientific use rests with the university and transcends the availability of a particular project leader or laboratory director. Thus, should a project head depart, the university is obligated to conduct an expeditious search for a qualified successor. In turn, the implication of this process is that there is continuity from construction to utilization of the new facility, since the basic objective of the facility is intellectual rather than economic. This process, then, has to be consistent with the basic premise that

construction of a new facility is not a construction project in the usual sense but a creation of an integrated organizational entity whose success will be judged by its intellectual products.

Note that, for these reasons, nuclear and high-energy physics laboratories have generally been built in America under contract with academic institutions. In contrast, major facilities for space science are supported by contract from government to industry. Once the space vehicles have been built and tested, then scientific payloads (which in themselves may be big or small science) are frequently created by academic entities, but their characteristics must strictly conform to conditions already built into the space vehicles that the scientific users generally had little choice in specifying.

Research in Big Science

Research in big science involves collaborative efforts by large groups. However, the dynamics of this collaboration has frequently been misunderstood. Indeed, the construction of an accelerator is a major collaborative

Fig. 5.3. Stanford Linear Collider main control room, 1990. Photo courtesy Stanford Linear Accelerator Center and the U.S. Department of Energy.

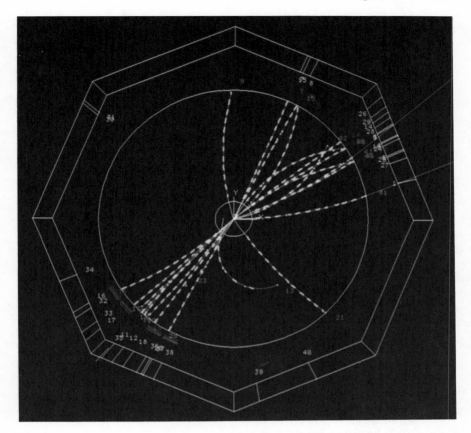

Fig. 5.4. Fifth Z-event observed at the Stanford Linear Collider, May 1, 1989. The interpretation of the event is as follows: an unseen Z decays into an unseen quark-antiquark pair, and one of these two particles radiates an unseen gluon. Each of these particles then materializes into a visible jet (a collimated group of fast, strongly interacting particles that leave tracks). One jet is seen between seven and eight o'clock, a second involves two straight tracks at about one o'clock, and a third consists of the group of particle tracks between two and three o'clock. Photo courtesy Stanford Linear Accelerator Center and United States Department of Energy.

effort, and frequently the potential users get involved in many phases of such construction. The potential users participate in workshops determining the fundamental design parameters of the machine, they maintain contact with the builders to make sure that provisions for future experiments are adequate, and they frequently get involved in the commissioning of the machine both to accelerate its completion and to become acquainted with its detailed operating characteristics.

Design and construction of particle detectors also tend to be major cooperative enterprises, involving in recent times frequently over 100 physicists from many institutions. Yet individual inventiveness and skill remain absolutely essential to the successful creation of a modern particle detector system. Data-taking with such a facility again involves many physicists because the machine usually runs 24 hours per day and the computer software needed to analyze the data is enormously complex (see Figs. 5.3 and 5.4).

Note that in big science of this type far more data are recorded than are required for the experiment's specifically identified primary goals. The real scientific exploitation of the data consists of "mining the tapes." It is during this later phase of data analysis that individual ingenuity becomes paramount. Frequently, important physics discoveries have been made years after the primary data were taken. The primary example of this at SLAC was the discovery of the tau lepton. Here a large collaboration of physicists built the colliding-beam machine SPEAR and then the Mark I detector. This led, among other triumphs, to the discovery of the Ψ/J particle and the elucidation of the spectroscopy of psions, which are composed of the charmed quark and its antiparticle. However, about two years after these discoveries Professor Martin Perl and his students carefully searched the data for an excess of coincidences of detected electrons with muons. Such coincidences can be explained only if initially a pair of particles that can independently decay into electrons and muons is formed. This conjecture was converted into what became irrefutable evidence for the existence of a third generation of leptons known as tau particles.

The Relation of Big Science to Academic Practice

It should be noted that throughout this process of big science at SLAC the motivation of the academic physicist participants remained exactly the same as it had been in smaller endeavors, that is, to uncover new basic facts of inanimate nature. However, because of the way in which the work must be carried out, there are indeed conflicts with traditional academic practices that must be resolved. Among these are

1. *Recognition of individual contributors.* Because most but not all of the participation by physicists is in the form of group activities, individual contributions cannot be easily traced through the publication record alone. Therefore, during faculty searches and promotion inquiries reference must be made to personal contacts, with bibliographical data being used for backup only. At SLAC we make a major effort to draw the speakers at major national and international physics conferences from the younger members of a large research collaboration.

2. *The tenure clock.* Attainment of a truly significant scientific result may require a time span not under the control of the young physicist participating

in the work. At the same time the "up or out" practices on the academic ladder require documentable accomplishment during a fixed time. The question is whether the "tenure clock" can be stopped while the individual participates in, say, the construction of a major detector.

3. *Thesis standards.* Ph.D. theses are expected to be "independent" pieces of work. As a practical matter this standard is frequently violated in many fields of natural science—big or small. Because "big science" research is carried out in groups and is frequently conditioned by the available facilities, true independence is hard to come by. At the same time, the graduate student may indeed make major and independent contributions to the instrumental part of his or her activity. However, departments are loath to recognize contributions to the design of instruments as a significant component of a thesis, even if they are intellectually highly challenging. This should be changed.

4. *Absenteeism.* The participation by the research physicist in experiments at SLAC is frequently controlled by the vagaries of the machine, the governmental financial support pattern, and other factors not under laboratory control. Thus a faculty member and his students may have to absent themselves from their teaching duties on a schedule difficult to predict, with consequent burdens on their colleagues. In most users' institutions this matter requires multiple teaching loads when the researchers return to campus. Universities will have to define the price they are willing to pay for participation in big science in greater flexibility in assignment of teaching duties.

5. *Quality of local facilities.* It is clearly desirable from the academic point of view that absences from campus of faculty and students collaborating in big science at other institutions be minimized. This would maximize the interaction of these individuals with their fellow academic colleagues and their contributions to academic life at the home institution. However, to make this practical the home institution cannot be permitted to let its supporting facilities—shops, computers, technical staff assistance—deteriorate; if that happens the academic people involved have no choice but to carry out an even larger part of their work at the big science lab. Recently the quality of support facilities at universities has slipped unacceptably. The fault for this is divided between the sources of government support and the academics themselves: financial support by the government has not grown as fast as most people hoped, but at the same time the principal investigators at most academic institutions have been less than responsible, using available funds for augmenting their academic personnel excessively, to the detriment of adequately building up the supporting structure.

All these points imply serious problems but none that cannot be solved by some flexibility and inventiveness.

Tensions between big science and the universities have arisen over the question of whether there should be a university or a branch of a university located in a big science facility. This is, of course, not an issue at SLAC, because Stanford University is in the fortunate position of being able to accommodate a two-mile accelerator on its seventeen-square-mile campus. Note, however, that when the University of Chicago attempted to establish a branch campus on the site of the Argonne National Laboratory a great howl arose from many other midwestern universities. They claimed that the University of Chicago was trying to take unfair advantage, relative to its sister academic institutions in the Midwest, of Argonne's resources. At the same time there is criticism, some merited, that the intellectual atmosphere at some big science facilities could be greatly improved if the relationship to universities were more intimate. Attempts in this direction have been made, for instance, at the branch of the State University of New York at Stony Brook, just outside the gates of Brookhaven National Laboratory.

Big Science and "Academic Freedom"

Much has been said and written on whether the advent of big science upsets the traditional values generally listed under the heading of academic freedom. Often expressed is the worry that as big science funds are expended in support of science, "who pays the piper calls the tune." In other words, there is concern that the sponsor, in this case the government, will unduly influence the conduct of the work, affect the selection of the principal personnel, and force the introduction of extraneous criteria into various program decisions. This is a problem a university faces irrespective of whether the science is big or small. A university such as Stanford continually confronts the issue of whether to accept a gift or grant from a donor or sponsor if there are too many "strings" attached. While totally unrestricted gifts to the university are highly desirable, most contributions are earmarked for a specific purpose. Yet when that purpose is defined in terms too narrow, the university can be and often is forced to reject the donation. It is illustrative to compare the situation of small science as supported at Stanford University before World War II with that of SLAC. A big part of prewar physics at Stanford University was the work initiated by Bill Hansen in high-power microwave electronics and sponsored by the Sperry Corporation. Yet the relationship between the Stanford faculty, the university administration, and the Sperry Corporation was a stormy one. A problem was that Sperry insisted on playing a major role in the selection of major technical personnel and in the topics to be pursued. Moreover, at times Sperry applied strong pressure to have the work be directed more to the generation of new patents rather than to the evolution of basic knowledge.

The relationship between Stanford University and the U.S. government in respect to SLAC compares favorably with this early situation. That relationship is governed by a contract between the U.S. Department of Energy and the trustees of the university that is renewable every five years. Under that contract the government supports the work at a financial level it chooses in response to annual program submittals by the university, but the university is not obligated to follow the technical and scientific conduct of these proposals except in the most general terms once funding is received. Under the contract the government has a right to approve the director and deputy director of the laboratory when they are first appointed, but it has no right to ask for their removal; the government has no authority to influence the selection of any other personnel or to control the participation by foreign nationals. Decisions about program are made by the laboratory director on the advice of a program advisory committee that passes on the scientific merit of each proposal for use of the SLAC facilities and on the projected capability of the proponents to carry out the work. Publications may not be held up for either national security or commercial considerations; patent review proceeds in parallel with submission of a manuscript to the publishers. In the remote eventuality that the government wishes to use the facilities it owns at SLAC for classified work, then the university has no obligation to carry out such activities. In summary, from the point of view of preserving the traditional academic values, these arrangements for government support of big science compare well with the prewar pattern of industrial support of small science.

Is There a Choice Between "Big" and "Small" Science?

This chapter should document that big science as typified by SLAC has indeed made necessary some changes in academic practices and methods of managing scientific enterprises. Yet one should not lose sight of the fact that the motivation of big science and small science remains the same; the expansion to big science is brought on by technical necessity, not by delusions of grandeur of the scientific community. We simply do not know how to obtain information on the most minute structure of matter (high-energy physics), on the grandest scale of the universe (astronomy and cosmology), or on statistically elusive results (systematic genetics) without large efforts and large tools. The evolution of technical and scientific fact has driven the changes, not a change in motivation or ethics of the scientific leaders.

Yet "big science bashing" has become popular. For instance, a recent article in *Issues in Science and Technology* attributed recent instances of scientific fraud to a decrease in morality brought on by big science, notwithstanding the fact that those instances occurred in "small" medical research and fraud is in fact virtually impossible within the large cooperative efforts of big science.

There is no conflict between big and small science as such, and in fact there is a continuum of scale among the different activities. There is no difference in motivation between the practitioners of big and small science. Much of the apparent but intellectually not real conflict between big and small science is simply caused by a perceived competition for resources. Critics point out with some merit that the cost per Ph.D. produced, the cost per scientific publication in refereed journals, the cost per Nobel Prize, or whatever other measures in cost vs. effectiveness the critic may choose, "big science" may not fare well. Yet that is not really the issue. First, this competition for funds need in fact not be real as long as support in basic science remains a very small fraction of the total national product, or even a small fraction of federally supported research and development. Historically, funding for big and funding for small science have risen or fallen together, not one at the expense of the other. Moreover, one should not demand comparable cost effectiveness of the multitude of scientific endeavors: If certain answers crucial to man's understanding of nature can be obtained only by large effort, is that sufficient reason for not seeking such answers?

PART II

SPONSORED RESEARCH AND EXTERNAL INTERESTS

CHAPTER 6

Big Science in Context:
Cornell and MIT

S. S. Schweber

When I first thought about my contribution to *Big Science*, I considered exploring further the changes the Massachusetts Institute of Technology (MIT) underwent after World War II[1] and giving a Rashomon-like account of these developments. The cast of characters was to have been drawn from the professoriate, the administration, and the board of trustees of MIT, the affiliated laboratories, the neighboring industries—new and old—and the armed services; each would give its version of the facts. I was after the answers to these questions: How in the decade following World War II did MIT achieve its position of dominance among institutions of higher learning as a source of technical advice and expertise for the government? Why did MIT enter in such a close partnership with the armed forces? The official answer given by MIT in 1963 that "only our overriding sense of national duty can justify our assumption of obligations [supported by the federal government] of such an order"[2] was not totally convincing. There were other questions, such as How did the mutual embrace of science and the military affect

1 Schweber, "Mutual Embrace"; see also Leslie, "Profit and Loss."
2 "Twenty-Six Campuses and the Federal Government." *The Educational Record* 44 (1963): p. 46, reprinted in *Fifty-Eighth Annual Report of the Carnegie Foundation for the Advancement of Teaching,* 1962–63.

MIT? How did it affect the curriculum, research activities, the hiring of faculty and the granting of tenure, the shaping of administrative policy? I thought that some partial answers to these questions and some insights could be obtained from a comparison of MIT with another institution of higher learning. I chose Cornell because I have been working with the papers of Hans Bethe, which are a rich source for materials on physics at Cornell from the mid-1930's to the 1970's. It seemed to me that an examination of the ethos of these two institutions, of their internal organization, and of some of the key individuals would highlight what is unique to each, and would help delineate two differing styles.

In this chapter I address the changes MIT and Cornell underwent after World War II by first considering each institution's self-image and character during the 1930's. First I outline some of that history and try to convey the tone set by the presidents of these two institutions, K. T. Compton and E. E. Day. For all their differences, MIT and Cornell also shared many similarities. At both institutions the science departments underwent important changes in the early 1930's. As at every other major American institution of higher learning, the advent of quantum mechanics was responsible for the change.[3] Next I focus on the physics departments at MIT and Cornell, make some observations about the conduct of World War II, and discuss some of the factors that shaped the postwar relations between the military and the physicists. Then I turn to some of Bethe's work during the war. An analysis of Bethe's activities helps explain why the physicists made such valuable contributions to the war effort. That section concludes with some observations concerning the impact of the wartime experiences on engineering education after the war. Finally, I briefly describe the setting up of the laboratories of nuclear studies at MIT and at Cornell, tell of the power struggles that accompanied their establishment, and draw some conclusions.

It may prove helpful to keep in mind a biological analogy to make coherent the various facets of the story I touch upon. I see the generation of physicists that matured with the birth of quantum mechanics as a "population" possessing traits that allowed it not only to adapt to existing conditions but in fact to dominate and transform the scientific and technological environment. These traits were intellectual brilliance and extraordinary experimental skills. These attributes enabled physicists to invent quantum mechanics, to construct cyclotrons, to develop atomic beams apparatus—and thus acquire mastery over the atomic and nuclear domains. The depression exerted a rigid selection pressure on the community. Only the very best survived, and these were an extraordinary lot: among the theorists, Bethe, Felix Bloch, J. Robert Oppenheimer, Rudolf Peierls, Edward Teller, Victor F. Weisskopf, Eugene Paul Wigner; among the experimentalists, Enrico Fermi, Ernest Lawrence, Isidor Rabi. During the 1930's they replicated themselves. A whole new generation was

3 Schweber, "Empiricist Temper Regnant."

selected and trained, primarily on American soil. The war gave them the opportunity to display their powers and in the process they acquired power. The physicists working on radar devices and atomic bombs had unlimited funds and equipment for experimentation, and as a result the technical knowledge and skills of the community were greatly increased during the war. Being a hardy, self-confident, wide-ranging, and resourceful new species, physicists occupied new niches after the war. At one level, the postwar developments could be narrated as the story of the physicists as colonizers.

Cornell and MIT, Compton and Day

As its name implies, the Massachusetts Institute of Technology began as a college of engineering and technology with vocational interests. MIT was described in its charter as a "school of industrial science."[4] Its original mission to train technicians and engineers, its dependence on the industrial world for the placement of its graduates, and the close ties of its faculty and administration with industry all gave the institution its character and culture. Practicality, usefulness, and the marketplace shaped its ethos. To a large extent, MIT's impressive growth during the decades around the turn of the century resulted from its success in developing a curriculum that made its graduates not only successful engineers but also able managers.[5] After World War I, taking to heart the lessons it was teaching to its students and making use of its vast scientific and technical resources, MIT added to its educational mission an entrepreneurial role.[6] In the early 1920's MIT's board of trustees approved the Technology Plan, designed to establish close bonds with industry. Karl T. Compton, who became president in 1930, further strengthened MIT's ties with industry. He gave new life to the Division of Industrial Cooperation and Research (DICR), which had been established in 1921 as part of the Technology Plan to make available—for a fee—MIT's "scientific and industrial experience and creative aptitude"[7] to industrial firms. DICR, Compton noted in 1932, "is designed to make as effective as possible the assistance which the Institute renders to business and industry in solving their technical problems."[8] In return, the Institute gained from the expertise of industrial firms and

4 Prescott, *When MIT Was "Boston Tech."*
5 See Noble, *America by Design.* Vannevar Bush ("Case for Biological Engineering," p. 34) once described an electrical engineer "as an individual who was not primarily a physicist, or a business man, or an inventor but who would acquire some of the skills and knowledge of each of these and be capable of successfully developing and applying new [electrical] devices on the grand scale which their inherent utility made possible." See also Carlson, "Academic Entrepreneurship."
6 Etzkowitz, "Making of an Entrepreneurial University"; see also Romanowski, "Peacetime to Wartime Transition."
7 Maclaurin, "Address to Alumni Dinner."
8 Noble, *America by Design,* p. 142.

obtained their support. DICR became the model for cooperation between industrial interests and educational institutions.[9] The legal arrangements that defined the relationship and the "cooperation" between MIT and its clients became the model for the contracts the Office of Scientific Research and Development (OSRD) wrote during World War II.[10] In 1936, at the height of the depression, DICR became self-supporting.[11]

When World War II broke out, DICR provided MIT the administrative structure necessary to implement the mobilization of scientific and technological resources K. T. Compton was advocating in the face of the fascist threat. With the Technology Plan MIT had developed mechanisms for taking on in-house projects to help industry solve technical, manufacturing, and managerial problems. During World War II the MIT Radiation Laboratory did the same for the government but on a scale that was inconceivable in the 1930's. The Radiation Laboratory was the prototype for the government-supported laboratories that were to proliferate at MIT. The pattern that had evolved during the 1920's and 1930's—and that became the norm during and after the war—was one of institutional involvement. But by participating massively in the war effort the Institute had transformed itself. By 1943 MIT was overseeing some $25,000,000 of government-supported contracts, whereas its total budget in 1939 was only about $3,000,000. Toward the end of the war in a report to his board of trustees Compton emphasized that "The value to our country of this type of institution in a time of emergency [is enormous]. . . . Its war value is parallel with that of a fleet or an army. . . . I submit that its value to our country justifies its maintenance on the highest possible plane of effectiveness . . . and that we have an obligation to take the necessary steps to insure such effectiveness."[12] The armed forces concurred and gave MIT their whole-hearted support in "the time of emergency" that the postwar period turned out to be. The Cold War, in particular the Czech coup and the Berlin blockade of 1948–49, set the stage for MIT's postwar partnership with the military. The Korean conflict cemented it.[13]

Cornell, in contrast to MIT, is a university. It owes its existence to the

9 *Ibid.,* pp. 143–47.

10 OSRD contract policy regarding fees, patents, and research classification "was originally hammered out in DIC." Romanowski, "Peacetime to Wartime Transition," p. 8.

11 Other components of MIT, however, were affected by the depression. Compton ("Report of the President," 1936) reported that "the depression brought about a decrease of nearly $400,000 in the operating income of the Institute, from $3,030,000 to $2,647,000. The student enrollment fell from 3,209 to 2,507 and the staff was decreased from 588 to 498." Interestingly, for Compton the depression was coming to an end in 1936, for he went on to state that "in spite of these losses and thanks to the whole-hearted cooperation of staff, alumni and Corporation, it can truly be said that the Institute emerges from the Depression in a stronger position than when it entered" (p. 17).

12 Compton, "Report of the President," 1944, p. 11.

13 See Needell, Chapter 11, and Kevles, Chapter 12, this volume.

unlikely association of two men of very different backgrounds: Ezra Cornell, a successful inventor–industrialist and a Quaker of humble background, and Andrew Dickson White, a highly educated scion of a wealthy patrician family, whose dream was to build a "truly great university." At the height of the Civil War, White outlined his conception of such a secular institution of higher learning in a letter to a potential donor. It would be a place, he wrote, where instruction would be open to all, where intellectual culture might restrain mercantilism and militarism, where "truth shall be sought for truth's sake," unfettered by sectarian requirements, and where "liberally minded men of learning" might find a base from which to "go forth and bless the nation."[14] Andrew White became Cornell's first president, and the university was molded by his enlightened liberalism.

Cornell is both a private and a public institution, and as a result it acquired a distinctive character of its own.[15] As a successful graft of a liberal arts college and graduate school with a land-grant component consisting of an engineering and an agricultural school,[16] Cornell was mindful of its ties with agriculture and the mechanic arts and of its responsibilities to the state and nation. Its dual mission was also imprinted on the science departments of the Arts and Science division: the ideals of pure research and the advancement of knowledge— ideals Cornell shared with other private liberal arts universities molded on the German pattern[17]—live in harmony with the American land-grant tradition of applied science and usefulness to the state and its citizenry.

The differences between the two institutions were reflected in the men at their helms. During the 1930's and 1940's, Karl Compton, the son of a Protestant minister, brought evangelical zeal to his mission of making science, technology, and MIT engines of progress in the service of industry and the nation. He was a positivist. In 1939 he formulated his opposition to Germany's fascism thus: "Authoritarian control is inherently contradictory to the spirit of science, and the pursuit of knowledge . . . [as] demonstrated by observation, experiment and experience. . . . Every injection of authority based on the prejudices or ambitions or objectives of people is a blow to scientific progress."[18]

14 Bishop, *History of Cornell*, pp. 41–42.

15 Becker, *Cornell University*.

16 The Morrill Land Grant College Act of 1862 had specified that "the leading object" of new land-grant colleges "shall be, without excluding other scientific and classical studies . . . to teach such branches of learning as are related to agriculture and the mechanic arts . . . in order to promote the liberal and practical education of the industrial classes in the several pursuits and professions of life." Becker, *Cornell University*, p. 34 and chapter 2.

17 For the case of Harvard during the first third of the present century, see Conant, *My Several Lives*, pp. 76–80; see also DeVane, *Higher Education*.

18 Compton, "Report of the President," 1939, p. 11. For much useful information on science and science policy during the 1930's, see Kevles, *The Physicists*. On Bush, see Nathan Reingold, "Vannevar Bush's New Deal" and the literature cited therein.

Both Karl Compton and Vannevar Bush—the two men who led MIT during the 1930's—were technological enthusiasts, but they were opposed to President Franklin Roosevelt's use of technology for the state's purposes. They were wary of Roosevelt's social and political agenda. Roosevelt had seen the depression as a challenge to be met by a concerted national effort, and he was eager to use technology to help bring the nation back to economic health. The Tennessee Valley Authority and the Grand Coulee Dam are monuments to that policy. Bush and Compton were against such governmental projects though they were not opposed to the federal government funding science, provided a scientific elite decided upon the allocations.

Throughout the 1930's Compton used the presidency of MIT as a platform for urging a greater role for scientists in guaranteeing the nation's welfare and solving the nation's economic problems. He felt strongly that a new type of government leadership was needed "whereby the scientific men of the country may be brought together to make an intelligent and co-ordinated attack on the great problems which are facing the nation."[19] During the first years of the New Deal, Compton actively campaigned for the support of science by the federal government. Upon being rebuffed by the Roosevelt administration, he turned his efforts to eliciting cooperation and securing support at the state and regional levels. Already at that time Compton was championing the idea of starting technically based enterprises derived from MIT's research projects, financed by venture capital—an idea that would come to fruition after World War II.

Although Bush and Compton had disapproved of technology-based projects to advance the government's political agenda, they heartily approved of enlisting science and technology in the defense of the nation. In fact, Bush thought that the United States could meet its defense needs by substituting technology for manpower, and in 1940 suggested that sophisticated technology, particularly electronics, could provide the margin for victory.[20] Bush and Compton had recognized early on the threat posed by fascism. After the outbreak of the war in Europe in September 1939, both of them placed their institution's resources in the nation's service and helped lead the effort to mobilize the scientific community to meet the challenge. In the summer of 1940, after the fall of France, MIT agreed to dedicate itself to "service in the crisis," placing the "interest of the nation" above the "self-interest of the institution."[21]

19 Compton, "The Government's Responsibilities."
20 Romanowski, "Peacetime to Wartime Transition."
21 Harrison, "Karl Taylor Compton: Scientist, Public Servant." Throughout the war, MIT assumed contractual responsibility for managing and financing the work done on its premises for the government. Arrangements for reimbursement by the government were governed by the principle that "the Institute should in the long run neither gain nor lose financially." Compton, "Report of the President," 1941–1942, pp. 11–12.

A year later, in a lead article in *Technology Review,* Compton urged that nothing stand in the way of military preparedness. In it he argued that it is not the mere "possession of scientific knowledge, engineering proficiency, and inventive skill" that characterized "a better man," but the readiness, under the threat of war, to "sacrifice the future for the present."[22] A few months before Pearl Harbor and a year after the Radiation Laboratory had been established at MIT, noting that the emergency was greater than most people realized and "that we must be prepared to go much further than we have gone thus far," Compton called for a partnership between scientists and the military as the most effective way of meeting the emergency.[23]

During World War II MIT's partnership with the government and the military services was cemented. Many individuals were responsible for establishing the networks of influence and power. Vannevar Bush, the first presidential science advisor, the first chairman of the National Defense Research Committee (NDRC), and later chairman of the Office of Scientific Research and Development (OSRD), was second in command at MIT before leaving for Washington to head the Carnegie Institution in 1939. Compton served on NDRC and OSRD while remaining president of MIT. MIT professors were attached to the highest echelons in the Pentagon: Philip Morse with the Navy, H. C. Hunsaker with the Air Force; Julius Stratton with the Secretary of War; others, such as William P. Allis, Clarence Bennett, Frank Bowles, and George Harrison, served as liaison between the services and the various OSRD wartime laboratories.[24]

More generally, the partnership envisioned and established by Compton flourished during the war.[25] A year after the war's end, Vannevar Bush com-

22 Compton, "Willingness to Make Sacrifices."
23 Compton, "Scientists Face the World of 1942."
24 For a list of MIT personnel who in 1942 were leading the Institute "to war," see Compton, "Report of the President," 1941–1942, pp. 6–8.
25 Rabi, who was the associate director of the Rad Lab, indicated how this came about in one of his reminiscences of his wartime experiences: "We had to set relations with the military. I was very forceful about that myself. For example, one group came from the Navy. They wanted certain black boxes, which they described, to be developed with certain voltages, and so on. I asked, 'What are they for?' Their answer was 'We prefer to talk about that in our swivel chairs in Washington.' I didn't say anything. Neither did I do anything—except continue to develop three-centimeter radar. They came back six months later—the same thing. I said, 'Now, look, let's stop kidding. Bring your man who understands aircraft, and we'll talk about your problems.' By that time, we had learned a lot about radar and tactical military applications. Well, the Navy did. We found that their problem was to knock off Japanese aircraft spying on ships. It turned out that they needed a shipborne height-finding radar to supplement and guide the radar equipment already in their carrier-based planes. And we made an agreement with the Navy. We'll develop that if you and we can do the whole thing together—a *partnership* [emphasis added]. We are in this war together. We can talk about the whole thing, whatever it is, and then our side will do its best to develop the appropriate radar. Which it did. It was a fantastically great radar—a very effective thing. As

mented: "World War II was the first war in human history to be affected decisively by weapons unknown at the outbreak of hostilities," a situation that "demanded a closer linkage among military men, scientists, and industrialists than had ever before been required."[26] Scientists generally, and physicists in particular, eagerly assumed their responsibilities in the partnership. Physicists, in fact, became its driving force. Moreover, civilian scientists appropriated the dominant role in the partnership. OSRD, which Bush headed, had been given broad powers and had put into civilian hands responsibility for and control over the development of the weapons to be used by the armed forces— functions and powers that had been the military's before the war. The relationship between science and the military in the post–World War II period was in part determined by the efforts of the Department of Defense to regain control over the planning and deployment of new weapon systems.[27]

The threat posed by the totalitarian states worried Edmund B. Day, Cornell's president from 1937 until 1949, as much as it did Bush and Compton. In the late 1930's he too had urged a comprehensive program of national defense. But Day was a social scientist, an economist and statistician by training, who saw the world in terms of men and women, their hopes and frustrations, their passions and vices, and he gave primacy to values, commitment, and morale over gadgets and technologies. During the two years before the United States entered World War II, Day lectured extensively on the topic "What really threatens American Democracy?" Four of these addresses were collected together in a book he titled *The Defense of Freedom*. Even though he often spoke somewhat euphemistically—the forces of isolationism were strong and demagogues such as Father Charles E. Coughlin had wide appeal—the book reveals Day as thoughtful, perceptive, wise, and often prescient, a man with an incisive intellect.

The most obvious danger to democracy, Day argued in February 1939, came from the great dictatorships of Europe and the Far East. Although he didn't believe that Germany, Italy, and Japan seriously threatened the United States by direct attack, nonetheless they constituted a menace in two important ways. First, they might "in their program of imperial expansion" precipi-

---

time went on, we set up an effective pattern of interdependence with the military. Fortunately, our money did not come from the military directly but from another government agency, the Office of Scientific Research and Development, under Dr. Vannevar Bush. Actually, we would use this money to develop a particular radar. We would then try to interest either our military men or the British in it. If they were interested, then they financed the production. After we learned to get along with the military men, we grew to have a deep respect for them. Respect for their devotion and hard work. We got along with them once they saw we were not there to take anything away from them but actually to help them." Bernstein, "Profiles, Physicist I."

26 Stewart, *Organizing Scientific Research*, p. ix.
27 DuPree, "National Security and the Post-War Science Establishment."

tate a general European war that would certainly become a world war. What was the United States to do in those circumstances? Day was well aware that as a means of defending democracy, war was a two-edged sword, with the Republic menaced both by conquest and "unavoidable political transformations 'to win the war.'" "To fight or not to fight," with the possible loss of democracy either way, was the "dilemma of democracy." But Day left no doubt that if war is the only means to preserve the political independence of people who want to preserve democracy, then it must be fought.[28]

The propaganda the Axis powers were spreading—in which democratic ideals become objects of contempt and scorn and democracy was branded as an outmoded form of government—constituted a second threat to American democracy. But the chief danger to democracy, Day emphasized, did not come from without but from within. The depression and the changes in the economy since World War I were posing a challenge not easily met. The disappearance of the sense of economic security had eroded confidence, and Day believed that this loss posed the greatest danger to democracy in the United States.[29]

Even in June of 1940, after the fall of France, when Day had seen the hazards of "a despotic and ruthless government [that] employs the full arsenal of science and technology,"[30] although he was no longer so confident that the oceans that separated the United States from Europe and Japan would give it the protection they "once so surely afforded," and he was urging a program of full mobilization for national defense,[31] he still felt that the chief threat came from within, from attacks that might break the national unity. Day was convinced that an essential defense against such attacks was "the better operation of our economic system" for "we have taken all the economic punishment we can stand. . . . If we fail to put our economic house in order America is headed for revolutionary changes whether or not there be attack from without."[32] The loss of economic security and of equality of opportunity for the many, the undue concentration of economic power in the hands of a few, had created attitudes that threatened the operation of democratic procedures. The problems of American democracy were thus also problems of the human spirit. But only under favorable social and economic settings could that spirit flourish and its highest accomplishments to date—democracy and civiliza-

28 Day, *Defense of Freedom,* pp. 10–11.
29 *Ibid.,* pp. 12–13.
30 *Ibid.,* p. 24.
31 In 1940 Day saw the basic problem facing his administration to be the maintenance "as far as possible" of the normal functioning of the university, while at the same time maximizing the university's direct contributions to the defense program. Day set up the University Council on National Defense, consisting of members of the board of trustees and the deans of the various colleges, with himself as chairman, to consider "the difficult questions of policy in connection with the defense program." Day, "Report of the President," 1940–1941, p. 5.
32 Day, *Defense of Freedom,* p. 34.

tion—be safeguarded.[33] Quoting Bertrand Russell, Day characterized the true signs of civilization as charity, brotherhood, peace, freedom, and justice, in contrast to the sentiments of Benito Mussolini: "Words are beautiful things. Machine guns, ships, aeroplanes are still more beautiful."[34] He ended his address with some deeply felt exhortations, to erect "some of our most important defenses," through a daily devotion to truth, justice, tolerance, and the common good.[35] For Day universities were the bastions of civilization, exemplars of the kind of bulwark he advocated to secure democracy in everyday life, and, especially, sanctuaries for those committed to ideas and "the intellectual life."[36]

In his inaugural address Day had noted some of the forces that made it difficult for universities to maintain the primacy of the intellectual function. One of these was "the current eclipse of the liberal tradition," the tradition that Andrew White had imparted to Cornell. Universities can develop only in an atmosphere that permits the independence of the communities of scholars.[37] Universities have the duty to guarantee and protect the freedom of inquiry of teachers and students and cannot allow activities within their walls that would threaten that freedom.[38] Echoing White, Day noted that "the love of money" is another external force of "great potency" that makes it difficult for universities to cultivate intellectual interests. Closely affiliated with love of money, though certainly not identical with it, was "the widely prevalent insistence upon vocational results in American education." The danger stemmed from the fact that "vocational interests are in many instances narrow in outlook and distressingly shortsighted."

Since Cornell was engaged in vocational education—in its Engineering College, its College of Architecture, its College of Agriculture, its Medical College, etc.—Day insisted that it must do so "in ways becoming an institu-

33 In an earlier address he had noted: "We are prone to think of [democracy] as a system of government rather than as a form of human relationship in which men and women of every class and creed live together in peace." *Ibid.*, p. 20.

34 Day quoted some other sayings of Mussolini: "War alone brings to its highest tension all human energy and puts the stamp of nobility on the people who have the courage to lead it." "Believe, obey, fight."

35 Day, *Defense of Freedom*, pp. 34–37.

36 Day, "Inaugural Address," p. 29.

37 At Day's inauguration Conant also had emphasized that "liberty and the life of the true university are closely linked." Democracy and the independence of universities "have marched forward and retreated side by side." Conant, "The Role of the Endowed University," p. 14.

38 When after World War II Cornell established a comprehensive course of study of contemporary Russian civilization, at the time a pioneering enterprise that aroused the criticism of conservative circles, Day responded, "It is part of the respect we owe to our youth to deny it no knowledge that will enable it to bear, as it will bear resolutely and willingly, and in the enduring tradition of freedom, the weight of the world that is descending on its shoulders." *New York Times*, Mar. 24, 1951, p. 13.

tion of higher learning devoted basically to the intellectual life": vocational education must be essentially professional in character. This, Day indicated, involved recognition of at least three governing principles: "an emphasis upon fundamental disciplines" over "practical techniques," a commitment to research, and a sense of "the social obligations of the vocation."

Day believed that what was done within universities and how these activities were supported from without must be consistent with these ideals and goals. Even though universities were no longer ivory towers, they were not meant to be entrepreneurial businesses nor were they meant to be places where secret research was carried out for the armed forces. "It is for the long pull that our universities exist."[39] Under Day, Cornell maintained its position in the front ranks of American universities and remained faithful to its ideals.

Physics at MIT and Cornell During the 1930's

The financial difficulties resulting from the voiding of the Cooperative Agreement between MIT and Harvard for the administration of the Gordon McKay endowment[40] and the transformation of the Throop Polytechnic Institute into the dynamic, pace-setting California Institute of Technology under the aegis of George E. Hale, Robert A. Millikan and Arthur A. Noyes[41] had resulted in MIT losing its status as the nation's premier institute of technology. In 1929 the board of trustees of MIT offered Karl T. Compton the presidency of the institution and charged him with the task of revitalizing MIT and making it once again the nation's outstanding institution in engineering education and research.[42] This Compton proceeded to do. Soon after assuming the presidency Compton revamped the administrative structure of MIT and made Vannevar Bush vice-president and second in command. A physicist by training,[43] Compton was convinced that the future of the institution depended on

39 Day, "Inaugural Address," pp. 32–34.

40 In 1903 Harvard received a large grant from the estate of Gordon McKay, a wealthy manufacturer of shoe machinery, for the establishment of an engineering college. Harvard sought to absorb MIT to satisfy the stipulation of the bequest. MIT demurred. But in 1914 a cooperative agreement was reached between the two schools whereby MIT would remain independent, the engineering faculties of the two schools would be merged under MIT authority, and MIT would open its doors to any Harvard student wishing to major in engineering—in return for three-fifths of the McKay endowment. The Cooperative Agreement was in effect until 1917 when the Supreme Court of Massachusetts voided it, finding that it violated the intent of the Gordon McKay will. See Prescott, *When MIT Was "Boston Tech."*

41 See Kargon, *Rise of Robert Millikan.*

42 Two years earlier Compton had been asked to investigate and make a report on the MIT physics department. See Harrison, "Karl Taylor Compton: Scientist, Public Servant."

43 Before coming to MIT, Compton had a distinguished career as a professor of physics at Princeton. His research activities were in the field of physical electronics: the study of electrical conduction in gases and thermionic and photoelectric emission.

strong science departments. He brought in 30-year-old John Clark Slater to head the physics department and encouraged chemistry and mathematics to widen their horizons. The department of electrical engineering, which had flourished under Bush's chairmanship, was further strengthened.[44] The other engineering departments, in particular the department of aeronautical engineering, were similarly transformed. By the end of the decade MIT was a new institution, and in large part Compton was responsible for the success of the change.[45]

Slater embodied all the qualities that Compton thought a scientist should have. He was brilliant, self-confident, an imaginative and accomplished researcher, and he had a vision. He believed that quantum mechanics would give answers to all questions about the structure of atoms, molecules, and simple solids and would become the foundation of an engineering practice that would design new materials with specified properties shaped to order by molecular strategy.[46] With the encouragement and support of Compton, Slater proceeded to build up physics at MIT. He brought in Philip Morse, an outstanding young theorist, George Harrison, an able experimentalist who specialized in optics and spectroscopy, W. B. Nottingham, a colleague of Compton's from Princeton who worked in physical electronics, and Julius Stratton, who had studied with Arnold Sommerfeld and worked on the propagation of electromagnetic waves.

Ties with industry were consolidated by establishing an acoustics and an optics laboratory. Starting in 1934 the physics department sponsored an annual electronics conference of three or four days; other conferences dealt with physical metallurgy and radioactivity. Slater also initiated activities in nuclear physics by having R. J. Van de Graaff associated with the department and later in 1938 getting M. Stanley Livingston to come from Cornell to design and build MIT's first cyclotron.[47] Equally important, Slater reformed undergraduate education at MIT. He revamped the introductory physics courses taken by all undergraduates at MIT whether they were science or engineering majors.

A measure of the transformation Slater wrought during the first decade of his chairmanship can be gauged from the dramatic increase in the size of the staff of the department and in the number of undergraduate and graduate students in it. The physics faculty was always large, mainly because of its

44 A typical appointment was that of Roger C. L. Guillemin, a physicist who had obtained his training with Sommerfeld.

45 Bush, *Pieces of the Action*, p. 32.

46 Schweber, "The Young Slater."

47 Both Van de Graaff's machine and the cyclotron were designed with medical research and treatments in mind. The cyclotron was constructed with a grant from the John and Mary R. Markle Foundation, which supported medical research. It accelerated deuterons to 14 million electron volts. Radioactive isotopes for medical applications were to be obtained by bombarding various elements with these deuterons.

considerable teaching commitments in the elementary courses. This allowed the department to diversify. Its faculty had a wide set of interests, wider perhaps than in almost any other physics department in the country. The diversity also reflected Slater's and Compton's strong feeling that it was "almost a duty in a technical institution to carry on work in various applications of physics which do not attract interest in an arts college," citing MIT's work in such areas as electronics, X-ray physics, optics, and acoustics. These studies might not have had the professional luster of nuclear physics, but industry eagerly snapped up physicists trained in these areas, and asked for more.[48]

The story of the buildup of physics at Cornell before World War II is similar to that at the dozen or so other American universities that were considered the premier institutions of higher learning. This growth, at Cornell and elsewhere, was facilitated by the great power in the hands of the president and the department heads. At Cornell the president was the chief administrative and the chief academic officer.

One of the characteristic features of the physics department at Cornell was that until the 1930's most of its faculty members were Cornell-bred. Most of them had attended Cornell as undergraduates and many of them had also obtained their Ph.D. there. Another feature of the department was that from 1887 until 1946 only three people headed it: Edward L. Nichols (1887–1919), Ernest G. Merritt (1919–34), and P. Clifton Gibbs (1934–46). The fact that in 1946 Lloyd P. Smith became the chairman, rather than the head, of the department is indicative of the changes brought about by Day.[49] Also worthy of note is the fact that from 1909—when the position was first created—until 1939 two of the three deans of the graduate school were physicists: Ernest G. Merritt (1909–14) and Floyd K. Richtmyer (1929–39).

Physics has always been strong at Cornell.[50] Edward Nichols, the founder and first editor of the *Physical Review,* came there in 1887. He brought Merritt, Frederick Beddell, and Richtmyer to the department and made it one of the foremost research centers in spectroscopy. By the mid-1920's it became apparent that quantum mechanics was altering the character of physics. To

48 Slater, "History of the Physics Department at MIT," p. 49.

49 In 1937 and 1938 a new system of department chairmanships was adopted. Thereafter chairmen of departments in the College of Arts and Sciences were appointed "for a specified term of years. Ordinarily the term of appointment will be for five years, with the presumption that one—not more than one—reappointment for a like term will be in order. The department chairman will be expected under this system to develop under democratic procedures a constructive administrative leadership for his department, always with the understanding that after a period of years administrative responsibilities will be relinquished and full professional responsibilities in teaching and research resumed." Day, "President's Report," 1937/38.

50 Paul Hartman has given an informative account of physics at Cornell in *Cornell Physics Department.* See also "Seventy Years of Physics at Cornell," mimeographed notes written in 1958 by "retiring professors Howe and Grantham." Both of these are available from the physics department of Cornell University.

keep abreast of the advances the department invited H. A. Lorentz, who spent the spring semester of 1926 in Ithaca.[51] That same year Merritt made an offer of a full professorship to Max Born at the very attractive salary of $8000 a year.[52] After Born turned down the invitation, Merritt attempted to attract Peter J. W. Debye and James Franck.

The sensitivity of the department to the changes in physics can also be inferred from its course offerings. The first edition of Richtmyer's *Introduction to Modern Physics,* which was based on a very successful course that he was teaching to the undergraduate physics majors, came out in 1928.[53] Quantum mechanics was brought into the graduate curriculum in 1928 when Earle H. Kennard started teaching a course on wave mechanics. In 1927 Gibbs initiated a program that brought distinguished physicists to the campus each summer.[54] The department also encouraged its young theorists to go abroad. Kennard spent his sabbatical year in 1926 and 1927 with Born and Niels Bohr. Lloyd P. Smith[55] in 1930 went to Caltech and the following year traveled to Germany to study with Sommerfeld on a National Research Council postdoctoral fellowship. As Sommerfeld was too busy, he was assigned to work with Hans Bethe, who was there as a young *privatdozent.*[56]

By the early 1930's it had become clear that the principal areas of research within the department—atomic and molecular spectroscopy, electron and ion physics—no longer were frontier fields. Intense discussions were held to decide which new fields of research ought to be supported. Merritt went to Leyden in 1931 to visit the low-temperature laboratory there and to Göttingen to acquaint himself with work carried on in Franck's laboratory. He also went to Berlin to confer with Max von Laue and others.[57] In 1933 Merritt recommended to the Cornell administration that the department expand its activities and go into nuclear physics, thus setting it on its modern course.[58] Not

51 Shorter-term visitors included Francis W. Aston, Arnold Sommerfeld, Paul Ehrenfest, Hendrick Kramers, and George P. Thomson.

52 Born was at MIT during the fall semester 1925–26 and had visited Ithaca during his stay. The offer also included an additional sum of $2000 for an assistant.

53 The course culminated with a discussion of Bohr's model of the hydrogen atom.

54 K. T. Compton came in 1927, W. F. G. Swann in 1928, A. H. Compton in 1929, E. C. Kemble in 1930, and W. V. Houston in 1932.

55 Lloyd P. Smith (1903–88) came to Cornell in 1926 as a Coffin Fellow and stayed on as an instructor while earning his Ph.D.

56 He did some research on Hartree-Fock methods and published a paper on the subject. L. P. Smith, "Calculation of the Quantum Defect." The acknowledgment states that "the writer is indebted to Dr. Bethe for suggesting the problem and for helpful discussions in connection with it."

57 Hartman, *Cornell Physics Department,* p. 182.

58 Lloyd P. Smith, who had come back to Cornell in 1933, greatly influenced this decision. He urged the department to appoint Bethe and threatened to resign to accept a position elsewhere if his recommendations were not followed. Cornell's offer of an acting assistant professorship came to Bethe "out of the blue." Bernstein, *Hans Bethe,* p. 43.

everyone supported Merritt's recommendation. In particular, Richtmyer, the most successful and best known of Cornell's experimental physicists and the dean of its graduate school, fearing that nuclear physics would take away support from his X-ray laboratory, opposed the move. Nonetheless the department went ahead and asked Livingston and Bethe to join it.

In retrospect, this was undoubtedly the most important decision taken by the department. Livingston, who had helped Lawrence build his cyclotron at Berkeley and "is generally credited with having made it actually run after Lawrence had the idea for it"[59] came in the fall of 1934 and immediately began building Cornell's first accelerator—the first to be built outside of Berkeley.[60] In early February 1935 Bethe arrived, and the following year Robert Bacher joined the department.

Gibbs, who had become head of the department in 1934, explained to Bethe when he arrived that the department "was changing from one in which research was done to provide thesis topics for graduate students to one in which graduate students could participate in ongoing research." Gibbs added that "not everyone agreed with this new emphasis on research, and there was some disagreement on which fields to expand into. It was the progressives versus the conservatives. The progressives had won the fight and now had the backing of the administration." The appointment of Bethe—a "theoretical nuclear man, and a foreigner to boot"—was one of the signs of change.[61]

Bethe, Bacher, and Livingston made Cornell into an outstanding center of nuclear research. Although Cornell's cyclotron produced deuterons at energies of only 1.2 million electron volts, Livingston and his associates developed an arc source that transformed it into a tool particularly useful for neutron research. Bethe "moved among the experimental physicists as a source of brilliant conjecture and practical aid."[62] He not only provided suggestions for experiments and the theory for their interpretation, but was intimately involved with their design and the analysis of the data.[63] At Cornell, as at the other centers where nuclear physics was being cultivated, theorists and experimenters worked intimately together.

The department kept abreast of developments in the frontiers of physics and maintained its standing as one of the best in the country by strongly

59 Bernstein, *Hans Bethe*, p. 44.

60 The accelerator was deliberately kept small because "in those days nuclear physics had not yet proved its worth" and was built at a cost of $3000. "A New Cyclotron for Cornell," draft, ca. 1940. E. E. Day Papers, Cornell University Library 3/6/8.

61 Bernstein, *Hans Bethe*, p. 46.

62 "Nuclear Physics at Cornell," unpublished report to Cornell's board of trustees, 1947.

63 In 1940 and 1941, when the design for a second larger cyclotron was being discussed, Bethe worked out a theory of the fringing fields and wrote a manuscript entitled "Elementare Theorie des fringing Effects." See also Van Vleck to Bethe, Dec. 10, 1941. Bethe Papers, Box 2, Cornell University Archives.

supporting nuclear physics. But in the process it was careful to make sure that other research in the department—in spectroscopy, X-ray and electron diffraction, optics, X rays, and electronics, and particularly in fields of importance in training students who would go to industry—did not suffer. To make itself better known the department in 1935 started sponsoring a series of annual summer symposia.[64] The importance of the sciences in President Day's agenda for Cornell was indicated by one of his first public appearances after his arrival at Cornell. On July 1, 1937, a few weeks after assuming the presidency, he gave the welcoming address to the Symposium on Metallic Phases that the department of physics had organized for that year.

In 1938 the faculty of the physics department, in response to a request from a committee of trustees and faculty, made a long and thorough study of their needs. Gibbs drew up a report that outlined "an integrated departmental program" incorporating the requests made by individual faculty members.[65] The program entailed capital expenditures of about $35,000[66] and an addition of about $30,000 to the annual budget to increase the number of teaching and research assistants and to enlarge the technical support staff. This sum was what the faculty considered necessary if they "are to serve [their] students adequately and are to maintain [their] position in the front ranks of university research." To place these figures in context: For the academic year 1920–21 the appropriation to the department was $87,000. By 1932 the departmental budget had increased to $127,000, of which some $25,000 went for research.[67] A year later, the impact of the depression was felt with a vengeance: the total research allocation was $9,000 and salaries were cut by 10%.[68] Only after World War II would the budget climb back to the 1932 level. The report also dealt with the standing of the department in comparison to physics departments at other leading universities. Its assessment was that out of the seventeen departments surveyed eight were superior to Cornell's in equipment

64 Symposium on Photoelectricity and Thermionics, July 4–6, 1935. Speakers included S. Dushman and I. Langmuir from General Electric and J. A. Becker, C. J. Davisson, H. E. Ives, and F. C. Nix from the Bell Telephone Laboratory, as well as local speakers; Symposium on Nuclear Physics, July 2–4, 1936; Symposium on the Structure of Metallic Phases, July 1–3, 1937.

65 The report, as well as the initial requests by the individual faculty members, can be found in the Bethe papers, Cornell University Archives.

66 The breakdown was as follows: about $8000 for teaching laboratory equipment, $15,000 for research apparatus, $12,000 of which was requested for nuclear physics, and around $12,000 for general utility-supporting equipment.

67 All the funds for research came from the university. From 1920 to 1930 over half a million dollars was appropriated by Cornell's Heckscher Research Council in support of research at the university. Over 80% of that sum was used to provide the services of trained assistants to members of the permanent staff.

68 Salaries at Cornell were low to start with. The average at Harvard in physics was $400 higher than the Cornell maximum! These figures are taken from Hartman, *Cornell Physics Department*.

and funding and five were equal; only two were considered better in theory and two were roughly equal.

The preamble to Richtmyer's request encapsulated the ethos of the "old order." At the time he drafted his statement Richtmyer was dean of the graduate school and a widely respected physicist.[69] Richtmyer was of the opinion that internal developments within physics and the interests of professors—not societal needs beyond the training of competent scientists—should determine the fields of research. Also, he believed that the individual researcher, not the team, was the fundamental element of scientific research. At Cornell, the turning point had been the decision to go into nuclear physics. But undoubtedly Richtmyer's views were widely shared.

The proposal by the department included plans for a new and larger cyclotron, the design of which was worked out during the following year. Its contemplated cost was approximately $50,000.[70] In June of 1941 the board of trustees of Cornell University accepted President Day's recommendation and appropriated the money necessary for the construction of the cyclotron and the building that was to house it. But the project was delayed "in view of the impossibility of securing the necessary materials for this highly important item of apparatus so long as the defense program is on."[71]

The Character of World War II

In an address to the nation two days after Pearl Harbor, Roosevelt declared, "We are all in it together, all the way. Every single man, woman, and child is a partner in the most tremendous undertaking of our American history." The long and hard war ahead would entail enormous sacrifices. The American involvement in the conflict came to be perceived as an all-out effort in pursuit of high ideals, a crusade not only against the Axis powers but also against racial prejudice and intolerance; the Four Freedoms heralded its aims and aspirations. The democracies—Great Britain and the United States—mobilized totally for war.

Neither Germany nor Japan had prepared itself for protracted "total" war. Their strategy had been predicated on the assumption that the hostilities

69 "[Richtmyer] was an organizer of the American Association of Physics Teachers; he was also an organizer of the Optical Society, and . . . active in fifteen professional bodies. He was, at one time or another, president of four of them: the American Physical Society, the Optical Society of America, the American Association of Physics Teachers, and Sigma Xi: he was vice-president of four others. He was the editor of the *Review of Scientific Instruments* and of the *Journal of the Optical Society of America.* Besides all this he was a life trustee of the National Geographic Society and active in church and a couple of local clubs. He had 94 papers and 60 meetings abstracts to his credit, mostly in X rays." Hartman, *Cornell Physics Department,* p. 168.

70 Day to Bacher, June 2, 1941. Day Papers, Cornell University Archives.

71 Day to trustee E. B. Whitman, Sept. 25, 1941. Day Papers.

would be brief and inexpensive. In the initial phase of the war the civilian component of their economy was left in place untouched, and even later the labor force was never fully committed to the war effort. By contrast, from the very beginning the British and Americans marshaled all their resources to fight the war, and they fought it with a vengeance. Roosevelt's objectives in waging the war—total defeat and unconditional surrender—determined its strategy. Roosevelt not only formulated the global aspects of that strategy but also oversaw, during the early stages of the war, the details of its execution. He kept himself informed of all aspects of the conduct of the war. He was the undisputed leader of the joint chiefs of staff—William D. Leahy, George C. Marshall, Ernest J. King, and Henry H. Arnold—men he had personally picked for the job as "the analytical minds and operational executants."[72] Eric Larrabee has perceptively observed that "there was a kind of fitness [in Roosevelt] being at the head of armed forces that remained essentially non-militaristic in nature, a sense that under his direction . . . they would be put to . . . purposes that he as leader of two liberal-democratic administrations had embodied." This perception of the nonmilitary nature of the military helped cement the partnership between the scientists and the armed forces.[73]

World War II was also a just war. It gave the scientists who worked on weaponry a sense of being engaged in a transcendent cause, and as with everyone else it spurred them to perform "at a higher pitch than ever before."[74] Louis Smullin, who worked at MIT's Radiation Laboratory throughout the war, spoke for most scientists when many years later he noted, "This was the last war probably, for which there was genuine enthusiasm, if that's the right word. It was clear who the villain was. It was clearly a war that had to be won. . . . And we were young."[75]

Everyone felt Roosevelt's charisma and authority. Vannevar Bush accomplished what he did because he was able to communicate directly with Roosevelt and could act in the president's name. Bush and Conant kept Roosevelt informed of the technical progress on building the bomb. Early on, they had conveyed to him the magnitude of the weapon's potential and had convinced him of the urgency of the enterprise. He shared the scientists' view that Germany was working on a bomb, and that they would win the war should

72 Larrabee, *Commander in Chief*, p. 15.

73 Larrabee, *Commander in Chief*, p. 626. After World War II this perception changed. P. M. Morse, who had worked closely with the Chief of Naval Operations during World War II, reported (in an interview with Schweber in 1986) that the attitude of Navy officers toward civilian consultants shifted dramatically in the late 1940's. There had risen a new Pharaoh who knew not Israel. The confrontation between Truman and MacArthur was symptomatic of the change.

74 Larrabee, *Commander in Chief*, p. 627.

75 Louis D. Smullin, interview with R. R. Romanowski, Mar. 15, 1982. In Romanowski, "Peacetime to Wartime Transition."

they succeed in building one before the U.S. Shortly after Los Alamos got started, Roosevelt, probably at Bush's instigation, sent a hand-written letter to Oppenheimer—whom he had never met—in which he reviewed the reasons for undertaking "under unusual circumstances" the "hazardous matter" Oppenheimer and his colleagues were engaged in, a task of such importance to the nation "that it must be guarded more drastically than any other wartime secret." "Nevertheless," Roosevelt continued, "I wish you would express to the scientists assembled with you my deep appreciation of their willingness to undertake the tasks which lie before them. . . . I am sure we can rely on their continued wholehearted and unselfish labors."[76]

Oppenheimer read the letter to the scientific staff at their weekly meeting, and shortly thereafter answered Roosevelt, "You would be glad to know how greatly your good words of reassurance were appreciated by us. There will be many times in the months ahead when we shall remember them."[77] Roosevelt became the incarnation of the war's aim for the scientists at Los Alamos. Many of them cried upon hearing that he had died.[78] Conant and Bush's direct access to Roosevelt gave the Los Alamos scientists the sense of being at the center of things, which in turn helped Oppenheimer create "an atmosphere of excitement, enthusiasm, and high intellectual and moral purpose."[79]

The enthusiasm for building the bomb was all-encompassing. No one at Los Alamos did any pure research. Only Richard Feynman found a little time to think and work on pure physics problems, and this on the bus rides to visit his wife bedridden in a hospital in Albuquerque. Not even on the physicists' weekend outings and hikes in the surrounding mountains—their communion with nature and rite of purification—did they talk about pure physics. The contrast with the situation in Germany and Japan is noteworthy. Werner Heisenberg developed his theory of the S-matrix in 1943 while working on problems related to the war effort; he thereafter lectured on the subject in Holland and Switzerland.[80] Similarly, Shinichiro Tomonaga wrote his paper on the quantum theory of fields in 1942 and 1943 while working on the theory of wave guides.

By early 1945—after they were convinced that a gun-triggered uranium bomb would work and that the Axis powers had been defeated—the Los

---

76 Roosevelt to Oppenheimer, June 29, 1943. Oppenheimer Papers, Manuscript Division, Library of Congress. Also partially reprinted by Smith and Weiner, *Robert Oppenheimer*, p. 260.

77 Smith and Weiner, *Robert Oppenheimer*, p. 260.

78 For the moving remarks Oppenheimer delivered at the memorial service for Roosevelt at Los Alamos, see Smith and Weiner, *Robert Oppenheimer*, p. 288.

79 I. I. Rabi, "How Well We Meant." Transcript of a talk given at the 40th anniversary of Los Alamos, 1983.

80 Dresden, *H. A. Kramers*, p. 273.

Alamos physicists intensified their efforts to produce an implosion-triggered plutonium bomb and also began deliberating the implications of a successful bomb. How to save civilization from the threat of the bomb had become the problem to be addressed. Bohr, the father figure of the community, set the example. He had come to Los Alamos with a secret agenda: to ensure that atomic energy "is used to the benefit of all humanity and does not become a menace to civilization."[81] It was appropriate that the man who had wrested the torch from Einstein and had taken over the intellectual leadership of the community as it asserted its dominion over the atomic and nuclear world should be the one to hand it the cloak of responsibility as it entered the arena of power and received some measure of power in return for its contributions. Bohr's insistence—before atomic bombs were developed—that the bombs' secrets be shared with Russia and that plans be made for the international control of atomic energy made a deep impression on Oppenheimer and the rest of the community at Los Alamos. Even though he failed to convince Roosevelt and Churchill about the correctness of his views and the perceptiveness of his vision, the fact that they had to listen to him carried a message they did not fail to notice.

Writing in the early 1970's, Michel Foucault noted that formerly intellectuals were the spokesmen of the universal and that the writer used to be intellectual par excellence: "a universal consciousness, a free subject." This "universal" intellectual was to be contrasted with those intellectuals who were merely "competent instances in the service of the State or Capital–technicians, magistrates, teachers." It seemed to Foucault that since World War II a new figure for the intellectual, that of the "specific" intellectual, had emerged. The atomic scientists led by Oppenheimer, Foucault argued, marked the "transition between the universal and the specific intellectual." Their efficacy came about because of their well-defined knowledge of the physical world, knowledge which they could draw upon in the political arena, and for which they could be attacked by political powers. At the same time, the physicists participated in the "discourse of the universal" because "the nuclear threat affected the whole human race and the fate of the world."[82] Bohr had made physicists into "specific" intellectuals, with Oppenheimer as the paradigmatic figure.

When it became clear that the tide of the war had turned, universities began formulating plans for postwar programs. Compton told MIT's board of trustees in 1943 that "as a result of faculty studies in recent years, and also as a result of developments during the war emergency, our attention is called to the desirability of increased emphasis on certain aspects of our curriculum as soon as the situation permits action to be taken." Compton singled out applied mathematics, electronics, instrumentation, and organic chemistry as fields in

81 Oppenheimer, "Niels Bohr and Atomic Weapons."
82 Foucault, *Power/Knowledge*, pp. 127–28.

which great opportunities existed. He informed the trustees that an initial sum of approximately $100,000 had been set aside "in order to insure our ability to take prompt steps in this matter as opportunities arise."[83]

By the following year the fields, besides the ones listed previously, that were destined to play important roles in "the scientific and industrial activity of the near future" were methods of propulsion, mechanisms for control of machinery, calculating devices, energy sources, plastics, organic chemistry, food technology, mechanics of materials, and hydraulics. By then, the executive committee of MIT had authorized the establishment of an electronics laboratory as a joint enterprise of the Department of Physics and Electrical Engineering and appropriated initial funds, had set aside a "substantial" sum for further work in instrumentation, had authorized the construction of the laboratory for the study of new propulsion devices, with provision for initial equipment and operation, had undertaken an important investigation of plastics for the plastics industry, had established a laboratory of food technology, and had appropriated funds for work on the mechanics of materials, applied mechanics, and hydraulics.[84]

Similarly, by 1944 it had become clear to the Cornell administration that the character of the physics enterprise had dramatically changed. Many of the leading members of the physics department working on wartime projects in government and industrial laboratories were being wooed to take attractive offers elsewhere. Bethe and Bacher received lucrative offers from the University of Rochester in 1944,[85] and Lloyd Smith was invited by the RCA laboratories in Princeton to head a new division that was to devote itself exclusively to "fundamental pure" research. At Cornell as elsewhere, by the fall of 1944 extensive plans were being drawn for the expansion of physics activities once the war was over.[86] A tug of war developed over the direction that the department was to take: whether to concentrate on "fundamental" or on "applied" physics.[87] Extensive discussions took place at Los Alamos between Bethe and Bacher, resulting in a memorandum by Bacher to Gibbs outlining "Plans for Nuclear Physics at Cornell University." Bethe and Bacher's conclusion was that "the most important plan of postwar research will be the high-

83 Compton, "Report of the President," 1943, pp. 19–21.
84 Compton, "Report of the President," 1944, pp. 12–13.
85 Bacher to Gibbs, Nov. 4, 1944. Bethe Papers.
86 Hiring activities at Los Alamos were intense. Feynman accepted an offer from Cornell in 1944, and Morrison did the same a little later. Several experimentalists were also added to the faculty of the department. By 1945 Bethe was holding meetings of the Cornell contingent at Los Alamos. The plans that Harvard formulated for the expansion of its science and engineering departments, as well as the records of the committee that formulated them, can be found among the papers of Harlow Shapley in the Harvard University Archives. Those of Princeton can be found in the departmental files deposited in the Mudd Archives, Princeton University.
87 Bethe to Gibbs, Nov. 20, 1944. Bethe Papers.

energy particle physics using a betatron source."[88] Eventually, the differences over the direction the department was to take were settled by creating a separate laboratory for nuclear physics that encompassed "fundamental physics."

Bethe and the War Years

When the war broke in September 1939, Bethe was not yet a citizen of the United States. After the fall of France in the spring of 1940, he was desperate "to make some contributions to the war effort." Unable to get clearance to work on classified projects, he devised projects of his own.[89] Introduced to the problem of analyzing the shock waves in gases surrounding a high-velocity projectile by Theodor von Karman, Bethe and Teller took it up and formulated a theory of the process that later became the basis for the use of shock waves to investigate the properties of gases. While completing the project, Bethe also worked on the penetration of armor by projectiles.[90] He produced a theory of armor penetration and shielding that became the point of departure of much work on these subjects during the war and proved to be very helpful in the manufacture of armor.

In March 1941 Bethe became a citizen of the United States, and on the day after Pearl Harbor he received his clearance to work on classified military projects. His first project dealt with microwaves and their uses in offensive and defensive weapons. MIT's Radiation Laboratory directors recognized that a well-developed theory covering microwave generation and propagation would save months of experimental labor that would otherwise have to be spent in searching, by trial and error, for the best size, shape, and arrangement of apparatus for a given purpose. They therefore asked Bethe and other theorists to work on the theory of microwave propagation. Most of the problems arising in practice involved cavities, wave guides, and similar devices, of shapes that did not permit solutions in closed form but were quite close to simpler shapes that had been treated exactly. Bethe moved, then, from problems integrable in closed form to the use of perturbation theory. He developed the foundations for such a treatment in a paper entitled "Theory of Diffraction by Small Hole," submitted to Lee DuBridge in January 1942, in which he solved "the problem of the effect of a small hole in a cavity upon the oscillations within that cavity." He proved that the usual Kirchhoff theory of diffraction, based on Huyghens's principle, failed "completely" when the hole is small compared with the wavelength, as was the case with his microwave work. His solution also indicated that much less radiation was emitted

---

88 Bacher to Gibbs, Dec. 6, 1944. Bethe Papers.

89 "Defense research is at last getting under way here [at Cornell] and for the time being it is to be mainly a voluntary project with the ideas coming from ourselves." Bethe to Von Karman, Oct. 29, 1940. Bethe Papers.

90 Bethe to Von Karman, Oct. 29 and Nov. 30, 1940. Bethe Papers.

through a small hole than would be expected from Kirchhoff's formula, the power being reduced approximately in the ratio of the radius of the hole to wavelength.[91]

The theory developed by Bethe made possible the theoretical study of the coupling of any number of cavities joined by small circular holes in their common plane boundaries. To make contact with experimental practice and with actual devices the theory needed to be extended to encompass noncircular holes, holes in curved surfaces, and holes of sizes comparable to the wavelength of the radiation or even larger. This last problem was of importance for the coupling of wave guides to cavities and in the computation of the angular distribution of the radiation emitted by horns. In February 1942 Bethe submitted a proposal to extend his earlier work for support by the Radiation Laboratory. He characterized the work "not as war research but rather as fundamental research which may serve as the basis for directly useful investigations" such as those currently undertaken at MIT. It therefore seemed to him entirely feasible, and in fact desirable, to have the work done by various theoretical physicists at their home universities "in view of the urgent necessity for training more graduate students in physics."[92] This arrangement would also mean lower cost.[93]

Bethe did work at the Rad Lab in 1942 for a brief period. In the summer of 1942 he was asked to join a study group under Oppenheimer at Berkeley that was concerned with the theoretical design of an atomic bomb and the estimation of its efficiency. The results obtained by this study group confirmed the feasibility of a uranium bomb, and in the spring of 1943 the Los Alamos Laboratory was established to develop and assemble an atomic bomb. Oppenheimer chose Bethe as the head of theoretical physics—one of the seven divisions of the laboratory—whose responsibility was summarized in the Smyth report as conditioned by "the impossibility of producing a small-scale atomic explosion by making use of only a small amount of fissionable material. Thus it was necessary to proceed from data obtained in experiments on infinitesimal quantities and to combine it with available theories as accurately as possible in order to make estimates as to what would happen in the bomb."[94]

The initial plan had been to assemble a uranium bomb by means of a gun

91 Bethe to DuBridge, Jan. 9, 1942. Bethe Papers.

92 Bethe, "Proposal of a Defense Research Project on the Theory of Electromagnetic Microwaves," p. 6. Bethe to DuBridge, Feb. 12, 1942. Bethe Papers, Box 2, folder entitled "Calculation for MIT Rad Lab 1942."

93 Gibbs, the department chairman, thought "each university could itself be a center for research with military application." Bacher, "Origins of the Floyd R. Newman Laboratory." Talk given at a symposium in honor of B. D. McDaniel, Cornell University, May 22, 1985.

94 Smyth, *Atomic Energy,* p. 214.

shooting a cylinder of fissile material into a hollow cylinder of fissile material surrounded by a reflector. It was important to know how neutrons would diffuse in the complicated shapes that resulted from this assembly. When a little later the problem shifted to the assembly of a plutonium bomb by implosion, difficult problems in hydrodynamics and shock waves arose.

All these problems were insoluble by analytical means and required a huge amount of numerical work. A decision was made to acquire IBM calculators to do the numerical work. These were electromechanical machines with the calculations done mechanically as in a desk calculator, but the sensing was done by electrical contact through holes in a punched card.[95] John von Neumann was a consultant at Los Alamos, and he contributed significantly to the solution of the implosion problem.[96] The project von Neumann oversaw at the Institute for Advanced Study to construct a mechanical and numerical integrator and computer (MANIAC) grew out of his computing experiences at Los Alamos.

I have sketched some of Bethe's wartime work because he is the supreme example of why theoretical physicists proved so valuable in the war effort. Bethe is as much at home in applied mathematics as in any branch of theoretical physics.[97] No calculation fazes him, and if analytic solutions cannot be obtained he resorts to extensive numerical work and the use of computers. And because he understands every facet of the experimental practice, he can interpret as well as suggest experiments. But it is his ability to translate his intimate knowledge of nuclear, atomic, and molecular properties into an understanding of the macroscopic properties and the behavior of materials, and into the design of macroscopic devices, that rendered his services so valuable to Los Alamos and later on to industry.

American physicists, in general, proved themselves gifted applied scientists and engineers in all the projects they worked on. The source of these qualities in the experimentalists was obvious. Their skills came from the demands of the experimental practice of the 1930's. Money was scarce and labor was cheap, hence graduate students built diffusion pumps and vacuum tubes rather than buying them. Before the war, experimentalists designed and constructed their apparatus and electronic circuitry from scratch—including the machining of the various parts, the winding of electromagnets, and the building of the components for their electronic equipment. Experimental physicists trained in the United States possessed another important trait: they knew a great deal of

95 Bethe, Introduction to *Computers and Their Role in the Physical Sciences,* ed. S. Fernbach and A. Taub (New York: Gordon and Breach, 1970).

96 Von Neumann's work on the Mach reflection of an oblique shock wave from a solid surface—which required a great deal of computational analysis—is widely acknowledged.

97 The following distinction is often made: applied mathematics refers to that branch of mathematical physics that does not involve Planck's constant and theoretical physics refers to the part that does.

theory because the course requirements during the first two years of graduate study at American universities did not differentiate between theorists and experimenters. For the theorists, close contact with experimentalists had given them an intimate familiarity and a deep understanding of machines, apparatus, materials, and experimental techniques. This was part of their training and a requirement for obtaining an academic position. Thus when Karl Lark-Horowitz wrote Bethe to inform him that there was an opening for a young theorist in his department at Purdue, he indicated that the department sought "a man who really has some ideas about experimental techniques, knows some physics, and has the ability to express himself clearly so that we have no trouble using him as a teacher."[98]

But there was another factor that played an important role in the case of theorists. Because, for the most part, only university careers were open to them and such jobs were scarce during the 1930's, the selection process was so demanding that only the very best survived. Those who did had outstanding talents: John Archibald Wheeler, Wendall Furry, Robert Serber, John Bardeen, Conyers Herring, Frederick Seitz, Willis E. Lamb, Philip Morrison, Emil J. Konopinski, Robert Christy, Morris Rose, Robert Marshak, to name but a few, and this list does not include the off-scale individuals like Julian S. Schwinger and Richard P. Feynman. All these theorists were an amalgam of pure and applied scientist.

In constructing their cyclotrons physicists acquired another trait that proved to be very valuable. "Development, as distinct from research, always requires the work of many scientists and engineers acting together; it requires conscious effort, planning, and plenty of money."[99] Physicists learned to plan and to work together in building cyclotrons; in the wartime laboratories the government supplied the funds that were needed and they learned how to spend money. All these talents were put to use in the design and construction of radar sets, of the first atomic pile under the stands of Stagg Field, of the first nuclear reactor at Hanford, and of the first atomic bombs, among the many useful devices physicists helped develop. Their competence as engineers was obvious to Bush, who still complained that the MIT Rad Lab staff should have been leavened with more engineers. Bush found that "DuBridge, Karl Compton, and Alfred Loomis had the bit in their teeth and they didn't pay much attention to my ideas as to how to run a laboratory."[100] Still, the physicists delivered.

Their ability as development engineers was similarly appreciated. They oversaw the manufacture of radar sets, proximity fuses, atomic bombs.

98 Lark-Horowitz to Bethe, Oct. 29, 1936. Box 9, Bethe Papers.

99 Bethe, after-dinner speech, American Physical Society, Feb. 3, 1961. Bethe Papers, Box 3.

100 Bush, Oral History Collection. LASC-MIT, vol. VI, p. 323, MIT Archives. See also Bush, *Pieces of the Action.*

Compton observed that because few industrial concerns could handle the construction of new radar systems out of a bewildering variety of exotic components, "it was the task of the research laboratory [physicists] to see that all these component parts were designed and put into production by suitable subcontractors all over the country."[101]

The war had made clear to the engineering community that it had much to learn from the physicists. More important, engineers came to recognize that science—the understanding of nature—was involved in modern engineering in ways far more intimate and complicated than in past times. What made the physicists the outstanding applied scientists and engineers they proved themselves to be was their ability to translate their understanding of the microscopic world into useful macroscopic devices. The physicists' mastery of quantum mechanics allowed them to infer the properties of materials at the extreme temperatures and pressures that exist in an atomic bomb. Bethe, Fermi, and the others converted their knowledge of the interaction of neutrons with nuclei into diffusion equations, and the solutions of the latter into reactors and bombs. Engineering education would clearly have to be revamped to keep pace with the wartime developments. The days of the "handbook"-trained engineer were over. Interestingly, it was the British who first recognized during the war that the education of their engineers was deficient. In 1944 a committee of the Ministry of Education was appointed to see how the demand by industry for engineers, particularly development engineers, would be met. The committee concluded that in the postwar period a new class of university-trained engineers, well-versed in fundamental science, would be needed by British industry.[102] Two years later, these findings were enlarged in a report on manpower to Parliament, which concluded, "Universities of a nation which is to remain a great industrial power must accept the responsibility for training technologists as well as scientists" and that "the academic organization which appears best suited for this purpose is one that includes instruction in engineering sciences at the undergraduate level and instruction and research in technological subjects at the graduate level."[103]

101 MIT, Office of the President. Box 70, Folder 55. Radiation Laboratory Summary. MIT Archives. The Rad Lab set up the Research Construction Company (RCC) to assemble prototype radar sets. RCC was large enough to supply the Army and Navy with "crash" sets but small enough to ensure careful assembly of models. "By the end of August 1945, approximately $25,000,000 worth of radar equipment had been directly supplied to the services by RCC and the Radiation Laboratory." Guerlac, *History of Radar*, p. 6.

102 "Higher Technological Education," Report of a Special Committee, headed by Lord Eustace Percy, appointed in April 1944 (London 1945). Quoted in "Report of the Dean of the Graduate School of Engineering to the President of Harvard University for the year 1946/7," *Official Register of Harvard University* 46 (1949): 387.

103 "British Report on Man-Power," Findings of a committee under the chairmanship of Sir Alan Barlow and presented to Parliament in May 1946.

Similar conclusions were reached at the leading American universities. At Cornell the Department of Engineering Physics was set up in 1948 to provide a type of education and training that would effectively bridge the gap between that of the basic sciences and engineering. The general aim was to prepare students for a prospective career in technical research and advanced engineering development in "the expanding technological activities in this country" by providing "graduates with the vigorous and exacting course of study which the curriculum of this department provides." The course of study—which took five years—was designed "to combine the broad training of the physicist with the knowledge of the properties of materials and the technological principles of the engineer."[104]

Vannevar Bush, who headed a panel to look into engineering education at Harvard after the war, prefaced his report with the observation that "the borderline between the engineer and the applied scientist is becoming dimmed. . . . Engineers, those who are in the forefront of advance, are becoming more entitled to be recognized as scientists in their own right. Applied scientists, under the pressure of war and its aftermath, have often become accomplished engineers as well."[105] To reflect these changes the Department of Engineering Sciences at Harvard was renamed the Department of Engineering Sciences and Applied Physics in 1946. In 1949 the faculty of engineering was merged with the faculty of Arts and Sciences, and a division of engineering sciences, consisting of the undergraduate department of engineering and applied physics and the graduate department of engineering was constituted. In reporting on the curricular changes that were under way, the dean of the new division noted that it should come as no surprise that the training of engineers had been deeply affected by the war. "The waging of war is inherently an engineering pursuit."[106] In 1951 the name of the division was changed to the Division of Applied Sciences.

The Postwar Developments

In his history of the physics department of MIT, Slater indicated that after the war the department's need for growth had to be somewhat tempered by the "rather *horrible example*" of the Rad Lab. Certainly, the laboratory had been an effective tool for wartime use. "But," Slater continued, "this is no way to run a university in peace time. The essence of a university is the training of the students by their older associates and professors, and to do this properly

104 Cornell University, College of Engineering, "Announcement for 1948/49," p. 68.
105 Quoted in van Vleck, "Blurred Borders of Physics and Engineering."
106 "Report of the Dean of the Graduate School of Engineering to the President of Harvard University for the Year 1946/7," *Official Register of Harvard University* 46 (1949): 390.

demands enough professors, or few enough students, so that they can effectively keep contact with each other."[107] The principle determining the size of the senior staff was that there be no appointments of "men not taking part in the teaching," that is, no appointments exclusively in research. Slater therefore dismissed from the beginning the idea of a separate research institute or laboratory—such as a continuation of the Radiation Laboratory—existing in parallel with the physics department. Hence the question became by how many and by what type of appointments should the existing staff be augmented. Being conservative by nature, Slater answered that financial caution demanded "as small additions to the department as possible," the number being determined by the department's teaching load. But even this allowed for considerable expansion, as a large increase in the number of students enrolling in physics was expected at both the undergraduate and graduate levels, since many veterans would be enrolling under the G.I. bill.[108]

However, events acquired a momentum of their own. In 1944 "Stratton received a flattering offer from industry, and had to make up his mind regarding his future."[109] Because he was a member of the physics department, he informed Slater, its chairman, of the offer. Together they proposed the setting up of a Research Laboratory of Electronics with Stratton as its director. The laboratory was conceived as a joint project of the departments of physics and electrical engineering, based on the premise that the applications of electronics lay in electrical engineering but that much fundamental work remained to be done in physics. Essentially, the Research Laboratory was to carry on many of the activities of the Rad Lab once the war was over and OSRD ceased to fund it. Thus, two birds would be killed with one stone. The proposal would keep both Stratton and something very much like the Rad Lab at MIT. Since the plan called for the creation of a laboratory under the control of two academic departments, rather than as a separate and independent organization as the Rad Lab had been, it satisfied Slater's demand that MIT not establish research institutes staffed by researchers who did not teach and were not appointed by a department. The idea was bought by Harold Hazen, the head of the department of electrical engineering at MIT, and by Compton and James R. Killian— who had in 1943 already appropriated $50,000 to expand MIT's activities in the field of electronics.

Stratton agreed to stay, and thus was born the Research Laboratory of Electronics. The department of physics was authorized to make several new

107 Slater, "History of the Physics Department at MIT."
108 Slater was of course right. By the beginning of the first postwar term, the department of physics at MIT had appointed 25 research associates—Ph.D. candidates who had worked in government laboratories during the war—and had admitted enough other graduate students to bring the graduate enrollment to about 90, "far ahead of any pre-war year." Slater, "History of the Physics Department at MIT," p. 55.
109 Ibid., p. 50.

appointments in the field of microwaves, "enough to ensure continuity between the Radiation Laboratory and the new Research Laboratory." Jerrold Zacharias and Albert Hill accepted offers to join the physics department and Jerome Weisner accepted an appointment in the department of electrical engineering. All three were staff members of the Rad Lab.

Shortly after VJ-Day an executive order by President Truman extended the funding of OSRD until June 30, 1946, to allow the armed forces to give out contracts to keep going work of the sort that OSRD had supported. The extension allowed MIT to continue receiving funds for running the Rad Lab. During that interval MIT set up the Research Laboratory of Electronics, obtained from the Signal Corps, Office of Naval Research, and Army Air Force the support for its operation,[110] and negotiated the transfer of most of the Rad Lab's scientific equipment to the new laboratory's Division of Basic Research. In his outline "Proposed Physics Program for the Research Laboratory of Electronics, MIT," Slater indicated that the laboratory's mission was one of application, the "transfer of . . . new methods from the physics laboratory to engineering practice."[111] While these negotiations were going on, the MIT administration initiated steps to establish a nuclear program using the Research Laboratory of Electronics as a model. Zacharias, who some months before Trinity had gone to Los Alamos to head one of its divisions, convinced Weisskopf and Bruno Rossi to join the newly established laboratory. In the fall of 1945, Zacharias was appointed director of the Laboratory for Nuclear Science and Engineering (LNSE) whose aim was "to encourage interdepartmental collaboration in researches bearing on the *useful application* of nuclear energy, particles, and products."[112]

In contrast to MIT, the establishment of Cornell's Laboratory of Nuclear Studies was instigated by faculty members interested in fundamental research. Lengthy discussions were held by the members of the Cornell faculty at Los Alamos throughout the spring and summer of 1945, resulting in a proposal that was submitted to President Day.[113] At three o'clock on the afternoon of Monday, September 24, 1945, a delegation of Cornell physicists led by Gibbs, the chairman of the department, met with Day to hear his plans for physics at Cornell. The physicists informed the president that they had all received offers to go elsewhere to conduct nuclear physics research, and while their preference was to remain at Cornell, the university would have to commit itself to provide "adequate opportunities for constructive work." Confronted with "an impel-

110 The initial contract was for $600,000 a year supplemented by additional sums for special projects.

111 Slater Papers, American Philosophical Society, Philadelphia.

112 Emphasis added. Compton, "Memorandum to the Institute Staff," Dec. 19, 1945. Slater Papers.

113 There exists an extensive correspondence between Bacher, Bethe, and Gibbs on these matters in the Bethe Papers.

ling issue of University policy," Day promised the physicists an answer within a month.[114]

Day took up the challenge. He committed himself to make university funds available to build an accelerator. In September 1946, the board of trustees unanimously voted to appropriate $1,200,000 for the "specific support of the Nuclear Studies Project." Writing to Bacher to inform him of the board's action, Day asserted that "no decision of the Board of Trustees during my term of office has been of greater importance to this institution and to the prospects of scientific research in this country."[115] In October 1946 the "great news" arrived that the Office of Naval Research "will undertake to execute a contract" for the construction of "the" accelerator for the Nuclear Studies Laboratory. The Newman Laboratory of Nuclear Studies was dedicated in October 1948, by which time the construction of a betatron was well under way.

Centers similar to the nuclear laboratories at Cornell and MIT were established on other campuses. All of them—and in particular LNSE at MIT, the Newman Lab at Cornell, and the Nuclear Lab at Chicago—attempted to recreate the atmosphere of Los Alamos: the sense of community, the exhilaration and joy of doing physics. All of them organized themselves so that they would be doing physics the way it was done at Los Alamos, with experimentalists and theorists working closely together and interacting strongly with one another. One further consequence of Los Alamos was apparent at these laboratories: theorists and experimenters had become peers.

The Office of Naval Research played a crucial role in establishing nuclear studies at both Cornell and MIT. But MIT, having defined LNSE's mission as "the useful application of nuclear energy, particles, and products," accepted the need for secrecy and the curtailment of scientific information exchange in some facets of the laboratory's work. Some measure of secrecy had existed in MIT's industrial research activities, and MIT had grown accustomed to such requirements in its government-supported wartime laboratories. MIT did not object to having "classified" courses taught there.[116] The summer study programs that Zacharias organized for the Navy were natural extensions of LNSE's mission.[117] At Cornell University, the Newman Laboratory of Nuclear Studies was committed to the production and the dissemination of new knowledge. Cornell was sensitive to the dangers accompanying the support of research by the military. Philip Morrison, who had joined Cornell in 1945,

[114] "Remarks by E. E. Day at the Dedication of the Laboratory of Nuclear Studies, October 7, 1948." Day Papers 3/6/8.

[115] Day to Bacher, Sept. 16, 1946. Bethe Papers.

[116] The first course on nuclear reactors at LNSE was given to Navy officers who were to man the nuclear submarines. The material of the course was classified when it was first offered.

[117] For details of some of these activities, such as projects Hartwell, Lexington, and Sage, see Schweber, "Mutual Embrace."

eloquently and presciently outlined these dangers in 1946. He was apprehensive that gradually the backers—the Army and Navy—would tighten "the now amicable contracts" and "the fine print will start to contain talk about results and specific weapon problems," with science "bought by war, on the installment plan," and subject to a crushing burden of secrecy.[118]

Although Morrison believed that physicists knew that the situation was a dangerous one and that it would be wrong to accept support from the armed forces, he feared that they would be compelled to do so. The war had taught them not only how a well-supported effort could greatly increase their effectiveness, but also that their field was no longer encompassed by what was possible for small groups of men to do. There was a real need for large machines—reactors, cyclotrons, synchrotrons, betatrons—to do the work of the future. Physicists needed support beyond the capabilities of the university. "If the ONR, or the new Army equivalent, G-6, comes with a nice contract, a physicist would be more than human to refuse." But, Morrison warned, "the result is necessarily bad. . . . The best security will always be a strong and healthy nation in which science has a recognized and independent place."[119] Morrison therefore called for the establishment of a National Science Foundation.

Epilogue

My account of MIT and Cornell indicates how the previous histories of these two institutions—one a technological institute, the other a university—shaped subsequent developments. Differing modes of governance took them along different paths. At MIT, academic policies were initiated and determined by the top administrators and the executive committee of the board of trustees, whereas at Cornell such policies were initially recommended by an autonomous faculty for approval by the administration and the board. The establishment of LNSE at MIT was the result of a decision made by Compton and Killian, whereas at Cornell's Newman Lab Bacher and Bethe were the instigators.

The differing character of these two institutions was also reflected in the leadership of their respective laboratories of nuclear studies. Bethe always remained the teacher and researcher, that is, remained the paradigmatic Cornell professor. His involvement in governmental activities was as that of a private citizen, in industrial consulting activities as that of a private individual. Zacharias, on the other hand, became the paradigmatic academic entrepreneur. And what more fertile soil to practice his entrepreneurship than MIT, the paradigmatic entrepreneurial university. He became involved in governmental

118 Morrison, "The Laboratory Demobilizes." Speech delivered at the atomic energy session of the *New York Herald* Forum, Oct. 9, 1946. Bethe Papers.
119 *Ibid.*

affairs by virtue of his institutional affiliation and position and by virtue of the institutional resources he could bring with him.

But the contrast should not obscure the fact that many of the postwar developments at the two institutions were quite similar. At both places the engineering curriculum was revamped and programs in applied science were instituted or strengthened as a result of the wartime experiences. Within each physics department a struggle developed between the "old-timers" and the conquering heroes, the nuclear physicists who returned from Los Alamos and built nuclear laboratories that were supported by funds from the Office of Naval Research and Atomic Energy Commission at unprecedented levels.[120] At Cornell, the power struggle was resolved by having a triumvirate govern the physics operations, following a plan drafted by Bethe in February 1945. This scheme left Smith, the chairman of the department, in charge of faculty and teaching, Bacher in charge of the semi-autonomous Newman Laboratory for Nuclear Studies, and Bethe as the coordinator and moderator between the two. The three were referred to as the father, the son, and the holy ghost.[121] That same day, the physics faculty adopted a resolution pledging to support the new arrangement, "to the purpose that we may better ensure the prestige of the University, the unity of the group, and the satisfaction of every individual in the group."[122]

At MIT the conflict was more bitter,[123] but the administrative structure that was set up was similar to the one at Cornell. Slater eventually resigned from the chairmanship in 1951, leaving the field to the nuclear physicists.

The power struggle that went on between the nuclear and high-energy physicists and the other kinds of physicists—at Cornell, MIT, and elsewhere—was a struggle to determine what physics is and how it should be done. The victory of the nuclear and high-energy physicists affected not only the subsequent development of physics but also that of the other sciences. For they were the scientists who populated the committees establishing national science

120 Zacharias in February 1946 could propose the building of a 90,000-square-foot structure to house LNSE. LNSE's annual budget for 1946–47 was over $1,000,000, and the requested budget for the following year was $1,441,100, with all moneys under Zacharias's control. The story at Cornell is similar. The proposed budget for research in nuclear physics that Bacher proposed in September 1945 amounted to some $2,000,000, of which $1,500,000 was for the construction of a 300-MeV high-energy electron accelerator, $50,000 was for a fast-neutron reactor, $300,000 was to house these facilities, and $200,000 was for auxiliary equipment. An extra $100,000 was asked for additional staff. Day and the Cornell board of trustees essentially accepted the proposal.

121 The proposal went on to detail the administrative structure for the running of the department and research laboratory and for the appointment of faculty, graduate students, and teaching and research assistants. The document also indicates that each "part" had an initial budget of roughly $200,000, which was provided by the University. Bethe Papers.

122 Resolution by physics faculty, Oct. 29, 1945. Bethe Papers.

123 "Slater and Zacharias almost came to blows." H. Feshbach, interview with S. S. Schweber, February 1988.

policy. Their influence reflected their enormous skill as applied scientists and engineers, and the role they had played in gaining victory over Germany and Japan. The authority and power of these physicists stemmed not only from their global understanding of the physical sciences and from their overall command of the applied science and engineering that went into the assembly of complex systems such as weapons, computers, and reactors, but also from the then-prevalent view that high-energy physics was the most fundamental branch of physics. High-energy physics and its associated theories were going to unravel the innermost workings of nature and illuminate the interactions between the "elementary" particles, allowing the high-energy theorist to reconstruct the world of atoms, molecules, and solids.

During the war and for a decade or so after the war, physicists had an overall competence that few other scientists had, one that gave them an overview of the defense enterprises they became involved with. Hence also their moral stand. Frequently, they were the ones who had the overall responsibility for the project; often, they were the only ones who were familiar with the working of the separate parts; consequently, they felt that a moral responsibility devolved upon them. But even as physicists became more specialized, as they began assuming more and more the role of the specialized professional, their sense of moral responsibility did not diminish. The nuclear threat that they brought into the world affected all of mankind and the fate of the entire planet, hence their discourse remained the "discourse of the universal."[124]

124 Foucault, *Power/Knowledge*, p. 128.

References Cited

Alvarez, Luis W. *Alvarez: Adventures of a Physicist*. New York: Basic Books, 1987.

Becker, Carl. *Cornell University: Founders and the Founding*. Ithaca, N.Y.: Cornell University Press, 1943.

Bernstein, Jeremy. "Profiles: Physicist I." *New Yorker*, Oct. 8, 1975, pp. 47, 109.

———. *Hans Bethe, Prophet of Energy*. New York: Basic Books, 1980.

Bishop, Morris. *A History of Cornell*. Ithaca, N.Y.: Cornell University Press, 1962.

Burchard, John E. *Q.E.D.: M.I.T. in World War II*. Cambridge, Mass.: MIT, Technology Press, 1948.

Bush, Vannevar. "The Case for Biological Engineering." In K. T. Compton, R. W. Trullinger, V. Bush, eds., *Scientists Face the World of 1942*, pp. 60–79. New Brunswick, N.J.: Rutgers University Press, 1942.

———. *Pieces of the Action*. New York: Morrow, 1970.

Carlson, W. Bernard. "Academic Entrepreneurship and Engineering Education: Dugald C. Jackson and the MIT–GE Cooperative Engineering Course, 1907–1932." *Technology and Culture* 29 (1988): 536–67.

Compton, K. T. "The Government's Responsibility in Science." *Science* 81 (1935): 347–55.

———. "Report of the President." *MIT Bulletin* 72 (1936): 8–27.

———. "Report of the President." *MIT Bulletin* 75 (1939): 9–21.

———. "Willingness to Make Sacrifices Is a Hallmark of the Character Essential to a High Standard of Civilization." *Technology Review,* June 1941, pp. 347–51.

———. "War Activities." *MIT Bulletin* 78 (1942): 5–18.

———. "Report of the President for 1941–1942." *MIT Bulletin* 78 (1942): 6–8.

———. "Scientists Face the World of 1942." In K. T. Compton, R. W. Trullinger, V. Bush, eds., *Scientists Face the World of 1942,* pp. 3–22. New Brunswick, N.J.: Rutgers University Press, 1942.

———. "Report of the President." *MIT Bulletin* 79 (Oct. 1943): 19–21.

———. "Report of the President." *MIT Bulletin* 80 (Oct. 1944): 11.

———. "Institute Evaluates Its War Record." *Technology Review* 48 (Nov. 1945): 39–41.

Conant, James B. "The Role of the Endowed University in American Higher Education." In *Proceedings and Addresses at the Inauguration of Edmund Ezra Day, 8 October 1937,* pp. 37–43. Ithaca, N.Y.: Cornell University, 1937.

———. *My Several Lives: Memoirs of a Social Inventor.* New York: Harper and Row, 1970.

Day, Edmund Ezra. *The Defense of Freedom.* Ithaca, N.Y.: Cornell University Press, 1937.

———. "Inaugural Address." In *Proceedings and Addresses at the Inauguration of Edmund Ezra Day, 8 October 1937,* pp. 25–41. Ithaca, N.Y.: Cornell University, 1937.

———. "President's Report, 1937/38." *Cornell University Officiations* 30 (July 15, 1938): 15.

DeVane, William C. *Higher Education in Twentieth-Century America.* Cambridge, Mass.: Harvard University Press, 1965.

Dresden, Max. *H.A. Kramers: Between Tradition and Revolution.* New York: Springer-Verlag, 1987.

Dupree, A. Hunter. "National Security and the Post-War Science Establishment in the United States." *Nature* 323 (1986): 213–16.

Etzkowitz, Henry. "The Making of an Entrepreneurial University: MIT and the Re-industrialization of New England." In Everett Mendelsohn, M. Roe Smith, and Peter Weingart, eds., *Science, Technology and the Military,* pp. 515–40. Sociology of the Sciences Yearbook, 1988. Dordrecht: Kluwer Academic Publishers, 1988.

Foucault, Michel. *Power/Knowledge.* Ed. Colin Gordon. New York: Pantheon, 1980.

Goodwin, H. M. *A History of the Departments of Chemistry and Physics at MIT, 1865–1933.* Cambridge, Mass.: MIT, Technology Press, 1933.

Greber, Lisa. "The Unholy Trinity: Physics, Gender, and the Military." B.S. thesis, MIT, 1987.

Guerlac, Henry E. *Radar in World War II.* Los Angeles: Tomash Publishers, 1987.

Harrison, G. R. "Karl Taylor Compton: Scientist, Public Servant." *Technology Review,* Dec. 1954, pp. 83–84.

Hartman, Paul. *The Cornell Physics Department: Recollections and a History of Sorts.* Privately printed, 1984.

Kargon, Robert H. *The Rise of Robert Millikan: Portrait of a Life in American Science.* Ithaca, N.Y.: Cornell University Press, 1982.

Kevles, Daniel. *The Physicists.* New York: Knopf, 1978.

Larrabee, Eric. *Commander in Chief: Franklin Delano Roosevelt, His Lieutenants and Their War.* New York: Harper and Row, 1987.

Leslie, Stuart W. "Profit and Loss: The Military and MIT in the Postwar Era." *Historical Studies in the Physical and Biological Sciences* 21 (1990): 59–86.

Maclaurin, Richard. "Address to Alumni Dinner." *Technology Review,* Jan. 1920, pp. 55–62.

Noble, David E. *America by Design: Science, Technology and the Rise of Corporate Capitalism.* New York: Knopf, 1977.

Oppenheimer, J. R. "Niels Bohr and Atomic Weapons." *New York Review of Books* 3 (Dec. 17, 1966): 7.

Prescott, Samuel C. *When MIT Was "Boston Tech."* Cambridge, Mass.: MIT Press, 1954.

Reingold, Nathan. "Vannevar Bush's New Deal for Research." *Historical Studies in the Physical and Biological Sciences* 17 (1987): 299–344.

Romanowski, Roslyn R. "Peacetime to Wartime Transition in Defense Research Policy at MIT." B.S. thesis, MIT, 1982.

Schweber, S. S. "The Empiricist Temper Regnant: Theoretical Physics in the United States, 1920–1950." *Historical Studies in the Physical and Biological Sciences* 17 (1986): 55–98.

———. "The Mutual Embrace of Science and the Military," in Everett Mendelsohn, Merritt Roe Smith, and Peter Weingart, eds., *Science, Technology and the Military,* pp. 3–45. Sociology of the Sciences Yearbook, 1988. Dordrecht: Kluwer Academic, 1988.

———. "The Young Slater and the Development of Quantum Chemistry." *Historical Studies in the Physical and Biological Sciences* 20 (1990): 339–406.

Slater, J. C. "History of the Physics Department at MIT." Slater Papers, American Philosophical Society, Philadelphia, n.d. [ca. 1948].

Smith, Alice Kimball, and Charles Weiner, eds. *Robert Oppenheimer, Letters and Recollections.* Cambridge, Mass.: Harvard University Press, 1980.

Smith, L. P. "Calculation of the Quantum Defect for Highly Excited S States of Para- and Ortho-Helium." *Physical Review* 42 (1932): 177–81.

Smyth, Henry de Wolf. *Atomic Energy for Military Purposes.* Princeton, N.J.: Princeton University Press, 1946.

Sorenson, Royal W. "Development and Characteristics of a 1,000,000-Volt Cascade Transformer at California Institute of Technology." *Journal of the American Institute of Electrical Engineers* 44 (1925): 373.

Stewart, Irvin. *Organizing Scientific Research for War: The Administrative History of the OSRD.* Boston: Little, Brown, 1948.

Stone, R. S. "Neutron Therapy and Specific Ionization (Janeway Lecture)." *American Journal of Roentgenology and Radium Therapy* 59 (1948): 771–85.

Van Vleck, J. H. "Blurred Borders of Physics and Engineering." *Journal of Engineering Education,* Dec. 1955, pp. 366–73.

CHAPTER 7

"I think Space Telescope was not in the
consciousness of astronomers. A majority of
astronomers favored it when pushed or
pressed, but most of them hadn't thought
much about it."[1]

The Biggest Kind of
Big Science: Astronomers
and the Space Telescope

Robert W. Smith

Most of the funds for U.S. science before World War II came from
industry, private foundations, and the states. During the war this
pattern was radically altered, and the federal government became
the chief sponsor of the scientific enterprise, a shift that was swiftly institutionalized in the years following 1945. This shift brought with it not only
much more money but also new obligations, as well as a new political framework within which scientists had to work. For some, there were also changes
in their forms of scientific practice, in particular an increasing reliance on
multidisciplinary teams. For many physical scientists, these various developments came together in the pursuit of big science.

In this chapter I examine a kind of big science in the making, in particular,
how approval was won for the Hubble Space Telescope program, big science
of the very biggest kind. I shall argue that at the heart of this process was
"coalition building," and that coalition building is crucial to understanding
how and why the telescope was approved, the telescope's design, its scientific
objectives, and so the kind of very big science that it represents. However, to
place my discussion into context, I shall begin by discussing optical astronomy

---

1 John Bahcall, interviewed by Paul Hanle, Nov. 3, 1983, p. 36, National Air and Space
Museum Collection.

and big science, for optical astronomers were initially the chief advocates of the telescope among the scientific community. I shall then briefly describe the overall policy-making process for the telescope in the United States before turning to two vital aspects of the coalition advocating the telescope: how a working consensus for the telescope was fashioned within an initially skeptical and at times hostile astronomical community, and how the coalition in favor of the telescope was extended to accommodate the interests of planetary scientists, easing approval for the telescope from its potential patrons in the White House and Congress.

Optical Astronomy and Big Science

Optical astronomers—that is, astronomers who work in the visible wavelengths of the electromagnetic spectrum—were generally slow to adopt the methods of modern big science. For many years after the war their ways of working were still overwhelmingly those characterized as little science, the type of science in which an individual conceives of and carries out a scientific program or directs a small group or laboratory in defining and executing a project with the aid of modest apparatus. Certainly some optical astronomers had access to powerful and costly telescopes, but even they did not generally become members of big, multidisciplinary teams. It is also noteworthy that the first branch of astronomy to become "big" (by the definition shortly to be adopted here) was radio astronomy, a discipline founded to a large degree by physicists and engineers who had been used to big-science ways of working during the war and who, initially at least, employed apparatus whose development owed much to the war.[2] Big science has nevertheless made major inroads into optical astronomy, in most spectacular fashion in the United States and Europe with the exceptional scientific, technical, social, and political demands of space astronomy, most notably the Hubble Space Telescope. But before introducing the Hubble Space Telescope, let me take a step back to make a few general points about the use of the term "big science" since it is a term that has been employed to describe a range of different activities.

A recent report by the Office of Technology Assessment, for example, notes big science "can mean large and expensive facilities. It can refer to large, multidisciplinary team efforts that entail cooperative planning and therefore require individual scientists to sacrifice some freedom in choosing goals and methods. Or it can refer to bureaucratic central management by government administrators."[3] When in 1986 the Task Force of the House Committee on Science and Technology produced a "World Inventory of 'Big Science' Research Instruments and Facilities," the criteria for inclusion of a scientific

2 On the history of radio astronomy, see, among others, Edge and Mulkay, *Astronomy Transformed,* and Sullivan, *Early Years of Radio Astronomy.* Of course, big science was not spawned by the war and certainly has its origins in the prewar period.

3 Office of Technology Assessment, *Mapping Our Genes,* p. 125.

facility were that it was constructed after 1920 and cost $25 million or more in 1984 dollars.[4] A definition focused solely on money, however, misses much. Certainly it is sometimes possible for scientists to work in the spirit of little science even with extremely expensive facilities. For instance, users of the 100-inch Hooker Telescope on Mount Wilson traditionally, as George Ellery Hale used to put it, "ploughed a lone furrow." Reflecting in 1977 on astronomical practice with big telescopes before World War II, Albert Whitford, director of Lick Observatory for a decade and one of the leading astronomers of his generation, emphasized its individual character. Whitford recalled how it had been a matter of taking one's own photographic plate out of the deep freeze, "warming it up and mixing it with your own developer, and coaxing the telescope into good mirror shape somehow, by opening and closing the domes at the right time, and then exposing a plate with high artistry: 'doing it yourself.' Real mastery of a beautiful and sometimes cantankerous instrument, a big telescope."[5] Even in the case of the International Ultraviolet Explorer, an international astronomical satellite launched in 1977 that cost well over $100 million to build, the users to a large degree have followed the methods of little science.

The common equation of big science—that big bucks plus a big machine equals big science—is therefore flawed. We would, moreover, do well to employ the notion of little science carefully. For example, among the characteristics that have been identified in big science are politicization, bureaucratization, high risk, and the loss of autonomy. Often the implication is that these characteristics are absent from little science, an implication not always borne out by the historical evidence. In addition, a periodization is sometimes implicit in the use of little science; that is, that big science emerged from World War II and before then the scientific enterprise consisted entirely of little science. To believe these points, as Michael Dennis has pointed out, is to believe myths. In talking about both big science and little science, then, it is important to recognize that these are both broad descriptions, not explana-

4 U.S. Congress, *World Inventory*, p. 1. Since the term first came into widespread use about 1960, "big science" has often been taken to mean expensive science with no reference to scientific practice. Steven Shapin, for example, in "Pump and Circumstance," described Robert Boyle's air pump—so costly an instrument that only the wealthy could afford one—as big science.

5 A. E. Whitford, interviewed by David DeVorkin, July 15, 1977, p. 50, American Institute of Physics Collection. Stephen G. Brush has argued in "Rise of Astronomy," that in the U.S. the transition to big astronomy—big in terms of teamwork and expensive facilities—began in the late nineteenth century. However, it seems to me that much of the astronomy done at even Mount Wilson and Lick in the 1920's and 1930's was not big science in the modern sense. Rather, as Whitford's recollection suggests, in its spirit it was often small science conducted with large telescopes; researchers essentially chose their own problems and generally worked alone or in a very small group, although they might be assisted by a small team of computers or a handful of technicians. On astronomical practice at Lick, see Osterbrock, Gustafson, and Unruh, *Eye on the Sky*.

tions, and that they have been used somewhat ambiguously in the past. Examinations of big science that take into account both cost and scientific practice are therefore likely to be more historically rewarding than those based on cost alone.[6]

Nevertheless, as Derek Price, one of the first to investigate the nature of modern big science, pointed out over 25 years ago, "Without doubt, the most abnormal thing in this age of Big Science is money. The finances of science seem highly irregular and . . . they dominate most of the social and political implications."[7] Most obviously, if large sums of money are not forthcoming, there can be no big science. And without $2 billion there could have been no Hubble Space Telescope, probably the most costly scientific instrument ever built.

The Hubble Space Telescope is a large space observatory at the heart of which is a 2.4-meter primary mirror. The optical system is a Ritchey-Chretien Cassegrain. Light falling on the primary mirror is reflected back toward a secondary mirror, which in turn directs the light through a hole in the primary so that it can be analyzed by a battery of five scientific instruments together with the telescope's fine guidance system, which acts as a sixth instrument. The Space Telescope was designed to be the most powerful optical telescope ever constructed. Marked by NASA as a payload for the space shuttle since the early 1970's, the telescope's position in space has been intended by its designers since the very earliest planning stages to give it an angular resolution better by an order of magnitude over that of ground-based telescopes. Although its supporters used cosmology as the main scientific justification for the Space Telescope, the large increase in capability promised by the instrument's resolving power, rather than its ability to tackle any particular scientific questions, was its chief attraction for astronomers. The design finally accepted for the Space Telescope was also such that, unlike ground-based optical telescopes that have to contend with atmospheric absorption, it could make observations at wavelengths ranging from 120 nanometers to 1 millimeter, that is, in the ultraviolet, infrared, and submillimeter as well as optical regions (see Fig. 7.1). (As it turns out, the telescope's primary mirror was not manufactured to specifications and suffers from spherical aberration. This flaw, soon discovered by astronomers and engineers after the telescope's April 1990 launch aboard the Space Shuttle, means that its sensitivity is significantly worse than planned. Although it is still more capable in some ways than ground-based instruments, the telescope in orbit is not nearly as powerful a tool for cosmology as astronomers had hoped; see Fig. 7.2.)

6 Dennis's comments on little science appear in Dennis, "A Change of State," p. 15. An excellent example of a paper that investigates changing forms of scientific practice in the context of big science is Galison, "Bubble Chambers." See also Klaw, *New Brahmins*, pp. 134–54.

7 Price, *Little Science, Big Science*, p. 92.

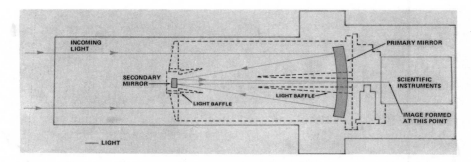

Fig. 7.1 Space Telescope light path. The optical layout follows a Cassegrain system, with light from the secondary mirror reflected through a hole in the primary mirror to a bank of scientific instruments. Photo courtesy NASA.

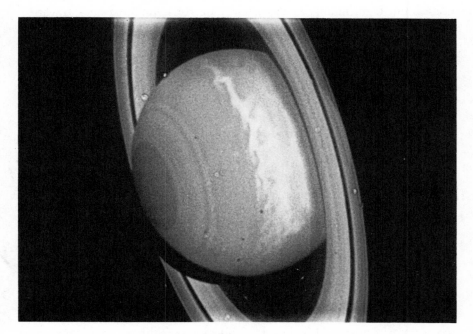

Fig. 7.2. An image of Saturn secured with the Hubble Space Telescope's wide-field/planetary camera in November 1990. Despite the flaw in the primary mirror, the telescope captures more detail than do ground-based telescopes. Photo courtesy NASA.

The Space Telescope's design and development were managed by NASA with the European Space Agency (ESA) as a minor partner. Approval for the telescope was won from the White House and Congress after a hard-fought three-year battle beginning in 1974; the building of the telescope began in 1977, and it was launched in 1990. The telescope's proponents also accepted from the earliest planning stages that its construction would be very largely the task of industrial contractors, for their resources and expertise would be essential to the elaborate "big technology" that would comprise the telescope. Its planning and building have nevertheless engaged large multidisciplinary teams of astronomers and other specialists, and its use will involve such teams, too. Designing and building the telescope has thus required what Robert Kargon has referred to as the "horizontal" association or cooperation of different sectors of society: government, industry, and academe.

Even when in the 1960's what became the Space Telescope program was first seriously discussed, the cost estimates were around $1 billion (1965 dollars) for a program more extensive than the current one. This was a price that everyone agreed put it well beyond the means of private patronage. The telescope's advocates accepted that if it was to come into being the telescope would, like nearly all of the U.S. big science facilities constructed since the war, have to be built with money from the federal government. The history of the Space Telescope to date is thus to a significant extent the history of how approval was won from the federal government for a big-science enterprise of a very big kind.

The Policy-Making Process

The development of a politically feasible Space Telescope program—that is, one that would be supported by astronomers and NASA and that the White House and Congress would ultimately fund—was not an orderly process.[8] That this should be so is hardly surprising. Although the Space Telescope is a joint program of NASA and the European Space Agency, NASA has been the dominant partner, and the telescope is chiefly an American creation. The coalition building, bargaining, and compromise entailed in winning approval for the Space Telescope were woven into the very fabric of American society, and policy definition in the U.S. form of democracy can at times be exceedingly complex and apparently disordered.[9] Is there nevertheless a structure to be discerned in the policy-making activities surrounding the Space Telescope?

8 This point is discussed at length in R. W. Smith, *Space Telescope*. Throughout the text I shall for convenience refer to the "telescope." It should be understood that this refers to the Space Telescope, its associated ground system, and the program to build the telescope at the particular period under consideration. Of course, the telescope's designs changed over time, and at any one time there were often competing designs, both for the spacecraft itself and various subsystems.

9 See, for example, Lindblom, *Policy Making*.

There are of course several models of policy-making, and I have elsewhere discussed some of these and their relationship to the case of policy-making on the Space Telescope.[10] One key point that should be noted, however, is that in the case of the Space Telescope one is dealing with the usual kind of policy definition for American big science. In the decentralized, pluralistic structure of the federal funding of post–World War II American science, any overall centralized planning has generally proved to be impossible and is widely seen as undesirable. Instead, policy definition is started at low levels in the collection of executive agencies (such as NASA), while higher policymakers (such as the Office of Science and Technology Policy) have played only a coordinating role at the end of the process.[11] Hence, for the Space Telescope to come into being, it was essential for its advocates to embed the idea of the telescope into NASA's own set of interests, for without NASA's support it would never be built.

Once this had been achieved, the term "ad hocracy" best captures the nature of the process by which approval for the telescope from the White House and Congress was sought and won by its supporters.[12] For the Space Telescope, policy-making did not just seem disordered, it *was* disordered. Policy-making is often the province of what are termed "subgovernments." Subgovernments are groups of individuals that make most of the routine and noncontroversial decisions in a given area of policy. Such a subgovernment might consist of agency officials, members of Congress, congressional staffers, and representatives of interest groups.[13] But once the funding of the Space Telescope had become a controversial issue, as we shall see that it did, the policy debate burst out of the sphere of the subgovernment that dealt with the more routine NASA policy-making. Policy-making on the Space Telescope was therefore hammered out in a variety of arenas according to ever-shifting rules and by ever-shifting players. It was a process in which no one ever had a complete grasp of what was happening.[14] The fundamental question of

10 See R. W. Smith, *The Space Telescope,* chapter 5.

11 Lambright, *Governing Science and Technology,* p. 202. See also Reagan, *Science and the Federal Patron.*

12 I am indebted to W. Henry Lambright for this term, which he employed during a commentary on two papers—one by me on the Space Telescope and the other by Howard McCurdy on the space station—at a NASA/National Air and Space Museum symposium in 1987.

13 On subgovernments, see, for example, Ripley and Franklin, *Congress, the Bureaucracy and Public Policy.*

14 The founding of CERN too was very "messy" in a political sense. Of course the Space Telescope and CERN are set in two very different political contexts, but perhaps the *ad hoc* nature of both approval processes was due in part to the policy-making having been taken out of routine political channels. Policy-making on the Space Telescope was not contained within a subgovernment, and for CERN, the policy was made before there was any sort of overall European bureaucracy within which it could be contained. On the early history of CERN, see Hermann et al., *History of CERN,* and Pestre and Krige, Chapter 3, this volume.

whether or not to approve the Space Telescope was in this *ad hoc* process of policy-making constantly being reframed as the issues bearing on the decision were themselves continually reshuffled and repackaged. To take one example: for about a decade the telescope was termed the "Large Space Telescope," but in 1975 NASA changed it to the "Space Telescope." (It became the Hubble Space Telescope in 1983.) As the Agency's deputy administrator told an astronomer, "in these days of stringent funding, we should not use titles such as 'large' or 'very large,' which suggest an opulence which neither NASA, science, nor astronomy is enjoying these days and which tend to invite reductions in budgets."[15] Nor were design choices and decisions about scientific objectives outside of the wider political process of winning approval. Rather, they were an integral element in the process of repackaging and reshuffling, in considerable part because of the necessities of coalition building, as well as the need to adjust the program to what the "market"—in the form of the White House and Congress—would bear. Hence issues of, say, congressional politics, which one perhaps might not expect to have any significant effect in shaping the telescope's design and its associated program, proved to be crucial. The Space Telescope should thus be viewed in many ways as the concrete realization of the interests supporting the program, and in particular of the coalition building that its advocates engaged in to win approval for the program. So in some degree it reflects the power relationships between the various institutions, groups, and individuals engaged in policy-making.[16]

15 G. Low to E. M. Burbidge, Jan. 28, 1976, Aucremanne Papers (File LST 1975 [sic]), NASA headquarters. On the importance of image in the launching of a program, see Lambright, *Governing Science and Technology*, chapter 2.

16 The notion of coalition building, it seems to me, is quite compatible with the general approach of some of the recent work in the social studies of science and the social construction of technology. Certainly the coalition that was constructed did much to shape the actual telescope, as I argue later in the paper, and the course of the telescope's design and construction is in agreement with some of the central tenets of this position: technology is not fixed by nature alone, technology does not stand in an invariant relation with science, and, in the words of John Law, "technological stabilization can be understood only if the artifact in question is seen as being interrelated with a wide range of nontechnological and specifically social factors" (see Law, "Technology and Heterogeneous Engineering," p. 112). Some students have also developed the systems metaphor to describe the development of technological systems. The leading exponent of this approach is Thomas Hughes. For him, the building of a technological system means that many factors must be knitted together. In so doing, those who build artifacts must consider not only the artifacts but their relationships to many other factors: social, political, scientific, and economic. Hughes sees these factors as interwoven with one another, and so each component in the system must be fashioned to interact harmoniously with the characteristics of the others. See, for example, Hughes, *Networks of Power*. The coalition building that I describe was therefore, in these terms, as much a part of the invention of the Space Telescope as the work done by industrial contractors designing pointing and control systems, precisely figured mirrors, and so on for the spacecraft. However, my use of coalition building in this analysis of the Space Telescope and big science derives largely from political science, a discipline that has attracted relatively little interest from historians or sociologists of modern science.

With this overall picture of the policy-making process for the Space Telescope in mind, I shall illustrate the process in more detail, first by examining the 1974 campaign to persuade Congress that astronomers regarded the Space Telescope as their number-one priority for space astronomy.

Astronomers, Priorities, and Coalition Building

By the mid-1960's, a large optical telescope in space for astronomy had begun to look to many people to be a serious technical possibility.[17] The chief scientific attraction for its proponents was that the image detail a space-based telescope could resolve would be fixed by the laws of optics and the quality of the telescope's optical and pointing systems, not by the vagaries of the earth's atmosphere. As a 1966 report on the capabilities of a large telescope in space contended, "Every one of the outstanding astronomical problems of current interest requires high resolution for further understanding." The 3-meter telescope—that is, a telescope with a primary mirror 3 meters in diameter—then under discussion was intended by its advocates to provide an improvement in angular resolution over ground-based telescopes of better than an order of magnitude.[18] The scientific potential of such an instrument was thus easily conceded by astronomers. After all, it was (and is) an article of faith for many astronomers that the history of much of their discipline has been driven by ever more powerful instruments. Galileo's use of the newly invented telescope was often invoked by the Space Telescope's advocates to "demonstrate" that an order-of-magnitude improvement in resolving power promises exciting and unexpected results. However, it was also obvious to those proposing such a large optical telescope in space—among astronomers, NASA, and industry—that the scale of the enterprise would require a major commitment from many astronomers.[19]

In NASA's early years, the pursuit of space astronomy was very much the province of a small number of principal investigators and their associated teams based in a university or one laboratory. This relatively small scale prevailed both for building the scientific instruments—usually with the aid of industrial contractors—and for securing and analyzing the data. However, by the mid-1960's, some astronomers and NASA managers were promoting the concept of what would later be called "guest observers," that is, observers who could propose astronomical observations to be made from a spacecraft even if they had not participated in its building. Given the critical attitude of many ground-based astronomers to optical astronomy from space, restricting the Space Telescope's observations to those selected by only a very limited group

17 R. W. Smith, *The Space Telescope*, chapter 1.

18 Munch, "Detectors for Diffraction-Limited Imaging," p. 16.

19 See, for example, the comments of the head of NASA's space science office to the American Astronomical Society in 1966: Newell, "Space Astronomy," p. 7.

(the principal investigators and their teams) would be no way to win friends
for the telescope. Certainly the telescope's price would mean that it would be
difficult to justify if it were for the benefit of a relatively small number of
astronomers. The volume of data that telescope would return in its planned
ten-year-plus life (much longer than was then typical for scientific satellites)
would be so vast that it would likely overwhelm a handful of principal-
investigator teams, and much of the data would perhaps never be examined. In
consequence, NASA early decided that for a mix of political and scientific
reasons the telescope would be a "national facility," to be launched into space
for the use of all astronomers: securing more potential users would win wider
support for optical space astronomy as well as ensure the participation in the
final program of many qualified scientists. Such a national facility, NASA also
stressed, would require a national effort, not one that was the responsibility of
one or perhaps a few university departments alone. NASA administrator
James Webb also judged that a project of the scale of the building and
operating of a Space Telescope might also require the agency to adopt new
institutional forms, and in 1966 he appointed an advisory group to consider
what kinds of institutions might be appropriate for projects of this scale.[20]

But in the mid-1960's such questions were largely moot. There was not
much support among astronomers for pressing ahead and building a large
telescope in space. Unlike, say, X-ray astronomers, who *had* to send experiments into space if they were to pursue their discipline because of the atmospheric absorption of X rays, optical astronomers could choose: astronomy from the ground or from space. The choice therefore involved very
different ways and styles of working. Put simply, for ground-based astronomers it meant little science, for those who wanted to pursue space astronomy,
most particularly astronomy from satellites, it meant big science and the need
to work on teams of scientists and with associated armies of engineers and
technicians. But it was big science of a particular kind. Physical scientists have
been used to taking charge of their own projects, but NASA's methods for
satellite astronomy emphasized, and were structured to ensure, control by the
agency, with the final authority for decision making resting firmly in the hands
of NASA managers. As David Hounshell points out in Chapter 9, for the

20 See James E. Webb to Norman F. Ramsey, Jan. 14, 1966, in Appendix A(1) of
"NASA Ad Hoc Science Advisory Committee Report to the Administrator 15 August 1966,"
and the report—it came to be known as the Ramsey Report—itself (copies in Space
Telescope History Project Files). The report advocated for the building and operation of the
telescope that NASA establish a consortium of universities. This would be a new kind of
institution for the agency, but from already existing institutions, such as the Brookhaven
National Laboratory and the Kitt Peak National Observatory, was very well known to high-
energy physicists and ground-based astronomers as the usual means of transforming the
concept of a "national" laboratory or observatory into concrete form. On NASA's frigid
response and the subsequent debate on the appropriate institutional means to manage the
scientific operations of the telescope, see R. W. Smith, *The Space Telescope*, chapter 6.

Chicago physicists working on the development of the atomic bomb, the shift to a big technology meant a loss of control to Du Pont, so here, with the pursuit of astronomy from satellites, optical astronomers were in many respects to lose control of their activities to NASA and the agency's industrial contractors. Space astronomy, then, placed new demands on astronomers, not only in terms of the reliability of their instruments and their methods of work, but also in how that work was to be directed and controlled. Thus it changed what it means to be an astronomer.

The choice between ground-based and space astronomy led to a divide. There were those who wanted to put optical astronomy into space, and there were those who remained convinced of the priority of ground-based astronomy, who were familiar with its techniques, and who were not inclined to enter new territory. Nor was this latter attitude due just to conservatism or unease with big science. What astronomers regarded as great scientific strides were taken with a variety of powerful ground-based telescopes throughout the 1960's. These included, for example, the exciting discovery of highly energetic quasars, objects that seemed to be much smaller than the known galaxies but were emitting vastly more energy.

In the United States, the divide between space astronomers and ground-based astronomers was also to a considerable degree the product of, and reinforced by, history and geography. To simplify somewhat, for west-coast astronomers with ready access to large telescopes at good sites, optical space astronomy was not nearly as appealing as for east-coast or midwestern astronomers, who generally had to contend with much poorer observing conditions and use less powerful optical telescopes than their colleagues in the West.

Some ground-based astronomers disliked space astronomy because of its links to the enormous, and to them largely wasted, expense of the U.S. space program. As one astronomer critic put it in 1966, "The cart has been put before the horse. Instead of presenting the orbiting observatory as an ancillary to the space program, the orbiting observatory has been offered as one of the important reasons for implementing the space program. As part of the campaign for selling the space program, the advantages of observation from space have been promulgated almost with Madison Avenue techniques. The key points in the logic of this sales technique run like this: You all know the wonderful discoveries that have been made with big telescopes, like those at Mt. Wilson and Palomar. O.K.? Now we have something that will make those big telescopes seem like a kid's spy glass. So although it's going to cost plenty, it'll be worth it."[21]

Other ground-based astronomers were critical—sometimes extremely critical—of space astronomy but nevertheless hoped to fashion what they judged to be scientifically worthwhile projects. The distinguished Caltech astronomer

21 Hoyle, *Man in the Universe*, p. 7.

Jesse Greenstein was one such, and he recalls that by about 1964 he had seen the writing on the wall: "You had to accept that if there was going to be space science, and if it was going to be supported no matter what you did, then you had to ride that wild horse, instead of letting people with only half-baked ideas claim the leadership."[22]

The issues surrounding the space astronomy to be done with the Space Telescope were not so much the possible scientific results to be achieved—if the telescope worked as planned astronomers agreed the data it would produce would be extremely exciting—as one of timing and priorities; when and how much money and effort should be expended on such an instrument? The space age was only a few years old, and launch-vehicle failures were common; compared to activities on the ground, optical space astronomy was a risky business. So, many influential astronomers suggested, why not take one's chances with cloudy weather, continue to do ground-based astronomy, and produce good science rather than chase the chimera of a large telescope in space? Optical space astronomy, by the standards of ground-based astronomy, was also extremely expensive, and so some astronomers contended the money would be far better spent on ground-based telescopes. Many large ground-based telescopes, one argument ran, could be purchased for the over $200,000,000 that NASA was providing in the 1960's for the construction of *three* orbiting astronomical observatories, all much smaller, less complex, and less expensive than the Space Telescope itself promised to be. Some ground-based astronomers also harbored fears that in its voracious appetite for money, space astronomy would eventually gobble up the funds currently available for ground-based activities.[23]

The small number of advocates of what in the late 1960's was termed the "Large Space Telescope" therefore faced an uphill battle to win support from their astronomer colleagues. Coalition building was thus very much the goal of the committee of astronomers assembled in the late 1960's to report for the National Academy of Sciences on the scientific uses of the Large Space Telescope.[24] The chairman of the group was Lyman Spitzer, Jr., a long-time enthusiast for and public champion of the idea of a large orbiting optical telescope.

Spitzer was one of the country's leading scientists. He had received his Ph.D. in astrophysics from Princeton in 1938, and after ending World War II as director of the Sonar Analysis Group, he went to Yale for a brief period before returning to Princeton in 1947 as chairman of the astronomy department and director of the University Observatory, positions he was to hold until 1979. He was also to be very closely involved with the U.S. fusion program.

22 J. Greenstein, interviewed by S. Weart, May 19, 1978, p. 209, American Institute of Physics Collection.

23 R. W. Smith, *The Space Telescope*, chapter 1.

24 National Academy of Sciences, *Scientific Uses of the Large Space Telescope*.

He was from 1953 to 1961 director of Project Matterhorn and from 1961 to 1967 chairman of the executive committee of Princeton's Plasma Physics Laboratory.

In 1946, he had written a report for the Rand Corporation entitled "Astronomical Advantages of an Extra-Terrestrial Observatory." Here Spitzer laid out in detail for the first time the kinds of astronomical observations of which a telescope above the atmosphere would be capable.[25] But Spitzer's report was classified. It took years to emerge into public sight and thus had no direct impact on the thinking of astronomers. Even his public efforts to enthuse his colleagues had met with little success. For a long time, they "were all quite startled to have a serious astronomer talking about what one could do" with large telescopes in space.[26] In 1953, for instance, the prominent astronomer Gerard Kuiper told a colleague, "I had not heard of the Spitzer satellite proposal. . . . Unless there should be some advantage in getting government services used to the notion that astronomers are capable of asking for a lot of money, I would regard the inclusion of this project hazardous and probably undesirable."[27]

But by the mid-1960's, following the opening of the Cold War in space and the provision of previously undreamt of sums for space astronomy, Spitzer was making more headway. Nearly all the other members of Spitzer's National Academy of Sciences committee were already strong advocates of the Space Telescope too, and so the point of its report was a foregone conclusion. The telescope's advocates argued that its major scientific justification was provided by cosmology. Nevertheless, the committee's members chose not to examine in any great detail what scientific questions the telescope would be able to address. Such specificity, when they knew the telescope was many years from construction, was not regarded as worthwhile. At this stage, the Space Telescope was essentially "all things to all people" as its advocates sought to bundle as many interests as possible into the proposed instrument. The committee's members therefore saw their role in a missionary light, to go out among the wider community of astronomers and expound on the scientific potential of such an extremely powerful new instrument. Their first meeting was therefore held at a bastion of ground-based astronomy with big telescopes, Caltech. In acting in this fashion, the committee members sought help to defuse the criticisms of opponents, enlist allies, secure the backing of the prestigious National Academy of Sciences, and so strengthen the Space Telescope's flimsy base of support (see Fig. 7.3).

The role of the various groups of astronomers assembled by NASA in the

25 Spitzer, "Astronomical Advantages."
26 Lyman Spitzer, Jr., interviewed by Paul Hanle, Oct. 27, 1983, p. 3, National Air and Space Museum Collection.
27 G. Kuiper to O. Struve, May 29, 1953, copy in F. K. Edmondson's files. I am most grateful to Professor Edmondson for providing a copy of this letter.

Fig. 7.3. An early Martin-Marietta conception, ca. 1970, of what was termed a Stellar Astronomy Module, in effect a version of the planned Large Space Telescope. The structure at top left is a space station; the use of the term "module" was intended to indicate that the telescope could be docked to the space station. Photo courtesy NASA.

1970's to plan the Space Telescope in detail was similar in part to that played by the National Academy of Sciences committee. By 1973 over 50 astronomers were active as members of several working groups pursuing studies related to the telescope. Their discussions and debates too ranged far beyond purely technical and scientific issues. Indeed, one of the reasons that NASA brought these groups into existence was to secure a sizable number of supporters for the telescope. After all, if the people who were planning the telescope and fully understood its objectives were not prepared to defend it if it ran into trouble, who would?

For three years in the mid-1970's, the Space Telescope did indeed encounter major opposition within Congress. The first shot in this lengthy battle was fired in June 1974 when the House of Representatives appropriations subcommittee dealing with NASA deleted all planning funds for the telescope from the agency's budget for fiscal 1975. The subcommittee's stated reason for rejecting the telescope was that it was not "among the top four priority projects selected

by the National Academy of Sciences." The subcommittee took as its justification *Astronomy and Astrophysics for the 1970s*, the 1972 report of the
Astronomy Survey Committee of the National Academy of Sciences. In part an
attempt by the National Academy of Sciences to help negotiate the claims of
astronomers for increasing funds for research, this report was also the committee's response to strong political pressures to set priorities rather than to
simply lay out a "shopping list" of desirable projects.[28] Chaired by Jesse
Greenstein, the Astronomy Survey Committee had in fact recommended four
first-priority projects for the coming decade. The Space Telescope was not
among them. Although the committee noted that the telescope "has extraordinary potential for a wide variety of astronomical uses,"[29] it had just squeaked
into the report as a second-priority project slated for the 1980's. In fact,
the Bureau of the Budget (later renamed the Office of Management and
Budget) had recommended to Greenstein that his committee not consider the
Space Telescope for the 1970's because of its cost.[30] Nor did NASA press
the telescope before the Astronomy Survey Committee, a decision perhaps
prompted by Greenstein's earlier criticisms of optical space astronomy and
known uneasiness about the cost of the telescope.[31] By early 1974, however,
the National Academy of Sciences' Space Science Board had concluded that
the impetus of the Greenstein study had been spent. This board judged that
some of the findings were obsolete because of new scientific discoveries.
President Nixon's decision of 1972 that NASA should build the space shuttle
had also radically altered the ground rules of space astronomy because the
shuttle was intended to allow astronauts to maintain and service spacecraft in
orbit regularly and allow them to be returned to earth if necessary. Hence, in
February 1974, the Space Science Board decided to embark upon a new review
of priorities for space science. This study was to elevate the Space Telescope to
the highest priority but was still some time from completion when the House
subcommittee deleted the telescope's planning funds (see Fig. 7.4).

What, then, could the Space Telescope's supporters do to restore the
telescope to the budget?[32] Although the project was in deep trouble, it was still
conceivable to the project's supporters in NASA and among the astronomers
and contractors that if senators and representatives could be persuaded in a
very short time that the telescope was a worthwhile enterprise, the Senate

28 James L. McCartney, "Negotiating Priorities for Research in Astronomy and Astrophysics in the 1970's: An Innovation in Science Policy," paper presented at George Sarton
Centennial, University of Ghent, 1984.
29 National Academy of Sciences, *Astronomy and Astrophysics*, p. 105.
30 Personal communication, J. Greenstein to P. Hanle, Oct. 23, 1984.
31 See also C. R. O'Dell to "Dear Colleague," June 26, 1974, Space Telescope Project
Scientist's Papers (Reading File 1974), Marshall Space Flight Center.
32 A number of aspects of the 1974 campaign have been examined by Paul Hanle, and I
shall in part be following his account, "Astronomers, Congress, and the Large Space
Telescope."

Fig. 7.4. Grumman's 1970 conception of what eventually became the Space Shuttle and what was then termed the Large Space Telescope. Photo courtesy NASA.

might pass a bill to fund planning studies. The disagreement in the House and Senate appropriations bills would then have to be resolved through contacts between the two bodies, probably a formal House-Senate conference. If the Senate view prevailed, the telescope would be restored to the budget. The telescope might be down, but because the entire legislative process must be gone through twice, it was not out.[33]

Everyone had accepted that the great bulk of the design and construction work for the Space Telescope would be the task of industrial contractors. Industrial contractors had thus been at work for some years defining the telescope and its subsystems, in part with the support of NASA contracts. These contractors, which included five major aerospace companies and two optical houses, had a strong economic interest in ensuring the telescope's survival, and they had already launched vigorous lobbying campaigns to get the planning funds reinstated. In later years there would be strong ties between

33 I consider the redesign of the telescope at length in *The Space Telescope*, chapters 4 and 5.

the contractors and the astronomer–lobbyists, but in 1974 these links had only just begun to be forged. The industrial contractors and astronomer–lobbyists might have the same short term aim—the reinstatement of the telescope in the budget—but the two groups were addressing rather different questions. For the astronomers the first order of business was to dispose of the question of the telescope's priority, the ostensible reason it had been removed from the budget. Following a suggestion from Congressman Burt Talcott, the ranking minority member on the House subcommittee, some astronomers decided that one way to do so was to enroll the members of the Greenstein committee in the telescope's cause.

NASA and the astronomers had been caught off guard by the House subcommittee's cutting of the telescope's funds. There was then no lobbying role for the professional society of astronomers, the American Astronomical Society. Although members of the society's executive council could speak out as individuals, the society itself was unable to champion the telescope lest this threaten its tax-exempt status. Nor was it clear, given the feelings of many astronomers toward space astronomy, that all the members of the executive board wanted to back the telescope. Even among those in the society who were enthusiastic about space astronomy there were some who favored other projects over the Space Telescope. Thus the American Astronomical Society could not act as an interest group; instead, it would be up to individual astronomers to go out and lobby. Also, some astronomers shunned political activities as base and beneath science, but two leading Princeton astronomers—John Bahcall and Lyman Spitzer—thought otherwise. They fully accepted that you cannot win at politics without playing. And for the supporters of the telescope this entailed negotiations, bargaining, compromise, coalition building, and, to some extent, the compromise of their original plans.

Spitzer had experience of lobbying Congress through his involvement in the fusion program as well as the Orbiting Astronomical Observatories. Indeed, it was after conversations between Bahcall, Spitzer, and Martin Schwarzschild (another Princeton astronomy professor) that it occurred to Bahcall and Spitzer that "we were the logical people" to lobby for the telescope.[34] Not only was the Large Space Telescope widely seen as the *Lyman Spitzer Telescope*, but Spitzer was also familiar with the workings of Capitol Hill and aware of the techniques and strategies needed to convince Congress to fund space astronomy. Beyond this, he enjoyed an extremely high standing among astronomers, both ground-based and space astronomers. Bahcall, the younger partner and himself a major astronomer at the Institute for Advanced Study, possessed great physical energy, political acumen (it was to turn out), and a relish for the fight. Both were members of the main group of astronomers planning for the telescope and so were fully aware of its scientific

34 John Bahcall, interviewed by Paul Hanle, Nov. 3, 1983, p. 3, National Air and Space Museum Collection.

potential and the latest thinking on design options. They also complemented each other excellently. Spitzer was every inch a distinguished Princeton professor, Bahcall his charming but sometimes brash and feisty foil.

Although Bahcall and Spitzer were not the only astronomers actively involved in the hastily devised lobbying campaign, they were, through their excellent contacts in NASA and among the astronomers, probably the most influential in drumming up support for the Space Telescope. Both, for example, were in close touch with the telescope's project scientist in NASA, C. R. O'Dell. At first O'Dell—who had joined NASA in 1972 from the directorship of Yerkes Observatory and had excellent contracts with astronomers outside the agency—had little idea of the workings of Congress, but he soon was given a crash course in the ways and functions of Capitol Hill through conversations with representatives of industrial contractors. O'Dell therefore acted as a conduit of information between the astronomers and NASA. As he watched the proceedings from the sidelines, he offered coaching to Bahcall and Spitzer on whom to contact.

As he sought to rally support for the telescope from the members of the Greenstein committee, Bahcall had found that "everybody was concerned that we not cut other projects out while we advocated Space Telescope. That was a really tough thing."[35] There was still opposition to the telescope from some astronomers and space scientists who preferred other projects to the telescope, but, as Bahcall pointed out, the opponents "were not organized. The critics also expressed arguments such as: There's a finite amount of money in Washington to support astronomy. If they dump so much into Space Telescope, there won't be enough to support ground-based astronomy. Or another sentiment that was often implicit was 'Space Telescope or space astronomy is East Coast astronomy. West Coast astronomy, i.e. ground based astronomy, will suffer if space astronomy is promoted at its expense.' There was also a real sentiment for not getting involved in politics. That is, astronomers and scientists worked in their laboratories, and they didn't confuse politics with science."[36] Despite such objections and whatever private concerns they might have had, all 23 members of the Greenstein committee were solicited and agreed to Bahcall's draft statement justifying the precedence of the Space Telescope over other future space astronomy projects.

With the updated report of the National Academy's Space Science Board also throwing its weight behind the Space Telescope as the number one priority for space astronomy, the issue of how highly astronomers rated the telescope disappeared, strengthening the hand of the telescope's advocates in the nego-

35 J. Bahcall, interviewed by P. Hanle, Nov. 3, 1983, p. 43, National Air and Space Museum Collection. Of course, it is by no means unusual for scientists to lobby Congress. See, for example, A. K. Smith, *A Peril and a Hope.*

36 J. Bahcall, interviewed by P. Hanle, Dec. 20, 1983, p. 52, National Air and Space Museum Collection.

tiations about reinstating the telescope to the budget. In fact, the telescope *was* returned to the budget, but with the planning funds cut in half. There were even more important changes: Congress granted approval only on the under- standing that NASA consider "substantial participation of other nations in a less expensive project to be launched at a later date."[37] In other words, NASA, the astronomers, and the industrial contractors would have to do a very substantial amount of revising and repackaging of the telescope and the planned program to build it, a repackaging that led, for example, to the name change to "Space Telescope" referred to earlier, together with more substantial changes, such as a reduction in the planned size of the telescope's primary mirror from 3 meters to 2.4 meters.

The congressional criticisms had nevertheless strengthened the coalition favoring the Space Telescope. First, the scientists now presented a solid front, in public at least. As Paul Hanle has pointed out, the congressional attack on the telescope helped to bring the remaining dissenting astronomers into line.[38] Second, links between the contractors and the astronomers, links that would prove crucial in lobbying campaigns in later years, were forged. Third, more astronomers now grasped clearly what sorts of political actions would be required to bring the telescope into being. John Heilbron and Daniel Kevles have argued that the "social consequences of big science are known: coopera- tion, interdependence, homogeneity among the lower echelons, entrepreneur- ism and dirigisme among the principal investigators."[39] But without such entrepreneurism, the telescope could not have been made salable; moreover, for the kind of costly big science that the telescope represented, its advocates came to accept that the mobilization of an entire scientific community was necessary to make it politically feasible.[40]

The Space Telescope and Planetary Science

The Jupiter Orbiter Probe (later redefined and renamed Galileo) was one space project that many preferred over the Space Telescope. Although not expected to be as expensive as the telescope, the Jupiter probe was estimated to cost several hundred million dollars and so raised many of the same sorts of questions as did the telescope. As it entailed a mission to Jupiter to probe the planet's atmosphere, it was also the favored project of planetary scientists.

37 U.S. Congress, *Congressional Record*, 93rd Congress, 2nd session, Aug. 21, 1974, H 29693.

38 Hanle, "Astronomers, Congress, and the Large Space Telescope." Hanle also dis- cussed the dismay of Jesse Greenstein over some of the aggressive campaigning to sell the telescope, campaigning that at times he thought potentially harmful to the interests of ground-based astronomy.

39 Heilbron and Kevles, "Mapping and Sequencing the Human Genome," p. 13.

40 R. W. Smith, *The Space Telescope,* chapter 5.

Deep-space astronomers and planetary scientists often tend to regard themselves as members of separate communities, each with its own set of goals, techniques, and programs. Hence it was not a given that supporters of the Jupiter Orbiter Probe would also support the Space Telescope. Moreover, during 1976 NASA was completing its plans prior to the expected incorporation of both projects in the agency's part of the fiscal 1978 budget (due to reach Capitol Hill in January 1977). A central question for NASA managers, then, was how to finesse the passage to approval of both projects without the two groups of supporters spoiling each other's chances of success.

The Jupiter Orbiter Probe was to be managed by the Jet Propulsion Laboratory (JPL), the leading institution in the United States for planetary science. The Jet Propulsion Laboratory is a NASA center, but unlike the other centers it is not a civil-service establishment. The facilities are government-owned, but the staff are all employees of the California Institute of Technology. Whereas directors of other NASA centers felt, and feel, themselves unable to walk into the Office of Management and Budget or onto Capitol Hill and lobby directly and openly for their programs, the director and staff of JPL have much more room to maneuver. As the Jupiter Orbiter Probe was a JPL project, there was decided unease at NASA headquarters that JPL and the planetary scientists might fight so hard for the Jupiter Orbiter Probe that they would knock out the Space Telescope in the process, or that the telescope's advocates might wreck the chances of the Jupiter Orbiter Probe.

An example of the kind of damage that could be done if one group started promoting its own project at the expense of another's had occurred in 1975. Then some Space Telescope advocates had criticized the NASA space science budget as "unbalanced." They protested privately to NASA and congressional staffers that a disproportionate number of NASA dollars had been spent on planetary science missions, while relatively little had been allocated to stellar and galactic astronomy, the principal charge of the Space Telescope as it was then defined. These claims had been fastened upon by the House subcommittee on appropriations dealing with NASA, the same subcommittee that had deleted all planning funds for the telescope the year earlier. The subcommittee exploited them to justify cutting $48,000,000 from a planetary mission, Pioneer Venus, pending a trade-off of the Space Telescope and Pioneer Venus the following year. As a report in *Science* put it, "Public internecine warfare over budgets among scientists of different disciplines is not unheard of, but it has been relatively rare in recent years, especially among basic researchers."[41]

41 Hammond, "Pioneer Venus," p. 270. See also U.S. Congress, *Congressional Record*, 94th Congress, 1st session, June 24, 1975, H 6010, comments by Mr. Boland, and anonymous, "House Committee," p. 282. When a senior group of scientists who acted as advisors to NASA asked the agency's deputy administrator in 1973 what they could do to help NASA's programs, his reply was to "help stop the fighting among the scientists and to get a

204 ROBERT W. SMITH

Another such outbreak might kill either the Space Telescope or the Jupiter Orbiter Probe, perhaps even both.

A 1975 NASA report pointed out that the Space Telescope could perform planetary science from its position in earth orbit but was "in no way" a substitute for a program of planetary flybys, the method planetary scientists much preferred for pursuing their research.[42] NASA headquarters neverthe-less pressed for the telescope's planned scientific instruments to be capable of performing high-quality planetary astronomy, often in the face of the diffi-dence of, and sometimes hostility from, those astronomers intimately involved in planning for the telescope and whose chief interests were stellar and galactic astronomy. As the then head of NASA's Office of Space Science has remem-bered, "There was a good indication that the astronomy community didn't give a damn about planetary observations. And a number of us thought that getting the planetary capability into the Space Telescope was desirable from two points of view—one, that you could do some damn good planetary science with it, and two, that politically it would help bridge the gap between the planetary and astronomical community. That might be one of the selling points."[43]

This issue was especially charged because funds for the Space Telescope and the Jupiter Orbiter Probe both required approval by Congress in fiscal 1978, that is, were presented in the president's budget in January 1977. In 1976 there was, in the understated words of the chairman of the Ameri-can Astronomical Society's Division of Planetary Sciences, "agitation" over NASA's reduction of funds for planetary science.[44] In April, for example, planetary scientist Clark Chapman had written to NASA administrator James Fletcher with a petition from another 117 of his colleagues. The petition urged NASA "to take appropriate steps to insure a stable, long-term, continuing program of planetary exploration. We are very concerned that if present management and fiscal trends continue, this vital scientific effort that has proved so rewarding during the past decade may disintegrate."[45]

As one well-informed public report put it in August 1976, the inability of "NASA to secure more than one new planetary start in the last four fiscal years has increased the importance of the space telescope in terms of planetary

base of support for space science [that] is nondivisive": memorandum, G. Low to J. Fletcher, Apr. 17, 1973, on "Activities During Week of April 8–14, 1973," Box 35, Folder 2, George M. Low Papers, Rensselaer Polytechnic Institute Archives, Troy, New York.

42 NASA, "Strategy for Outer Planets Exploration," p. E6.

43 Oral History Interview, N. Hinners with R. W. Smith and J. N. Tatarewicz, Nov. 16, 1984, p. 39, National Air and Space Museum Collection.

44 W. Baum to N. Roman, June 8, 1976, Space Telescope Program Scientist's Papers, NASA headquarters (ST–Faint Object Camera Files).

45 Clark Chapman to Fletcher, Apr. 7, 1976, copy in George M. Low Papers, Box 34, Folder 1, Rensselaer Polytechnic Institute Archives.

observations." The same report noted that the National Academy of Sciences Committee on Planetary and Lunar Exploration has recently "stressed that adequate instrumentation should be designed to enhance the [Space Telescope's] usefulness in observing planets." The article continued, "Some planetary researchers are concerned . . . that the heavy involvement in the space telescope program of scientists interested in observations outside the solar system may prevent adequate planning for effective use of the instrument inside the solar system."[46] While planetary scientists had on the whole been somewhat indifferent toward the Space Telescope in earlier years, their difficulties in promoting their own more favored projects meant that they were now eager to secure a "piece of the action" in the telescope.

One result was that Nancy Roman, NASA's Space Telescope Program Scientist, who had long considered it important to make the telescope useful to planetary scientists, established a small group to examine how appropriate the telescope's proposed scientific instruments were for planetary science.[47] Roman's aims were to reassure planetary scientists that their voice was being heard and to underscore that the telescope would indeed be useful for planetary research.

Nor were these activities designed simply to revise the rhetoric about the Space Telescope's scientific potential. The extension was exhibited by choices of hardware, too. For some years the project's participants had planned that the detector for the main camera aboard the telescope would be a Secondary Electron Conduction Vidicon, or SEC Vidicon for short. The SEC Vidicon had been under development at Princeton since 1964 through a series of grants and contracts from NASA. As is often the case with astronomical detectors, a mature "off-the-shelf" product—in this case a Westinghouse television-type tube—was being adapted to astronomical ends. The chief advantages for astronomers of the SEC Vidicon were that it covered relatively large areas of the sky and worked well in the ultraviolet region of the spectrum. However, the SEC Vidicon performed poorly in the red, a region of particular interest to planetary scientists. Planetary scientists argued, for example, that the Space Telescope would be extremely useful to them for long-term studies of the atmospheres of the planets. Unlike planetary flybys, which take a spacecraft to a planet for only a short period, the telescope would make possible studies over several years. For such investigations, examination of the absorption bands of methane, for example, planetary scientists stressed the need for a detector with good response in the red.[48] The planetary scientists therefore

46 See Covault, "Longer-Range Planetary Plans Sought," pp. 40–41.
47 R. W. Smith, *The Space Telescope*, chapter 7.
48 See, for example, the comments of Bradford A. Smith, in the minutes of the Space Telescope Operations and Management Working Group meeting, Oct. 18–19, 1976, copy in the Space Telescope Project Scientist's Papers, Marshall Space Flight Center.

pushed hard for the red-sensitive Charge Couple Devices (CCDs) to be considered as an alternative to the SEC Vidicon, despite the facts that CCDs had
barely entered astronomical service and still faced an imposing array of developmental problems. When this pressure was added to an unease among
some NASA staffers about the SEC Vidicon's overall performance, the NASA
managers in charge of the Space Telescope program chose to open a competition for the detector.[49]

NASA headquarters also worked directly with the supporters of the Space
Telescope and the supporters of the Jupiter Orbiter Probe to prevent an
outbreak of verbal fisticuffs. The then head of NASA's Office of Space Science
has recalled that he told the Jet Propulsion Laboratory "not to get any activity
going anywhere that was aimed at shooting down the Space Telescope, and
then working with the planetary scientists themselves, the leaders, the lobbyists, to really get them to support actively their program, but don't attack the
other one, or you'll start fratricide. And on the other side, working with the
[astronomers] . . . and the industry, telling them the same thing, to not take aim
at the planetary program."[50]

As one of the leaders of the lobbying effort for the Jupiter Orbiter Probe
has remembered, "There was an awareness all along in this effort that one
should be very careful about questions which certainly did materialize from
the press and from representatives of Congress, about trying to prioritize. You
know, do you want Space Telescope or Galileo? That was the danger that we
faced, and questions that seemed to raise that spectre would occasionally come
down, and so it was a very clear point that in no way was that to be regarded as
a legitimate question. We needed both of them. They addressed different
questions and were different kinds of instruments. . . . We were fully cognizant
of the ongoing [Space Telescope] effort, not merely neutral, but supportive.
This is a project that's going to be useful to [planetary] science as well, but it's
addressing astrophysical questions that are very important."[51]

In fact, during the budget hearing in Congress, the Space Telescope was
funded but Galileo was deleted by the House appropriations subcommittee dealing with NASA. The leading Space Telescope advocates now rallied
around the Galileo mission. A lobbying campaign was mounted to save
Galileo, and after a hard floor fight in the House of Representatives in which
the House subcommittee's recommendations on Galileo were decisively and

49 Smith and Tatarewicz, "Replacing a Technology," pp. 1226–33.
50 Oral History Interview, N. Hinners with R. W. Smith and J. N. Tatarewicz, Oct. 17,
1984, p. 29, National Air and Space Museum Collection. See also Oral History Interview,
C. Chapman with J. N. Tatarewicz, Oct. 10, 1984, pp. 27–28, National Air and Space
Museum Collection.
51 Oral History Interview, C. Chapman with J. N. Tatarewicz, Oct. 10, 1984, p. 27,
National Air and Space Museum Collection.

Fig. 7.5. The almost completed Space Telescope in the clean room of the Lockheed Missile and Space Company in 1988. Photo courtesy NASA.

208 ROBERT W. SMITH

dramatically rejected, the Galileo mission was reinstated in the NASA budget.[52]

The hastily assembled and somewhat uneasy alliance of the astronomers and planetary scientists had held, and both Galileo and the Space Telescope had been approved. But for the stellar and galactic astronomers who represented the great majority of those planning the telescope, there had nevertheless been a price to be paid for the support of the planetary scientists. This had come in the form of increased accommodation of their interests in the telescope's design and planned use, a price that NASA managers had deemed worthwhile and even necessary for coalition building. With the coalition assembled, it was still over a decade before the final touches were put on the telescope, and it was readied for launch (see Fig. 7.5).

Conclusions

As Daniel Kevles has noted, the sheer bigness of big science is enough to arouse questions,[53] and in the case of the very big science represented by the Space Telescope, the key question was whether or not to approve its construction. In order to win such approval for the telescope, a scientific community had to be mobilized and allies had to be secured. The telescope's advocates were therefore compelled to devote much effort to making the telescope not just technically feasible but also politically feasible. In this chapter I have examined two aspects of this process: securing a working consensus among ground-based and space astronomers in favor of the telescope, and securing the support of planetary scientists. In both cases, the key element of my analysis has been the coalition favoring the telescope and the ways members of the coalition sought means by which it could be strengthened. Nor, as I have argued, were these activities only political, involving negotiations and compromises among different groups; instead, they also involved the hardware and design of the telescope as well as its planned scientific objectives. The process of winning approval for the telescope included negotiation of the question of what the telescope itself would be. Although in this chapter I have devoted most attention to the astronomer members of the coalition, for a fully rounded account one needs to consider all the other members of the coalition—NASA officials, various members of the executive branch of government, congressmen and congressional staffers, other interested scientists, sympathetic journalists, and so on—and the various links between them. Even this limited study reveals that for the investigation of the kind of very big science that the telescope represents, the university, laboratory, or single scientific community are in themselves alone inappropriate units of analysis; rather, the

52 U.S. Congress, *Congressional Record*, 95th Congress, 1st session, July 19, 1977, H 23668–78.

53 Kevles, *The Physicists*, p. 395.

historian must study the *assemblage* of these institutions, groups, and individuals and how they in turn are shaped by and themselves shape the science and technology that underpins big science in the making.

Acknowledgments

This paper is based upon work partially supported by the National Aeronautics and Space Administration under contract NASW-3691 and by the National Science Foundation under grant SES-8510336. Any opinions, findings, and conclusions or recommendations expressed in this chapter are those of the author and do not necessarily reflect those of the National Aeronautics and Space Administration or the National Science Foundation. Sections of this chapter are based on material in *The Space Telescope: A Study of NASA, Science, Technology, and Politics* by Robert W. Smith, with contributions by Paul Hanle, Robert Kargon, and Joseph N. Tatarewicz (New York: Cambridge University Press, 1989), and I am grateful to Cambridge University Press for permission to employ this material. Quotations from and citations of interviews recorded in the collection of the American Institute of Physics are by permission of the Center for History of Physics, American Institute of Physics. I am also grateful to the participants at the Big Science Workshop for their helpful comments on the initial draft of this chapter, as well as to Allan Needell for his reading of a later version.

References Cited

Anonymous. "House Committee Votes Pioneer Venus Delay, Seeks Choice Between It and LST." *Aerospace Daily,* June 20, 1975, p. 282.

Brush, Stephen F. "The Rise of Astronomy in America." *American Studies* 20 (1979): 41–67.

Covault, Craig. "Longer-Range Planetary Plans Sought." *Aviation Week and Space Technology,* Aug. 16, 1976, pp. 38–41.

Dennis, Michael. "A Change of State: The Political Cultures of Technical Practice at the MIT Instrumentation Laboratory and the Johns Hopkins University Applied Physics Laboratory, 1930–1945." Ph.D. diss., Johns Hopkins University, 1990.

Edge, David O., and Michael J. Mulkay. *Astronomy Transformed: The Emergence of Radio Astronomy in Britain.* New York: Wiley, 1976.

Galison, Peter. "Bubble Chambers and the Experimental Workplace." In Peter Achinstein and Owen Hannaway, eds., *Observation, Experiment, and Hypothesis in Modern Physical Science,* pp. 309–73. Cambridge, Mass.: MIT Press, 1985.

Hammond, Allen L. "Pioneer Venus: Did Astronomers Undercut Planetary Science?" *Science* 189 (1975): 270–71.

Hanle, Paul. "Astronomers, Congress, and the Large Space Telescope." *Sky and Telescope,* Apr. 1985, pp. 300–305.

Heilbron, John, and Daniel J. Kevles. "Mapping and Sequencing the Human Genome: Considerations from the History of Particle Accelerators." In *Mapping Our Genes.*

Federal Genome Projects: How Vast, How Fast. Contractor Reports, vol. 1, pp. 160–79. Washington, D.C.: U.S. Office of Technology Assessment, 1988.

Hermann, Armin, John Krige, Ulrike Mersits, and Dominique Pestre. *History of CERN*, Vol. 1, *Launching the European Organization for Nuclear Research*. Amsterdam: North Holland, 1987.

Hoyle, Fred. *Man in the Universe*. New York: Columbia University Press, 1966.

Hughes, Thomas P. *Networks of Power: Electrification in Western Society, 1880–1930*. Baltimore: Johns Hopkins University Press, 1983.

Kevles, Daniel J. *The Physicists: The History of a Scientific Community in Modern America*. New York: Vintage Books, 1979.

Klaw, Spencer. *The New Brahmins: Scientific Life in America*. New York: Morrow, 1968.

Lambright, W. Henry. *Governing Science and Technology*. New York: Oxford University Press, 1976.

Law, John. "Technology and Heterogenous Engineering: The Case of Portuguese Expansion." In Wiebe E. Bijker, Thomas P. Hughes, and Trevor J. Pinch, eds., *The Social Construction of Technological Systems: New Directions in the Sociology and History of Technology*, pp. 110–34. Cambridge, Mass.: MIT Press, 1986.

Lindblom, Charles. *The Policy-Making Process*. Englewood Cliffs, N.J.: Prentice-Hall, 1968.

Munch, G. "Detectors for Diffraction-Limited Imaging." In *Space Research: Directions for the Future*, pp. 25–27. Washington, D.C.: Space Science Board, 1966.

National Academy of Sciences. *Scientific Uses of the Large Space Telescope*. Washington, D.C.: National Academy of Sciences, 1969.

———. *Astronomy and Astrophysics for the 1970s*. Vol. 1. Washington, D.C.: National Academy of Sciences, 1972.

National Aeronautics and Space Administration. *Strategy for Outer Planets Exploration*. Washington, D.C.: NASA, 1975.

Newell, Homer. "Space Astronomy Program of the National Aeronautics and Space Administration." In *Astronomy in Space*, pp. 1–8. NASA SP-127, Washington, D.C.: NASA, 1967.

Office of Technology Assessment. *Mapping Our Genes. Federal Genome Projects: How Big, How Fast?* Washington, D.C.: Congress of the United States, 1988.

Osterbrock, Donald E., John R. Gustafson, and W. J. Shiloh Unruh. *Eye on the Sky: Lick Observatory's First Century*. Berkeley: University of California Press, 1988.

Price, Derek. *Little Science, Big Science*. New York: Columbia University Press, 1963.

Reagan, Michael D. *Science and the Federal Patron*. New York: Oxford University Press, 1969.

Ripley, Randall B., and Grace A. Franklin. *Congress, the Bureaucracy and Public Policy*. 4th ed. Chicago: Dorsey, 1987.

Shapin, Steven. "Pump and Circumstance: Robert Boyle's Literary Technology." *Social Studies of Science* 14 (1984): 481–520.

Smith, Alice K. *A Peril and a Hope: The Scientists' Movement in America, 1945–47*. Chicago: University of Chicago Press, 1965.

Smith, Robert W. (with contributions by Paul Hanle, Robert Kargon, and Joseph Tatarewicz). *The Space Telescope: A Study of NASA, Science, Technology, and Politics*. New York: Cambridge University Press, 1989.

Smith, Robert W., and Joseph N. Tatarewicz. "Replacing a Technology: The Large Space Telescope and CCDs." *Proceedings of the IEEE* 73 (1985): 1221–35.

Spitzer, Lyman. "Astronomical Advantages of an Extraterrestrial Observatory." Appendix 5, "Preliminary Design of an Experimental World Orbiting Spaceship." Douglas Aircraft Company, Santa Monica Plant Engineering Division, Report SM-11827, 1946.

Sullivan, Woodruff T., III, ed. *The Early Years of Radio Astronomy: Reflections Fifty Years After Jansky's Discovery.* Cambridge, Eng.: Cambridge University Press, 1984.

U.S. Congress, House of Representatives, Committee on Science and Technology. *World Inventory of "Big Science" Research Instruments and Facilities.* Washington, D.C.: Library of Congress, Congressional Research Service, 1986.

CHAPTER 8

Background to History:
The Transition from
Little Physics to Big Physics
in the Gravity Probe B
Relativity Gyroscope Program

C. W. F. Everitt

F riends have imagined that I, as a professional physicist who has sought to write history professionally, must wish to write a history of the NASA program I work on, the test of general relativity based on orbiting gyroscopes known as Gravity Probe B. Far from it. For one, I doubt my ability to reach a just detachment. For another, a leader in a program can never know some things—such as, for example, how his colleagues see their work in relation to his. For a third reason, most cogent, the charm of history to me rests, like the charm of travel, in encounter with the unknown. "The past is a foreign country; they do things differently there."[1] Autohistory loses this. Rather than embalm one's own past, one should move on, leaving historical analysis, if appropriate, to other minds.

Granted these views, what can a physicist engaged in a space program add to a debate about the historiography of big physics? The answer lies, I think, in helping to identify critical questions. How, for example, does a small laboratory research effort make the transition to being a big space project? How do the three cultures—NASA, academia, and aerospace—learn to live and work together? What influence do national advisory committees like the Space

1 Hartley, *The Go-Between,* chapter 1.

Science Board (or Space Studies Board, as it is now called) have? How do factors so mundane as NASA procurement regulations and the 18-month-long budget approval cycle each year through the Office of Management and Budget (OMB) and Congress change the way science is done? How do the pessimism-realism of the NASA comptroller's office about costs and the OMB's fear of the "camel's nose under the tent" (program commitments made surreptitiously) alter program planning? Are monster budgets the wisdom of experience or "self-fulfilling prophecies," hard-won truth or "learned helplessness," in a bureaucratic world so Kafkaesque that we are forced to think that the real victor in World War I was the Austro-Hungarian Empire?

History and the Issues of History

If I begin with institutional and external questions, it is not from placing institutions above ideas, or from any Tolstoyan conviction about impersonal forces in history. Gratitude returns to individual actions. I, from a distance of 30 feet, have witnessed an exchange between two Congressional staffpersons lasting twenty seconds that added $1 million to our budget authorization. Likewise, from a wall seat at a Space Science Board meeting I have heard two sentences from different speakers, one calm, one impassioned, so transform a debate that a straw vote of 8 to 6 against a report[2]—at which, according to one observer, my face turned white—was followed an hour later by an almost unanimous vote of approval. These are chance examples. About others, such as why the board commissioned that report, I know little. A friend, formerly in Washington, has remarked, "Some day you and I should get together over a beer and I will tell you what really happened at [a specified] meeting when your program was given the go-ahead." That beer remains undrawn. The point is merely that individual actions occur in institutional settings with institutional constraints, and their success depends on timing. As a prominent, strongly supportive NASA official put it at one meeting I did not attend, "Look, you keep telling me to fly, and I keep telling you that I am standing on the fourth-floor window-ledge flapping my arms as hard as I can. What more do you expect me to do?" Six months later the same man, unprompted, was able to intervene smoothly and decisively to help the program forward.

Technical achievement under pressure also hinges on the individual. It is impressive to watch a colleague with little time and antiquated equipment home in on the one inspired decision that brings success. But note the word *pressure*. Physicists are driven creatures, some of whom opine that they should be left to craft works of genius in isolation. Not so. Accept money and expect pressure, whether from the funding agency or from colleagues in whose imaginations dwell other uses for taxpayer largesse. About this there is noth-

2 National Research Council. *Strategy for Space Research.*

ing unique to big physics and nothing new. Admirers of James Clerk Maxwell will recall the harsh words written in *Nature* on two occasions[3] about the Cavendish Laboratory and its alleged unproductiveness under his direction. And physicists who grumble at bureaucrats should recognize they too are under pressure. The program monitor's highest reward is the knowledge that he picked a winning horse and helped train it to take the jumps. His deepest fear halfway through the race is that he may have backed a loser.

Just as the human story in big physics involves relationships between individuals and institutions, so in the design of scientific apparatus the intellectual story is one of relating individual ideas to the grand idea. Too dominant in our culture, scientific and popular, is the notion of the "breakthrough." Every fight should end in a knockout, every ball game in a home run. A good experiment may start from a single idea, but that is not what makes it go. Henry Cavendish's epic achievement of 1798 in "weighing the Earth" lay not in applying a torsion balance to measure the gravitational constant (the Rev. John Michell's idea, not his) but in the sustained force of intellect he brought to the design of his apparatus and to the exposure and removal of error. Gravity Probe B, similarly, while involving a few breakthroughs, like the recognition that mechanical gyroscopes can be made to perform far better in space than on Earth, has depended even more on what is nowadays somewhat pretentiously called "systems thinking": a sustained effort by a group of physicists and engineers to grasp, demonstrate, and interweave techniques and ideas from many different intellectual disciplines.

In big physics, individual ideas must be related to the grand idea, and those who raise funds must be alert to human affairs, but there is a further subtlety. These two very different realms of discourse intermingle. Demands for money must simultaneously address technical truth and political truth. A brilliant plan costing three times what Congress or NASA will settle for is futile; an acceptably priced fiasco will be—a fiasco. Moreover, these truths, unlike those about inalienable human rights, are not self-evident and eternal. Rather, they are in continual flux. People and policies in Washington come and go; yesterday's technical show-stopper and yesterday's minor difficulty change places. Politics may be the art of the possible; this kind of technical-political-managerial enterprise is better seen as the art of reaching correct decisions from insufficient information. How that happens or fails to happen raises profound historical questions.

Gravity Probe B began with an idea of Leonard Schiff's, first published in *Physical Review Letters*, February 1, 1960.[4] NASA support for it commenced

3 Anonymous editorial, "Physiology at Cambridge," on which see a letter from Maxwell to Lewis Campbell, Mar. 4, 1876, in Campbell and Garnett, *Life of James Clerk Maxwell*, p. 392; Guthrie, "Remonstrance to a Respected Daddie Anent His Loss of Temper."
4 Schiff, "Possible New Experimental Test."

with a modest research grant,[5] awarded jointly to the Department of Physics and the Department of Aeronautics and Astronautics at Stanford University in March 1964, retroactive to November 1963. My involvement came a year earlier in October 1962 when at the invitation of William Fairbank I joined the Stanford physics department as the program's first full-time research associate. The eight years to 1971 were spent forming the general scheme of the experiment and developing preliminary component hardware. The first bow to flight was in 1971 when NASA commissioned Ball Brothers Research Corporation (now Ball Aerospace) to perform a Mission Definition Study.[6] The 1970's mainly saw a group of some six to eight physicists and engineers at Stanford demonstrating specific technologies. The transition to a space program took five years, beginning around April 1979 and culminating on March 30, 1984, in a decision by the NASA administrator to authorize a limited engineering test of flight hardware known as STORE (*Shuttle Test Of the Relativity Experiment*). STORE in somewhat simplified form is scheduled for shuttle flight in August 1994. Now with six active faculty members, a combined research and administrative staff of 34, a total of 31 graduate and undergraduate students, a subcontract from Stanford to Lockheed of around $10 million in 1991, with additional separate $1 million spacecraft study contracts to both Lockheed and Fairchild, Gravity Probe B is big physics. Launch of the science mission is expected in 1997, rather more than 37 years after Schiff's suggestion.

People occasionally express amazement, and even disapproval, that any individual or group should dedicate so many years to a single experiment. Had we been forewarned, we would never have armed. But balance is necessary. All NASA science programs since the 1960's have suffered lamentable delays. When, in 1978, a NASA manager of great perspicacity told a review panel of which I was a member that the canonical interval between conception and execution of a space experiment was ten years, we were shocked. In retrospect, her caution looks optimistic. The Hubble Space Telescope, for which the first Phase A study was completed in 1967, was launched in July 1990—and Robert Smith in Chapter 7 conveys some idea of why it took 23 years. The Gamma Ray Observatory, which followed proposals made to NASA in 1965, will go in 1991. Judicious historiography may someday bring insight as well as castigation to these delays.

Gravity Probe B too has met the bureaucratic boa constrictor, but there is more. A program so dependent on what I shall call *interdisciplinary invention* could not have been shortened by more than say 30%, even with unlimited funds. The right comparison is not with the three years of the Manhattan Project (which followed thirty years of nuclear physics) nor with the wartime development of microwave radar but with the eighteen years from William

---

5 NsG 582, later NGR 05-020-019.
6 Ball Brothers Research Corporation, "Mission Definition for Stanford Relativity Satellite."

Crookes's demonstration that cathode rays are deflected by a magnetic field to J. J. Thomson's discovery of the electron, or the seventeen years during which James Watt and his associates labored in improving the performance of the steam engine by a factor of four.

In what follows I refrain, as promised, from offering a history of Gravity Probe B. The play, like Viola's in *Twelfth Night,* is not yet played out. Something can be said, however, about the transitional events from 1979 to 1984, if not as they were, at least as they appeared to be, and something also of the influence on us of a man who never knew Schiff's work, William Walter Hansen.

Schiff's Idea, Interdisciplinary Invention, and the Hansen-Terman Heritage

Schiff calculated that an ideal gyroscope in orbit around the Earth would, according to general relativity, undergo non-Newtonian precessions of two kinds with respect to the framework of the fixed stars: (1) a *geodetic* effect due to the gyroscope's motion through curved space-time, yielding at 650 kilometers altitude a precession of the gyroscope in the orbit plane amounting to 6.6 arc-seconds per year, and (2) a *frame-dragging* effect due to the Earth's rotation, whose magnitude varies with the inclination of the orbit but is in a 650-kilometer polar orbit expected to be 0.042 arc-seconds per year. In polar orbit the two effects are at right angles, as shown in Fig. 8.1. Conceptually, no experiment could be simpler. All it takes is a gyroscope, a telescope, and a star, each referred to the next and the star referred to distant quasars. Realization is more elaborate. Gaining the precision hoped for—a measurement of frame-dragging to one part in 300 and of the geodetic effect to one part in 50,000 or better—requires a telescope three orders of magnitude better than typical "very good" star-tracking instruments and a gyroscope with errors from nonrelativistic disturbances a million times less than those of the best gyroscopes used for inertial navigation.

Given the huge worldwide investment in gyroscope technology since World War II, all this may seem chasing the rainbow. In truth, there is no absurdity. Two technologies, space and cryogenics, transform the problem. Operating in orbit eliminates the support torques that limit the performance of conventional earthbound mechanical gyroscopes. Operating at low temperature (1.8 degrees above the absolute zero) allows us to exploit the properties of superfluid helium to stabilize the apparatus and to use superconductors to provide new ways of shielding the gyroscope against magnetic fields and reading its direction of spin.

Figure 8.2 is a view of the flight instrument. Four gyroscopes, each arranged to measure both relativity effects, are mounted along with a "drag-free proof mass" in a massive block of fused quartz (weight 51 pounds), rigidly

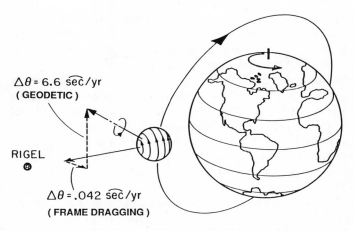

$\Delta\theta = 6.6 \; \widehat{\text{sec}}/\text{yr}$
(GEODETIC)

RIGEL

$\Delta\theta = .042 \; \widehat{\text{sec}}/\text{yr}$
(FRAME DRAGGING)

Fig. 8.1. The two relativity effects predicted by Leonard Schiff.

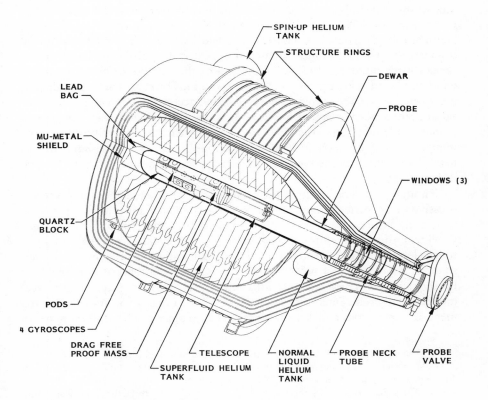

SPIN-UP HELIUM TANK

STRUCTURE RINGS

DEWAR

PROBE

LEAD BAG

MU-METAL SHIELD

WINDOWS (3)

QUARTZ BLOCK

PODS

4 GYROSCOPES

DRAG FREE PROOF MASS

TELESCOPE

SUPERFLUID HELIUM TANK

NORMAL LIQUID HELIUM TANK

PROBE NECK TUBE

PROBE VALVE

Fig. 8.2. The Gravity Probe B flight instrument.

attached to a quartz telescope. Each gyroscope is a quartz sphere, the size of a ping-pong ball (diameter 1.5 inches), coated with a thin layer of the metal niobium, spinning at 10,000 revolutions per minute, and electrically suspended in high vacuum. The gyro-telescope structure is enclosed in a 10-foot-long cigar-shaped chamber ("the probe") inserted into a dewar vessel (a glorified thermos bottle) containing 400 gallons of liquid helium and capable of staying cold for two years. The whole is surrounded by a spacecraft (not shown) comprising among other items a ring-shaped solar array, electronics boxes, telemetry, a roll-reference system, a sun shield for the telescope, and thrusters that direct the flow of escaping helium gas from the dewar so as to provide almost ideally smooth and precise pointing and translational control of the spacecraft.

Simultaneous discovery. Whoever ponders that mystery may do so here. Beyond Einstein's three "classical" tests, Schiff's was the first experimentally plausible proposal for a test of general relativity to have appeared in 45 years. In November 1959, just two months before Schiff, G. E. Pugh advanced almost the identical proposal, choosing as his publication medium the oddest of all vehicles—a Weapons System Evaluation Group memorandum[7] from the Pentagon! Pugh's route to his idea was quite different from Schiff's. It followed a suggestion from H. Yilmaz[8] that tracking data on an artificial satellite might reveal frame-dragging through a rotation of the satellite's orbital plane, an effect predicted years earlier by W. Lense and H. Thirring. This, as Pugh saw, was hopeless given the limits then on tracking accuracy and orbit prediction,[9] but a gyroscope experiment might be feasible. Chance, not war, determined Pugh's mode of publication. His article contained nothing military; having joined the Weapons System Evaluation Group a year earlier he happened to hear Yilmaz speak at the New York meeting of the American Physical Society in January 1959.

Though Pugh had some of the relativity wrong, his memorandum is impressive for its penetration into the Newtonian disturbances affecting a spinning body in orbit, and above all for the brilliant concept of a "drag-free" satellite. Ordinary satellites, though nominally in free fall, are in reality subject to accelerations from aerodynamic drag, solar radiation pressure, and other sources amounting to a few times 10^{-8} of the acceleration of gravity at the Earth's surface. These accelerations affect gyro performance. Pugh's idea, independently reinvented two years later by B. O. Lange of Stanford's Department of Aeronautics and Astronautics,[10] was to place a spherical test mass (in

7 Pugh, "Search for the Gravitational Carolis Force."

8 Yilmaz, "Proposed Test of the Nature of the Gravitational Interaction."

9 Modern laser tracking methods and Global Positioning System (GPS) receivers are on the fringe of being able to attempt the Yilmaz experiment.

10 The independence of Lange from Pugh is attested by D. B. DeBra, who was sitting next to Lange in the audience at a NASA-sponsored meeting on relativity at Stanford when Lange had the idea.

Pugh's mind the gyroscope itself) in a cavity within the spacecraft to serve as reference for the true gravitational orbit. The mass, being shielded by the surrounding vehicle, is not subject to drag. By sensing its position within the cavity, one obtains a reference signal for controlling gas thrusters that make the spacecraft chase after the test mass. Drag-free operation is essential to Gravity Probe B.

It is much to be regretted that we at Stanford have never done justice to Pugh's achievement. I myself, though long aware of his memorandum's existence, never saw a copy until 1981. Even Schiff, the most scrupulously honorable of men, shortchanged Pugh, principally I suspect from that curious literal-mindedness that those who knew Schiff could not but puzzle over, which probably saw Pugh's work as deficient because it contained a mistake in relativity and was not published in a refereed journal. Still, nothing would have happened had it not been for two men newly arrived at Stanford that academic year, William Fairbank of the Department of Physics and Robert Cannon of the Department of Aeronautics and Astronautics.

I have tried elsewhere,[11] in the one piece of historical delving I have done on Gravity Probe B, to comprehend the events that preceded and followed a much-recounted meeting between Schiff, Fairbank, and Cannon at the now-no-longer existent swimming pool in the now-no-longer exclusive men's gymnasium at Stanford. The problem lies in reconciling Schiff's detailed working notes with the vivid, if not wholly consistent, recollections of the two other members of the trio. That is as may be. More important are matters of vision. Fairbank, already known for several spectacularly precise experiments, performed while he was at Duke University, brought a zeal for low temperatures and an aura of difficulties surmounted. Cannon, from MIT, brought an expert understanding of gyroscope technology, formed in part through his contact with C. Stark Draper and the MIT Instrumentation Laboratory. And both men were ambitious. W. A. Little's picture[12] of Fairbank bursting on the Stanford scene like a whirlwind from the south, a prophet uttering strange words about long-range order in momentum space, is appealing. Cannon's vision, formed in reaction to Draper's vast operation, was to think ahead to the opportunity space might provide for improving gyro performance not by factors of two or four but by many orders of magnitude. Half an hour with Schiff clinched matters. Cannon's remark that evening to his wife—"I have met a man who needs a gyroscope even better than the ones we have been talking about"—remained in her memory twenty years later.

Gyroscopes in space and linear accelerators on the surface of the Earth have little apparent connection, yet it was Bill Hansen, inventor of the rhumbatron and the electron linear accelerator, the central figure in Chapter 2, who gave Gravity Probe B its institutional setting.

11 Everitt, "Stanford Relativity Gyroscope Experiment."
12 Little, "Organic Superconductivity," p. 359.

That most famous of inept questions, "Can there any good thing come out of Nazareth?," may serve to remind us that genius, though it needs a setting and a culture, does not always originate in mature centers of excellence. Hansen, who grew up in Fresno, California, when Fresno's greatest distinction, as noted by the *Encyclopaedia Britannica* five years after his birth, consisted of being "the only place in America where Smyrna figs have been grown with success,"[13] entered Stanford in 1924 and graduated with an engineering degree in 1928. Drawn to physics through David Webster, the new head of Stanford's moribund physics department, he obtained a doctorate for work on X rays, and spent two years at MIT learning mathematics and the beginnings of microwave technology before returning to Stanford as an assistant professor in 1934. It is astounding that this homegrown product of a mediocre university—for Stanford was that—should so transform things that when he died at 43 of beryllium poisoning fifteen years later his colleagues were left wondering how to bring what he had done under control. And all this without guile or ruthlessness. No one who has followed Hansen's career can miss his humanity: the warm atmosphere that he and Edward Ginzton established in the Stanford Microwave Laboratory while building up the accelerator program; his generosity, personal and financial, to the Varian brothers; the unselfish help, too little acknowledged, that he gave to Felix Bloch in developing nuclear magnetic resonance. It is tragic that he died eighteen months before the start of two brilliant decades of discovery at HEPL, the High-Energy Physics Laboratory containing the machine he had built.

One thing Hansen bequeathed us, mundane but strongly influencing program logistics, was 14,000 square feet of laboratory space in a prime location on the Near West campus. This came to Gravity Probe B with the clearing at the Main Bay and first End Station of HEPL, from 1985 on. But universities—whatever fundraisers may think—do not live by bricks and mortar alone. More profound was Hansen's spiritual gift (shared by Frederick Terman, builder of Stanford's engineering school) of bringing physicists and engineers together in creative exchange.

Bill Fairbank often remarked that the first discovery a graduate student needs to make is that it is possible for him to make discoveries, and that this realization usually comes from being at a place where significant things are happening. Similarly, when Bill himself at 42 came to Stanford from Duke, he quickly sensed that here was a place of new opportunity, brilliant as his research at Duke had been. Cannon from MIT felt the same. Fundamental to all this, not formal but atmospheric, was the Hansen-Terman vision of entrepreneurial collaboration.

A proper historical investigation would have to examine many questions to grasp how Stanford, seemingly in the 1930's a *nouveau-riche* fun school, could become transformed into a center of research, and of this particular kind

13 *Encyclopaedia Britannica*, 11th ed., vol. 11, "Fresno."

of research. In Chapter 2 Galison, Hevly, and Lowen admirably describe Hansen's impact, and Stuart W. Leslie in an absorbing article[14] has sketched Terman's role, but much remains puzzling. To some people, at the end of World War II Stanford seemed in decline, a decline reversed only by the unexpectedly brilliant presidency from 1947 to 1966 of J. E. Wallace Sterling. Yet many who helped the reversal were in place when Sterling arrived, and some like Hansen were soon to vanish. Did Terman the engineer single-handedly persuade Sterling the historian to put so much into building science and engineering? Did Stanford make Silicon Valley or did Silicon Valley remake Stanford? What influence did the shift of the medical school to the campus have? (Certainly it affected HEPL.) These are all important matters. For the narrower interest of Gravity Probe B, however, the necessary question concerns the process, referred to above and now to be defined, of *interdisciplinary invention*.

That collaborations such as ours do not happen automatically was borne in on me in 1969 when at Cannon's behest I showed our work to a former dean of an east-coast university, an engineer of great distinction. His comment was that his university's engineers should visit Stanford to find out how it was done. When twelve years later I was asked east to explain, I named two requisites: good will and a genuine need on both sides. True, but not, as I now realize, an explanation of why collaborations work more readily in one place than another.

Speak of interdisciplinary research and most people fall asleep. Like motherhood it is an art all the world believes in and half the world practices. Yet having myself worked with geologists for five years (1955–60) during the early days of paleomagnetism and plate tectonics, I can with some assurance contrast ordinary collaborations with the process forced upon Hansen and upon us. Most interdisciplinary research consists of bringing together fixed expertises for a new purpose. Exciting as that can be—and in paleomagnetism I found it exciting enough to write a critique on the different cultures of physics and geology[15]—it differs markedly from the interdisciplinary invention espoused here.

Gravity Probe B is a physics experiment testing one of the most abstruse of scientific theories, general relativity. Its success depends on new engineering ideas, but (and this is the subtlety) these engineering ideas depend in turn on new physics from another field, cryogenics. The disciplines intermingle far more than is ordinarily the case.

Take the gyroscope, the suspended spinning sphere described earlier and illustrated in Fig. 8.3. Several years were to pass before even the basic design was established. Some support for the gyro rotor is needed even in space. To begin with, Schiff, Fairbank, and Cannon all assumed that it would be a

14 Leslie, "Playing the Education Game."
15 Everitt, "Studies in the Magnetism of Baked and Igneous Rocks."

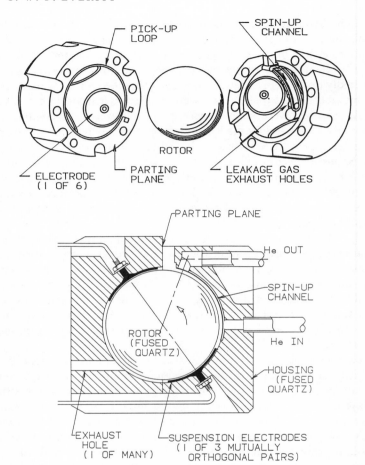

PICK-UP LOOP

SPIN-UP CHANNEL

ROTOR

ELECTRODE (I OF 6)

PARTING PLANE

LEAKAGE GAS EXHAUST HOLES

PARTING PLANE

He OUT

SPIN-UP CHANNEL

ROTOR (FUSED QUARTZ)

He IN

HOUSING (FUSED QUARTZ)

EXHAUST HOLE (I OF MANY)

SUSPENSION ELECTRODES (I OF 3 MUTUALLY ORTHOGONAL PAIRS)

Fig. 8.3. The Gravity Probe B gyroscope.

magnetically supported superconducting sphere, not as now an electrically supported one. Two groups, one at the Jet Propulsion Laboratory (JPL), the other at General Electric, were developing "superconducting gyroscopes" of that kind with grandiose claims for the future, and given Fairbank's mastery of cryogenics theirs was the obvious scheme. The program's first doctoral dissertation, completed in 1963 under Cannon's direction, concerned the dynamics of a magnetically levitated superconducting body during spin-up.

Though superconductivity is essential to Gravity Probe B, this "superconducting gyroscope" proved to be a false trail both for us and for inertial navigation. Why? Because in seeking an improved gyro suspension scheme, the groups at JPL and GE were addressing the wrong problem, as may be seen from a line of reasoning that dawned on me years later in 1972.

Any gyroscope in the form of a suspended almost spherical body will experience (nonrelativistic) disturbing torques from the action of the suspension forces on the deviations from perfect roundness. Now the support system—any support system—acts by exerting pressure (positive or negative) on the surface of the sphere. The disturbance one is trying to eliminate depends primarily on two factors, pressure and asphericity, and only secondarily on the details of the suspension mechanism. To put the issue more technically, the disturbing torque is the derivative of the energy in the system with respect to the orientation of the gyro spin axis, and the only way in which one suspension scheme may be superior to another is if it allows more of the energy withdrawn over one region of the sphere to be coupled back in elsewhere. The condition one seeks should resemble that of a body floating with neutral buoyancy in a (frictionless) fluid. Magnetic suspension had many complications and no intrinsic tendency to meet the ideal any better than other established schemes, such as the electrical suspension invented by Arnold Nordsieck of the University of Illinois in 1953. Far more to the point was to find ways of reducing the support pressure—space—and improving the roundness of the sphere.

Why superconductivity, then? For two reasons. First, it allows another source of disturbance on the gyroscope to be removed, the large eddy-current torques that act on a spinning sphere of normal metal even in weak magnetic fields. Second, superconductivity provides a means for reading the direction of spin of a perfectly round, perfectly homogeneous sphere.

From Nordsieck on, engineers committed to the development of gyroscopes with spherical rotors had struggled with the problem of readout. Various techniques, optical and electrical, had been devised before 1960, but none could be adapted to our experiment. Schiff's earliest notes reveal his awareness of the issue. Soon Fairbank proposed a characteristically ingenious solution based on the Mossbauer effect, but that too had difficulties.

An important moment in my own education came in late 1962, when Howard Knoebel, Nordsieck's successor at Illinois, visited Stanford a month or so after my arrival. Hardly knowing what I was saying, I mentioned something about readout, and he instantly replied, "Well, you are worrying about the right problem. The readout is the difficult part." A few months later Bill Fairbank and I hit upon the idea of a readout based on the "London moment" in a spinning superconductor. In 1952 Fritz London,[16] following R. Becker, F. Sauter, and G. Heller,[17] had calculated that a rotating superconducting body should develop a magnetic moment proportional to spin speed and *aligned with its instantaneous axis of spin*. Here is a marker applicable even to a perfect sphere. Figure 8.4 illustrates the London moment readout in its primitive form. Surrounding the gyro rotor is a superconducting loop connected to a SQUID (*S*uperconducting *QU*antum *I*nterference *D*evice), a

16 London, "Macroscopic Theory of Superconductivity," p. 83.
17 Becker, Sauter, and Heller, "Über die Stromverteilung in einer supraleitenden Kugel."

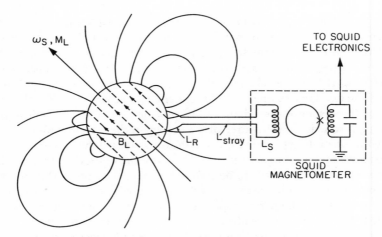

Fig. 8.4. Reading out the direction of spin of the gyroscope by the London moment.

device capable of measuring very weak magnetic fields. As the spinning sphere tilts, the magnetic field through the loop changes by an amount proportional to angle, and with an appropriate calibration technique the angle can be determined.

The London moment readout was in some degree an act of faith, for no magnetometer with the required sensitivity existed then. We had ideas, but several years went by before Zimmerman and Silver[18] in 1964 invented the SQUID, and several more passed before we adopted it. Another task was to devise a means of spinning up the gyroscope. That might seem a small matter; it was not. In a relativity experiment the goal is to eliminate disturbing torques on the gyro rotor, whereas to start the rotor spinning a torque must be applied. The problem is to find a way of applying a torque and then switching it off— by some thirteen orders of magnitude! Our final approach consisted of passing gas through a circumferential channel of rather elaborate design cut in the housing and then pumping out the system to let the rotor coast freely in high vacuum.

So much for the basic gyro concept, thought through by 1967 after five or more years of steady interaction between physicists and engineers. Transforming this into a flight-quality gyroscope took a further continuous elaboration of interdisciplinary invention in four areas: (1) suspension, (2) readout, (3) spin-up, (4) manufacturing technology. A brief nonhistorical summary may illuminate the complexities of the process.

Suspension. Given that Nordsieck had already invented the electrically suspended gyroscope, and that suspension units were commercially available

18 Silver and Zimmerman, "Quantum States and Transitions in Weakly Connected Rings."

from Honeywell, it might seem that little remained to be done in this area. Far from it. Most fundamentally, we had to develop a multilevel suspension system capable of operating both on Earth and continuously through a range of gravity levels in space. Beyond that, several deep technical problems embracing the physics and the engineering had to be attacked in adapting the system to a cryogenic gyroscope operating in the laboratory. One was electrical interference between the suspension and the London moment readout. Another, wholly unforeseen, was that the 20-kilohertz signals of alternating current used in suspending the ball generated large amounts of heat in the housing, raising the gyroscope above its superconducting transition temperature. A third, even more startling, was that sometimes at low temperatures, though never at room temperature, a perfectly well-behaved gyro rotor would spontaneously explode minutes or hours after it had been levitated. The elaborate train of physics—engineering detective work that led to an understanding of this phenomenon, and to its cure by a redesign of the suspension system, is one of the odder episodes in the history of Gravity Probe B.

Readout. If the solution to gyro suspension was principally adaptation of an existing engineering system, the solution to readout was a total novelty conceived by physicists and developed by the combined group with much help from outside. It depended on two subsidiary inventions: the SQUID and a scheme for producing ultralow magnetic fields by successive expansion of a series of superconducting lead bags. The SQUID was in no sense a Stanford contribution, though it followed in part from a phenomenon, flux quantization, discovered simultaneously by two groups, one here and the other in West Germany. By happy chance the ultralow field technology, conceived and developed at Stanford, has provided what appears to be the ideal environment for the testing of SQUIDs.

Spin-up. The spin system may be thought of as an engineering design; it originated with Dan Bracken, a graduate student in the Department of Physics, in consultation with myself and Don Baganoff, a professor in the Department of Aeronautics and Astronautics. That was only half the story, however. Once the gyro has reached full speed (10,000 revolutions per minute), the pressure must be reduced to an exceedingly low level (10^{-11} torr or 10^{-14} atmosphere). For years we had no idea how to accomplish this. Eventually the insight of John Lipa and John Turneaure created a technique known as "low-temperature bakeout." After the spin cycle the gyro housing is warmed two or three degrees above its normal operating temperature (1.8 kelvins) for a few hours and then allowed to cool down. The pressure collapses. Important in this work was a remarkable award-winning honors thesis on helium adsorption isotherms at low temperatures by a physics undergraduate, Eric Cornell.

Manufacturing technology. Rotors with sphericity ten or more times better than any previously available, extremely uniform superconducting coatings, materials of extreme homogeneity free in the extreme of magnetic contaminants, a housing cavity spherical to a few millionths of an inch whose surface incorporates a complex spin-up channel surrounded by a raised wall projecting nearly a thousandth of an inch, a total structure that can be cycled repeatedly to low temperatures without damage, special means for joining superconducting wires to the superconducting readout loop—all these and more are needed for a satisfactory gyro design. Attaining them has required a wide range of new metrology and manufacturing techniques, a joint effort by physicists, mechanical engineers, and electrical engineers, a precision machining company, a manufacturer of roundness-measuring instruments, a group from another university with experience in optical instrumentation, a NASA center, experts on sputtering, experts on clean rooms, and a gentleman with many years' experience in the rarely combined skills of engineering design, optical polishing, and quartz machining. As Winston Churchill said of another alliance, we have had to become "somewhat mixed up in some of our affairs for mutual and general advantage."[19]

This mixing up characterizes all our work. The helium dewar developed by Lockheed combines new physics and engineering principles tailored for space, including a "porous plug" device for controlling liquid boil-off in low gravity, invented in the Stanford physics department and engineered for space at NASA Marshall Center and JPL. The instrument for measuring quartz homogeneity is an engineering device invented by physicists. The "Kalman filter" for processing relativity data is a physics tool developed by engineers. Even mathematical techniques cross-fertilize. Methods from nuclear physics theory have revolutionized the analysis of gyro performance. Methods from spacecraft orbital dynamics simplify a correction to Schiff's formulae for the Earth's imperfect sphericity.

If the strength of the Hansen-Terman heritage appears in the easy collaboration on Gravity Probe B, that strength should not be taken for granted. Institutional structures can wreck such unstructured gifts. The impressive conjunction of physics and engineering mastery gained so surprisingly by the Cavendish Laboratory under Rutherford in the 1920's did not long survive. Whether in its second century Stanford will prefer Hansen to hubris remains to be seen.

Systems, Size, and Elegance: Design of the Dewar-Instrument Package

He who enters NASA's world enters a world of reviews and reports. During 1980 two important events took place on Gravity Probe B's long march toward flight. In April a committee of the Space Science Board produced the first draft of a "Strategy for Space Research in Gravitational Physics in the 1980's," which among other things strongly endorsed the project's science. In August NASA appointed an *ad hoc* Technology Review Committee made up of fifteen eminent physicists and engineers, who spent five days on

19 Speech, House of Commons, Aug. 20, 1940.

site at Stanford reviewing technical issues. After commenting on the importance of the science and the "long period of difficult technology development," that committee summarized its findings with the statement that "the remarkable technical accomplishments of the dedicated Stanford team give us confidence that when they are combined with a strong engineering team in a flight development program this difficult experiment can be done."[20] Despite such glowing reviews we were soon facing fresh obstacles that put the whole enterprise in jeopardy.

By 1980, besides individual technologies, there existed a fairly complete overall design for the experiment, and there had been, in addition to the Ball Brothers Mission Definition Study of 1971, three more engineering studies, two by Ball and one (a "Phase A" study) performed at NASA Marshall Center in 1979. Why then did four years go by before it was possible to implement the Technology Review Committee's recommendation of combining the Stanford team with a strong engineering team—Lockheed—in a flight development program? The story reveals something of the complex interactions among pricing, systems design, experience, and institutional constraints in space mission.

For several reasons, all making good sense at the time, NASA decided to explore the prospect of forming the engineering team in-house at the Marshall Center. Stanford had an excellent relationship with the Marshall Center developed over thirteen years. The center has first-class cryogenic expertise. Doing Gravity Probe B in-house would usefully diversify the center's activities. Finally, not least important, in-house development would save on the program's *apparent* cost. NASA's accounting procedures are such that the salaries of engineers in the field centers are largely covered from the centers' funds, and not therefore from the scarce resources of a NASA Headquarters program office. At the Marshall Center, the direct charge per person to a program was $14,000 per man-year, as opposed to the average for the aerospace industry of $120,000 per man-year. Fictitious though the saving is, it constitutes a part of reality. Often the only way to do a program is to do it in-house.

Accordingly, in fiscal 1981, NASA Headquarters began funding the Marshall Center's performing a "Phase B" engineering study of Gravity Probe B. To understand this term, it should be explained that NASA flight programs are customarily executed in four phases:

Phase A, a preliminary feasibility study.

Phase B, spacecraft design and mission planning, sufficiently detailed to allow realistic pricing and scheduling.

Phases C/D (always done together), design and fabrication of the spacecraft.

The Phase B study,[21] completed in August 1982, was of great value. It laid

20 Rosendhal, "Stanford Gyro Relativity Experiment."
21 "Gravity Probe B Phase B Final Report." Huntsville, Ala.: Marshall Space Flight Center, 1983.

out accurately many programmatic and technical issues previously ignored. It seriously addressed pricing. It influenced all that we have done since. Nevertheless, because of the peculiar ways universities and NASA centers each do business, the study was undertaken in very disadvantageous circumstances, and it was subject to an unforeseeable external constraint linked to the IRAS (*InfraRed Astronomy Satellite*), a joint U.S.–Netherlands–U.K. program dedicated to the first major all-sky survey of infrared astronomical sources.

When in 1971 Ball Brothers completed the Gravity Probe B Mission Definition Study, the company, desiring experience with dewars in space, applied internal development funds to build a prototype dewar embodying many of the features needed for our program or any other. This decision stood Ball in good stead; the company secured the contract to build the IRAS dewar, planned to operate at a temperature of 1.8 kelvins and keep helium liquid for one year. Ball constructed the dewar in 1986 and 1987; it incorporated a JPL version of the Stanford porous plug; cryogenic testing on the ground was done partly at Ball and partly at JPL.

As happens in any program of such novelty, there were problems. Valves failed to seal; burst disks ruptured; plumbing leaked; most worrying of all, thermal tests appeared to indicate a much shorter liquid hold-time than expected. Such tales grow in the telling: for most of our Phase B study, the story was that IRAS would not stay cold for longer than six months or possibly four.

Since bigger dewars stay cold longer, the obvious answer was to enlarge our dewar. This conclusion, supported by detailed calculations at the Marshall Center, matched a Stanford concern that the main magnetic shield for the gyroscopes needed to be larger in diameter and therefore longer. The consequence of these and other concerns was a dewar 14 feet long and 5 feet in diameter, and a spacecraft weighing 5300 pounds rather than the 2800 computed earlier.

Why, it may be asked, with the space shuttle does one care about weight? Payloads far larger than 5300 pounds can be taken into orbit. Actually, taking 5300 pounds to a height of 600 or 650 kilometers (as is needed for drag-free operation) is not so easy. Even with launch from the Vandenberg Air Force base—then assumed to be available—an apogee-perigee kick stage would probably have been required. But the larger objection is cost. Years of NASA experience have shown that the cost of a spacecraft is closely correlated with its weight, modified only slightly by its complexity. Double the weight and you will double the price. This we had done. From a rough estimate of $100 million in 1980 dollars, the cost for Gravity Probe B had jumped to over $200 million 1982 dollars, even with the nominally lower manpower costs for Marshall Center personnel. With manpower fully accounted for (as some people demanded), the figure was nearer $360 million. Disaster. We had priced ourselves out of the market.

Most troubling was the sense of powerlessness. A year before Phase B ended, everyone could see what was happening, yet nothing could be done. In August 1981 a very experienced and astute senior manager at the Marshall Center urged us to form a "tiger team" to reexamine the whole design, but with IRAS as it was the tiger had no claws. NASA engineers, so often blamed for "buying in" on new programs, have no wish to be trapped. Companies like Ball Aerospace with doubtful products to defend are suspect. University principal investigators obviously know nothing of the real world. Worse, puzzling as it must seem, crucial people at both Stanford and the Marshall Center were unavailable. The leading dewar expert at the Marshall Center was tied up in another program. Two Stanford physicists, whose extraordinary talents might have done much, were heavily committed elsewhere and unable to travel. Here was another obstacle. During the 1980 technology review one visitor asked what the greatest difficulty in the experiment was. Almost without thinking I responded, "Marshall Center travel funds." Flippant as the answer sounds, it contained a deep truth. Congressional restrictions on NASA travel are severe to the point of insanity. Yet without on-site technical education, hard thought is impossible.

Such were some of Phase B's trials. In retrospect my principal feeling is one of grateful surprise for what was achieved. More was needed. By December 1982, rumor—that evil-featured traveling companion of big physics—had begun whispering round the scientific community that Gravity Probe B was in trouble.

Next, IRAS to the rescue. Launched after much agonizing on January 25, 1983, IRAS proved spectacularly successful in both infrared astronomy and cryogenics. Within ten days the helium in the dewar had settled to a boil-off rate lower even than the most hopeful estimate. Doom and gloom had been factitious. The experiment lasted 311 days and characterized more than half a million new infrared objects. For Gravity Probe B, that might have been the start of dewar redesign, but a bolder course presented itself. Why not try a radical redesign of the instrument to fit within the six-foot-long IRAS dewar, now flight-proven? This promised many advantages, not least a well-established price of $10 million for the dewar, in contrast to the appallingly high figure of $35 million spelt out in Phase B.

Here the benefits of hard-won management experience became apparent. A year earlier Stanford had retained the services of Bradford Parkinson as management consultant in the hope that as the program developed he could be persuaded to join us as professor (research) and program manager—which happily he did eighteen months later in September 1984. Brad once before had been through a crisis like ours, as U.S. Air Force manager for the Navstar Global Positioning System (GPS) program. Then, he and a small group of Air Force engineers had spent a week in seclusion totally rethinking the design of the GPS spacecraft. In March 1983, following his suggestion, we and Ball

Aerospace formed a similar team for Gravity Probe B. An intense five-day study[22] persuaded us that although the IRAS dewar really was too small, the nearly identical "stretched" dewar for COBE (COsmic Background Explorer), only one foot longer than IRAS, might be adapted to our purpose. Equally important was a rethinking of power requirements. In Phase B the anticipated power needed had reached the very high value of 576 watts. Radical (indeed brutal) surgery cut this to 143 watts. A rough pricing analysis put the program's total costs, even if done in industry, at the much more acceptable figure of $135 million 1983 dollars.

It is important to recognize that abrupt "tiger team" efforts like the Stanford–Ball study are not substitutes for the elaborate detail of a Phase B study. Their value is in laying ground rules. In large studies, as we had found earlier, change is extraordinarily difficult: everyone's assumptions have to be changed together. Take power. Ask an engineer how much power he needs and you will get one answer. Tell him how much he can have and you get another. Limits must not be absurd: a 100-watt task may not be feasible with 0.1 watt, but offer 20 watts and once the screaming and the shouting have died down an ingenious solution will often emerge to meet it. Do not be so foolish, however, as to apply the limit in only one area: you will get nothing. Everyone must feel the pinch, and everyone must feel the drive toward elegance in design.

With this, consider once again the dewar–instrument package as conceived by Stanford and its STORE subcontractor, Lockheed, and shown earlier in Fig. 8.2. The apparatus comprises the quartz-block instrument assembly developed by Stanford, containing the gyroscopes, the telescope, and the drag-free proof mass, all in the 10-inch-diameter "dewar probe." The dewar, while larger than COBE's, is still smaller than designed in Phase B; it contains 500 gallons of liquid helium and is expected to stay cold for two years. Some appreciation of the design challenge is gained from knowing that the total heat load from all sources on the huge helium tank has to be less than 80 milliwatts.

To claim elegance for one's own work would be presumptuous, but few of the ideas are mine. If, more broadly, some engineering designs are born elegant, some achieve elegance, and some have elegance thrust upon them, then in Gravity Probe B such elegance as is achieved in the design of the dewar–instrument package has been thrust upon us by the desperate needs to keep down weight and cost. What are the design's distinguishing characteristics?

Elegance in integration is *multiplicity*—solving one problem in ways that aid another. Superconducting gyroscopes, for example, need low temperatures; low temperatures stabilize the instrument assembly against mechanical creep and thermal distortion. Other multiplicities occur throughout the de-

22 Everitt, ed., "Account of the Restructuring of the GP-B Relativity Gyroscope Program."

sign, one of the most interesting being the use of the escaping helium gas to provide thrust for the spacecraft's pointing and drag-control systems.

Elegance is *optimization*. Take the "dewar probe." Its diameter should be just enough to contain the instrument assembly and allow for pumping the gyroscopes to a pressure low enough for spin-up. No more, or the lead-bag magnetic shield surrounding the instrument becomes unwieldy and the heat input into the dewar becomes excessive. A 10-inch diameter just does it: space for the instrument assembly: 5.6 inches of clear aperture for the telescope: room around that for spin-up plumbing and electrical leads: adequate pumping: a workable thermal design. The layout also matches the best configuration for the gyroscopes: all four in line on the satellite's roll axis. Meeting all the requirements, however, takes extreme attention to design detail, especially in the "neck" region between cold and warm temperatures.

Elegance is *assembly*—an apparatus readily put together and taken apart. Assembly, often a challenge in engineering design, is especially difficult in long-lived cryogenic systems, this one above all. Building the dewar with its complex thermal design is hard enough, but once assembled it at least can stay assembled. The problem is the instrument. It must, with equally stringent cooling requirements, yield to repeated assembly and disassembly. Tricky, especially since the dewar, in order to preserve the lead-bag magnetic shield, must be kept at liquid helium temperatures.

The solution combines (1) a sealed dewar probe to facilitate instrument testing, (2) an airlock to permit satisfactory insertion of the warm probe into the cold dewar, and (3) a clever new device due to Lockheed, the "Axial Lok," which simultaneously clamps in the installed probe and establishes heat paths from it to the vapor-cooled shields.

Elegance is *tolerance-ordering*, where "tolerance" means the uncertainty allowed in some manufacturing operation. Precisions differ. Take the quartz gyro–telescope assembly. Great precision is possible in figuring isolated flat or spherical surfaces; less in making two surfaces parallel; less still in making parts of predetermined length or diameter. Artful design orders operations to bring precision just where it is needed.

Elegance is *simplification*. As engineering designs evolve they gain false sophistication—empty but seductive ingenuities. Ruthlessly, agonizingly, these must be stripped away. An early problem in Gravity Probe B was telescope pointing, made difficult by floppiness in the dewar's structure. One solution—"elegant" but complex—was to supplement the spacecraft's attitude controller with a fine pointing system inside the dewar probe. Later a stiffer dewar (adopted for other reasons) removed this need. Conceptual elegance gave way to real elegance: a simple design that works.

Elegance, finally, is *work-arounds*—averting the risks, endemic to all space programs, of costly delays during fabrication or failures in orbit. For the latter consider two, each in the control systems, lost drag control and lost telescope readout in one axis. Tricks with the gyroscopes aid both. First, one of the gyroscopes, still spinning, may double as a proof mass. Second, with proper planning the lost pointing information may be recovered from the gyro readouts with surprisingly little loss of the desired data on general relativity.

Throughout this review of elegance what is so striking is the way in which cost constraints and technology are interwoven in big physics. With unlimited resources some (not all) of the elegances would be unnecessary.

Shuttle and STORE

With IRAS successful and Gravity Probe B restructured to be affordable, all after 1983 might be thought to be plain sailing. By no means so. Certainly there was a strong interest at NASA Headquarters and elsewhere in Washington in the notion of a program scaled down in cost and size without any loss of science performance. How to proceed was still far from obvious. Even if the mission's cost was $135 million (and not everyone believed it), that was still enough to require a "New Start" through OMB and Congress, a process fraught with peril and delay. A special problem, but also ultimately a special advantage, was the nature of the scientific community likely to support relativity experiments. Most would-be physicists—and physicists are not well represented in NASA advisory groups, which are mainly composed of astronomers, earth scientists, life scientists, solar scientists, geodesists, and others directly engaged in NASA programs.

During Phase B two very different approaches to developing Gravity Probe B were aired. One started from the recognition that what had been done up to 1980 was, as the Technology Review Committee emphasized, development of individual technologies rather than systems. A plausible course before proceeding to flight would be to demonstrate on the ground a complete instrument package with a telescope, at least two gyroscopes, and a science data-reduction system simulating the space system. The difficulty was that then NASA would have to commit some $30 to $40 million in advanced funding before the start of the flight program. Given the way NASA program offices are structured, such funds would be hard to break loose.

The alternative started from the observation that Stanford, apart from a subcontract from Johns Hopkins Applied Physics Laboratory from 1969 to 1972 for a small drag-free control system, had very little flight experience. Some people thought it wise for us to seek flight experience on the space shuttle with some very simple experiment—a Get-Away Special (GAS) test of a room-temperature gyro, for example. Here the difficulty was that such a test, however simple, would be a very large drain on manpower, and a diversion from the prime goal of Gravity Probe B.

Many months were spent pondering these and other suggestions for a limited program start before it finally became clear, around August 1983, at the time of NASA's submission of its budget for fiscal 1985, that the right answer would be a fusion and extension of the two ideas, to consist of building the final dewar–instrument package, testing it in an engineering "experiment rehearsal" on the space shuttle, and then bringing it back for refurbishment and integration with a spacecraft for the Science Mission. That is the program we call STORE.

Programmatic choices are not absolute truths. A good decision is one that intelligently conjoins many diverse factors, technical, managerial, and political. One is not even choosing between apples and oranges, but rather seeking, with limited information and uncertain dollar outlay, for the most desirable combination of apples, oranges, and kiwi fruit. STORE, as originally conceived, gave just that. It was technically sound because it addressed the central technical challenge of Gravity Probe B—integrating the dewar–instrument package and subjecting it to rigorous environmental tests. It was managerially sound because it forced Stanford and its chosen aerospace subcontractor, Lockheed, into a fruitful marriage focused on a flight mission that would minimize Gravity Probe B's technical and programmatic risks through the "experiment rehearsal." And it was politically sound because such a rehearsal, conducted with hardware that would be reused in the Science Mission, was seen by NASA, the Space Science Board, OMB, and the Office of Science and Technology Policy and on Capitol Hill as the right major step, prudent, acceptably priced, and imaginative in its use of the shuttle. Any flight less than STORE would have been a diversion. More, given Gravity Probe B's perceived risks, would have been impossible to sell.

The building of a full-scale instrument package for ground tests is something we have done under the name FIST (*First Integrated Systems Test*) as the first major step in STORE. Why then was that not an appropriate idea? Approval for a nonflight program of that size would, as already remarked, have been difficult, but the real and deep flaw was managerial. Without an explicit commitment to flight Lockheed would have been unlikely to bid the program, the Stanford University administration would have been unlikely to allocate the resources necessary for it (20,000 square feet of space in the prime Near West campus area, plus $650,000 capital investment for new and refurbished buildings), and Gravity Probe B itself would have been less likely to attract the good people we have been fortunate to find. More subtle, but even more critical, would have been the loss in urgency. Recall that up until 1984 the Gravity Probe B group was a laboratory research group. Few team members had the experience of working to deadlines—that is not the way of research in mazy academia. The shock of being confronted with a real flight program, with launch date, milestones, preliminary design reviews, critical design reviews, critical paths, Baseline Control Board, and the like, was profound and salutary. Developing a ground test unit for itself would have helped, but nothing like so much.

How the STORE program was sold through NASA, the OMB, and Congress, what has happened since, and whether the *Challenger* tragedy of 1986 has changed the picture, are all questions interesting to us as we go forward, and possibly to anyone who might some day choose to study our successes and our blunders. Perhaps I have said enough to show how complex life is for those who choose to pursue big physics in space.

Acknowledgments

My three principal senior colleagues are Bradford Parkinson, who serves as Program Manager and Co-Principal Investigator for Engineering Systems, John Turneaure, who is Hardware Manager and Co-Principal Investigator for Cryogenic Systems, and Daniel DeBra, Co-Principal Investigator for Engineering Design. The Stanford professional and administrative staff includes T. Ale, F. Alkemade, R. Anglim, D. Bardas, P. Bayer, J. Breakwell, T. Brosz, S. Buchman, P. Carini, D. Charleston, K. Davis, P. Ehrensberger, D. Freeman, D. Gill, J. Gill, C. Gray, G. Green, G. Gutt, R. Hacker, L. Ho, M. Jarnot, J. Kasdin, C. Kaye, M. Keiser, B. Lange, T. Langenstein, H. Larabell, S. Lester, J. Lipa, J. Lockhart, B. Muhlfelder, A. Ortega, B. Richet, M. Sato, M. Simon, J. Stamets, M. Taber, T. Van Hooydonk, R. Van Patten, J. Wade, C. Warren, M. Wood, Y. Xiao, D. Yon, and P. Zhou. The graduate students include H. S. Chou, C. Cohen, M. Condron, J. Crerie, M. Jacobs, Y. Jafry, H. Jin, D. Kalligas, C. Kee, H. Lee, K. N. Lee, H. Lee, X. Qin, M. Reisenberger, M. Tapley, H. Uematsu, T. Walter, P. Wiktor, C. H. Wu, and J. Zhu; the Lockheed staff includes R. Cowden, C. Everson, R. Parmley, G. Reynolds, J. Salmon, and some 30 others.

When this chapter was in preparation, William Fairbank, who had been such a powerful inspiration to us all, died very unexpectedly. The loss is a profound one.

References Cited

Anonymous editorial. "Physiology at Cambridge." *Nature* 9 (1874): 278–79.

Becker, R., F. Sauter, and G. Heller. "Über die Stromverteilung in einer supraleitenden Kugel." *Zeitschrift für Physik* 85 (1933): 772.

Campbell, Lewis, and William Garnett. *Life of James Clerk Maxwell.* London: Macmillan, 1882.

Everitt, C. W. F. "Studies in the Magnetism of Baked and Igneous Rocks." Ph.D. diss., London University, 1959.

———. "The Stanford Relativity Gyroscope Experiment (A): History and Overview." In J. D. Fairbank, B. S. Deaver, Jr., C. W. F. Everitt, and P. Michelson, eds., *Near Zero: New Frontiers of Physics,* pp. 587–97. New York: Freeman, 1988.

———, ed. "Account of the Restructuring of the GP-B Relativity Gyroscope Program." Stanford University report supported by NASA contract NAS8-38543.

Guthrie, F. "Remonstrance to a Respected Daddie Anent His Loss of Temper." *Nature* 19 (1879): 384.
Hartley, L. P. *The Go-Between*. London: Hamish Hamilton, 1953.
Leslie, Stuart W. "Playing the Education Game to Win: The Military and Interdisciplinary Research at Stanford." *Historical Studies in the Physical and Biological Sciences* 18 (1987): 55–88.
Little, W. A. "Organic Superconductivity: The Duke Connection." In J. D. Fairbank, B. S. Deaver, Jr., C. W. F. Everitt, and P. Michelson, eds., *Near Zero: New Frontiers of Physics*, pp. 358–70. New York: Freeman, 1988.
London, F. *Superfluids*, vol. 1, *Macroscopic Theory of Superconductivity*. New York: Wiley, 1953.
National Research Council. Space Science Board. *Strategy for Space Research in Gravitational Physics in the 1980's*. Washington, D.C.: National Academy Press, 1981.
Rosendhal, J. D. "An Assessment of the State of Technological Development of the Stanford Gyro Relativity Experiment." Washington, D.C.: NASA, 1980.
Schiff, L. I. "Possible New Experimental Test of General Relativity Theory." *Physical Review Letters* 4 (1960): 215.
Silver, A. H., and J. E. Zimmerman. "Quantum States and Transitions in Weakly Corrected Rings." *Physical Review* 157 (1967): 317–41.
Yilmaz, H. "Proposed Test of the Nature of Gravitational Interaction." *Bulletin of the American Physical Society* 4 (1959): 65.

CHAPTER 9

Du Pont and the Management of Large-Scale Research and Development

David A. Hounshell

S ince the Du Pont Company established its first formal research and development laboratory in 1902, the firm has been among a handful of U.S. corporations pursuing industrial research and development on a consistently large scale. From at least 1940 until the early 1980's, the company was an intensively research-driven, technology-driven enterprise, depending on the commercial development of its own research ideas for its sustenance. The spirit of this enterprise is perhaps best depicted by the words of Pierre S. du Pont, one of the founders of the modern Du Pont Company, who in 1907 enunciated a broad policy about the company's research and development programs that, although sometimes under stress, has endured to this day:

> In our Experimental Laboratory we should at all times endeavor to have in force some investigations in which the reward of success would be very great, but which may have a correspondingly great cost of development, calling for an extended research of possibly several years, and the employment of a considerable force. I outline this policy for two reasons: first, that it will tend to build up a line of well-trained men whose continuous employment will be certain. Second, and more important, the value of the Laboratory will eventually be much greater on this account.[1]

1 Du Pont to C. M. Barton, Aug. 17, 1908, quoted in Hounshell and Smith, *Science and Corporate Strategy,* p. 45.

Du Pont has clearly pursued a strategy of large, high-risk, high-reward research and development projects. This strategy has produced many successes and not a few failures.

Today Du Pont spends about $1.4 billion per year on research and development from sales of about $33 billion.[2] Of course, not all of this money is spent on risky research. Nor is all of it devoted to work at the frontiers of the various branches of science in which the company is involved. Much of Du Pont's research and development budget is spent with reasonably certain results in areas that some would consider mundane. This includes money spent for limited product and process improvement, for example. But still the company spends a good fraction of its research and development budget on high-risk, high-reward enterprises. Some of the projects on which this money is spent might even qualify as big science.

"Big science" is one of those concepts difficult to define precisely. The expression "I can't describe it, but I know it when I see it" is highly appropriate with big science. The term usually identifies government-funded science projects that entail massive expenditures on large-scale equipment around which large teams of researchers work. The Stanford Linear Accelerator is big science; the Manhattan Project was big science. The superconducting supercollider will be big science; fusion research such as that embodied in the Tokamak Fusion Test Reactor is big science. The chapters in this book seek to go beyond the simple step of labeling one project "big science" while describing another as something else. They seek to abstract commonalities in these projects that look like big science, to classify them, and to analyze them in the belief that such a process will lead us to a deeper, if not entirely new, understanding of big science.

Toward this goal, I seek in this chapter to develop a reasonably clear view of how the Du Pont Company has managed its big research and development projects so that we can grasp the important similarities and differences between big science within industry and the government-funded big science projects that dominate the existing historical scholarship and are the subjects of the other chapters in this volume. I propose to do this by means of three case studies drawn from Du Pont's history: the development of nylon, Du Pont's involvement in the Manhattan Project, and the development of Delrin acetal resin.[3]

This chapter chronicles how, because of both internal and external factors, the establishment of a small, elite program of fundamental research within the Du Pont Company's corporate (or central, as opposed to industrial department) research organization became a dominant model for all the company's research. Du Pont's involvement with the Manhattan Project confirmed the

2 Du Pont Company Annual Report, 1988. E. I. du Pont de Nemours and Company, Wilmington, Del.

3 Virtually all the Du Pont–related material discussed in this chapter is derived from Hounshell and Smith, *Science and Corporate Strategy*.

validity of the nylon model even though the company came into conflict with physicists at the University of Chicago's Metallurgical Laboratory. By using the nylon model to structure its research programs in the post–World War II era, as highlighted in the history of Delrin, Du Pont exposed itself to serious problems in managing research and, more important, in charting a viable strategy to maintain its historic growth and earnings rates.

The Development of Nylon, 1927–40

The development of nylon has probably played a greater role in shaping the post-1940 history of Du Pont than any other factor or set of factors.[4] This important twentieth-century material, which, among a myriad of other uses, graces women's legs, reinforces tires, helps climbers scale mountains, brushes our teeth, and carpets our floors in homes and offices, has earned Du Pont and its shareholders perhaps as much as $20 billion since its commercialization in 1940. Nylon has served not only as Du Pont's most successful product, but also as a model for the corporation's research and development programs.

To understand both nylon's history and Du Pont's research and development programs, one must comprehend that since 1921 the company has been a decentralized firm, managed multidivisionally. This means that Du Pont is a company of many companies; a president and an executive committee are responsible for the development and execution of overall corporate strategy. They maintain responsibility for oversight of relatively autonomous industrial or manufacturing departments and direct responsibility over several staff departments, including engineering and central research. Each industrial department is responsible for its own manufacturing, marketing, and research and development functions, and the general manager (now known as the "group vice-president") of each industrial department has effectively been able to do anything he wanted provided that his department's earnings remained consistently good. (As this book went to press, a major reorganization at Du Pont invested greater control in the company's chief executive officer and eliminated the company's executive committee.)

At the time of nylon's commercialization, the diversified Du Pont Company was composed of ten industrial departments, including the Rayon Department, which manufactured a wide range of viscose rayon and cellulose acetate fibers for both the apparel and the industrial fibers markets. Du Pont had been in the man-made fibers business for almost twenty years. Its new miracle fiber, however, was not the creation of the Rayon Department's large research and development organization. Rather, nylon emerged from a small elite fundamental research program established in 1927 by Charles Stine, the head of Du Pont's central research organization.

4 The invention and development of nylon are discussed in Hounshell and Smith, *Science and Corporate Strategy*, pp. 223–74.

Stine's department was a remnant of a once large and centralized organization that prior to Du Pont's decentralization of 1921 had done all of the research and development for the company. Seeking to improve the size and quality of his small organization, Stine proposed what he termed a "radical departure" in Du Pont research: conducting fundamental research aimed at establishing a solid scientific foundation under Du Pont's diversified businesses. Stine argued that Du Pont's seemingly disparate businesses—paints, plastics, explosives, dyestuffs and related organic chemicals, synthetic ammonia, rayon, cellophane, heavy chemicals—really possessed common scientific bases. If these bases were better understood, Du Pont's businesses would inevitably benefit. Because of the short-range focus of each industrial department's research division, fundamental research was not getting done (and certainly, Stine argued, the universities were not doing the kind of research he had in mind). Only the central research unit could engage in such important work on a long-term basis, thus fulfilling its logical role as the central laboratory in the diversified chemical company. By taking this approach, Stine argued, Du Pont's image as a scientific organization would be greatly bolstered, and it would be able to recruit researchers of higher caliber.

Stine identified several areas in which his organization could contribute to the company's welfare. These included research in catalysis, high-pressure reactions, physico-chemical phenomena, chemical engineering, and polymerization. The executive committee approved Stine's proposal and appropriated funds for him to build a new laboratory (which when completed became facetiously known by those who did not work there as "Purity Hall") and to recruit high-caliber researchers for each of the areas he had outlined.

With some difficulty, Stine succeeded in hiring an instructor in chemistry at Harvard, Wallace H. Carothers, to head the fundamental research group in polymers and polymerization. Like other academic chemists who had declined Stine's very generous offers, Carothers was suspicious of industrial chemistry; he accepted Du Pont's offer only after repeated assurances that by "fundamental" research, Stine meant "pure" research—research with no strings attached. And, indeed, this is the kind of research Carothers pursued for the next two years. He and his group, consisting of up to eight recently minted Ph.D.'s, massively documented the nature of polymers and polymerization, supporting the theories proposed by the German chemist Hermann Staudinger.

Then, two developments in 1930 brought an end to what has been called the "academic era" of research at Du Pont in the first half of the twentieth century. Most important, in the same month Carothers and his group quite unexpectedly discovered neoprene synthetic rubber and the first wholly synthetic fiber. For research that was to have no immediate commercial objectives, Carothers's work suddenly took on great commercial implications, especially since Du Pont was a manufacturer of rubber chemicals and two man-made fibers, rayon and cellulose acetate. These implications were enhanced by the appointment of Elmer K. Bolton as Stine's successor when, a few months after Carothers's discoveries, Stine was promoted to Du Pont's executive committee. Unlike Stine, who had above all sought *prestige for* his fundamental research program, Bolton was a hard-nosed industrial research director who now wanted *products from* Stine's program. Indeed, as director of research in Du Pont's Organic Chemical Department, Bolton had voiced opposition to Stine's proposal for a fundamental research program. Now it was his responsibility.

Bolton's succession resulted in two things. First, the responsibility for the development of neoprene was swiftly given to his former department, which had broad experience in commercial-scale organic reactions and some expertise in rubber chemistry. Second, Bolton and his new assistant, Ernest B. Benger (who had directed research in the company's Rayon Department), were quick to push Carothers to do more with synthetic fibers. The first fibers (aliphatic polyesters) made by Carothers had turned out to be highly unstable; they melted at low temperatures and fell apart in water. Bolton and Benger wanted Carothers to synthesize a polymer that could be spun into a strong, stable fiber of commercial value.

For a brief while Carothers and his group tried in earnest. But this work did not fire his scientific imagination, and he soon moved on to work on large ring compounds, an area in which he published pioneering papers, just as he had with linear condensation polymers. Yet in 1934, sensing that Carothers was vacillating about the future course of his research, Bolton strongly encouraged him to return to the fiber question. Carothers thought about new approaches to obtaining a polymer of high molecular weight that would be stable when spun into a fiber and outlined a new attack on the problem. He suggested a specific synthesis to one of his assistants, who after spending five weeks preparing the intermediates, polymerized the first polyamide (nylon). The qualities of this polymer when spun into a fiber—good stability at relatively high temperatures and resistance to hydrolysis—led to an intense period of making other polyamides and checking their fiber properties. Synthesizing other polyamides entailed polymerizing every known combination of dibasic acids and diamines with carbon chains between two and ten atoms long (some 81 possible compounds). This work was done almost entirely within Carothers's fundamental research group in Purity Hall and, perhaps much against Carothers's own intentions, had become the principal focus of his group.

By the spring of 1935, Carothers had determined that a 5-10 polyamide was the optimal candidate for fiber development. (The numerical designations for various types of nylon polyamides come from the number of carbon atoms in the diamine and the dibasic acid, respectively.) But Bolton vetoed the 5-10 polymer. Believing that the pentamethylene diamine intermediate would be far too expensive, he advocated a 6-6 polymer, the intermediates of which could be made from the abundant compound benzene.

Up to this point the nylon project was essentially a piece of work done in Carothers's fundamental polymer research group and represented but a small part of the central research organization's overall budget. In 1934, Bolton's organization employed almost 120 scientists and research engineers with a total budget of about $900,000.[5] The expenses of Carothers's group, including salaries, would probably have come to less than $75,000. Du Pont's total research budget was $5.7 million in 1934, and its research and development personnel totaled almost 850 scientists and research engineers. (In the same year, the United States Department of Agriculture's research budget was $16 million, well down from its earlier high of $22 million.)[6]

Despite its modest beginnings, the nylon project quickly became a crash program to commercialize the world's first synthetic fiber. (Carothers, who at this time was suffering from a worsening case of chronic depression, essentially dropped out of the nylon development project; he did, however, finish writing the very important patent applications upon which Du Pont built a very substantial proprietary position.) When Bolton made his decision that nylon 6-6 would be the candidate for development, the fiber was truly a laboratory curiosity. Commercialization required proving the fiber in existing markets, which meant scaling up the laboratory operation from pushing the molten polymer through a hypodermic needle in milligram quantities to spinning and drawing it in gram and kilogram quantities (see Fig. 9.1). Such scale-up required the synthesis of the intermediates from which nylon 6-6 was polymerized, not an easy task because neither intermediate was commercially available in the United States and because synthesis of both required high pressures. Development also meant evaluating how well the new fiber performed in commercial textile processes such as knitting, weaving, dyeing, and finishing. These requirements dictated that Du Pont have expertise not only in polymerization (which Carothers's group effectively supplied) but also in high-pressure synthesis and commercial fiber manufacture.

Fortunately for Du Pont's central research unit, it could rely upon the company's Ammonia Department, which possessed outstanding expertise in high-pressure synthesis, and its Rayon Department, whose staff knew the man-made fibers business as well as anyone. The nylon project therefore became a joint venture, with the central research department taking responsibility for polymerization and melt spinning, the Ammonia Department attending to large-scale synthesis of intermediates, and the Rayon Department concentrating on the textile end. Bolton retained overall responsibility for the project, but he relied heavily on Benger for close management of the project. The Rayon Department's research unit charged its second-in-command, Er-

5 Data on Du Pont's research and development workforce and expenditures, including those of the central research unit, appear in Hounshell and Smith, *Science and Corporate Strategy,* pp. 288–91.

6 Dupree, *Science in the Federal Government,* p. 345.

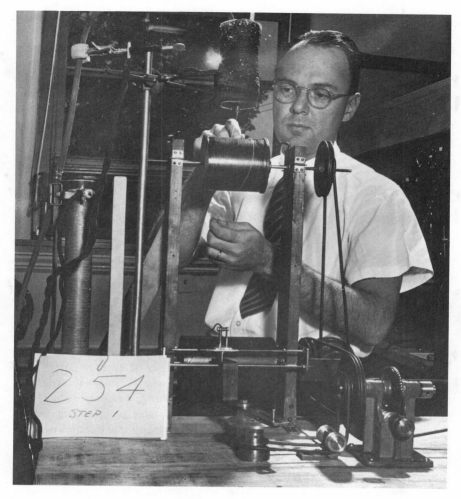

Fig. 9.1. Donald Coffman, an early member of Wallace Carothers's group, demonstrating the first successful, laboratory-scale wind-up of nylon after the molten polymer emerges from the spinneret, 1938. Photo courtesy Hagley Museum and Library.

nest Gladding, with active supervision of its end of the project. Gladding assigned George Preston Hoff the duty of being his department's liaison with the central research organization. Most of the nylon research and development was carried out at Du Pont's Experimental Station five miles north of the center of Wilmington, Delaware, where the central research unit had always been located.

Understanding how the central research organization managed its research is important to a full appreciation of the nylon project and Du Pont's influence on the way research was done on the plutonium end of the Manhattan Project. Shortly after he became the director of central research, Elmer Bolton established what he called the Steering Committee, which he chaired. The committee was composed of Bolton's assistant director of central research (Benger), the director of the Experimental Station, the assistant director of the Experimental Station and his assistant, and the research supervisors (who were one step above the group leaders). The Steering Committee met weekly (after 1935 twice weekly), and attendance was absolutely mandatory; members were expected to organize their schedules around the committee's meetings. The function of the committee was to coordinate the research of the department. Committee members discussed the research being done by the various groups and by the department as a whole. To keep in touch with researchers directly, the committee established the research review, in which group leaders and individual researchers gave presentations on their work at least yearly and sometimes more frequently. The committee authorized and monitored all research projects, including nylon, through this process.[7] One member of the Steering Committee, Crawford H. Greenewalt, a research supervisor whose specialty was chemical engineering, played in addition to Benger and Bolton an active role in the nylon development project.

Although the history of nylon's development from a laboratory specimen in 1935 to a commercial product less than five years later is a fascinating story, only a few salient points are important to comprehend here. The central research department brilliantly orchestrated nylon's development because of its managers' ability to settle very early—to "freeze," in their words—on the fundamental elements of the product and process. Bolton's decision to develop nylon 6-6 instead of the more easily polymerized 5-10 has already been cited. As important was the department's decision that melt spinning was the best way to produce nylon fibers. Spinning experts in the Rayon Department strongly advocated employing one of the two methods it used for the commercial production of rayon and cellulose acetate (solution or "wet" spinning and solvent or "dry" spinning, respectively). But managers in central research believed melt spinning to be a far better way to do the job, even though researchers encountered one difficulty after another in making this approach work on a scale larger than the hypodermic needle. These managers resisted the temptation to work on all three spinning processes simultaneously, choosing instead to focus all efforts on what appeared to be the most technically elegant approach.

Nylon research managers also organized the development project in a parallel rather than linear fashion. They did not hold up the project's development because one step of the process was not falling into place. The best

7 The creation and functioning of the Steering Committee are discussed in Hounshell and Smith, *Science and Corporate Strategy*, pp. 308–9.

244   DAVID A. HOUNSHELL

example of this is what happened with sizing. Sizing is a kind of protective coating put on fibers so that they can be processed smoothly by textile manufacturers, such as knitters or weavers. Because nylon is hydrophobic, repelling water, conventional water-soluble sizes would not work, and researchers had great difficulty finding a compound that would. Rather than holding up the project, researchers designed the commercial plant with a big blank spot on the blueprints labeled simply "sizing area." Nobody knew what the compound would be, how it would be applied, and what other processes would be affected. In fact, the commercial plant was virtually completed before the sizing problem was solved.

Most important, the nylon project succeeded brilliantly because its managers kept the project focused on one commercial target—women's full-fashion hosiery. Nylon is a very versatile material, and it was tempting for managers to try to develop the fiber for all or many of the markets they thought it could penetrate. But the managers wisely resisted. They saw that the greatest initial market opportunity for nylon was in women's hosiery where silk was commanding prices of from $3 to as high as $9 per pound. Nylon had many silk-like properties but was better for stockings because it was so resistant to abrasion and stable in water. The entire development effort focused on displacing silk in women's hosiery with nylon, and when the commercial plant started up, the company simply could not keep up with demand (in part because of increasing trade problems with Japan that soon deteriorated into a total end to silk imports in the United States). With such a tight focus, Du Pont was able to commercialize nylon in an extraordinarily short time and without a great outlay of money. Only after the commercialization of nylon for stockings did Du Pont develop the material for new applications in lingerie, as a tire cord, as a carpet fiber, and as a versatile plastic, among other end uses.

Another important element in the success of the nylon project was the way in which the scale of the project moved deliberately from the laboratory to semi-works to pilot plant to commercial operation. At each step along the way data about the fiber and its manufacturing processes were generated and digested to improve both the fiber and the process at that stage and for the subsequent stage. Use of semi-works was by no means an innovation stemming from the nylon project; Charles Stine had been instrumental in making the semi-works stage a routine part of any scale-up operation at Du Pont.[8] But the smoothness with which Du Pont and nylon moved through these various scale-up stages reinforced their importance for the project's managers.

The company spent $4.3 million on nylon's precommercial research and development and sank almost $9 million into the first commercial plant and $2.5 million into a plant to manufacture intermediates. Approximately 200 research scientists and engineers from the central research, Ammonia, and

8 Hounshell and Smith, *Science and Corporate Strategy,* p. 51.

Rayon departments had been involved in the project (plus, of course, the many engineers assigned to the routine design and construction of the plants).

With the January 1940 opening of the first commercial nylon plant, the project's managers knew that their insistence on focusing the project on stockings and the division of the project into its logical parts (polymerization and spinning, intermediates, development of the fiber for a specific market) had paid off—and in a big way. They believed that they had developed an ideal approach to managing research and development—from fundamental research all the way through commercial development. Nylon became a model, an archetype for Du Pont's research and development on large projects, including that leading to the Hanford Engineer Works of the Manhattan Project.

Du Pont and the Manhattan Project

Du Pont's role in the Manhattan Project is well known through the works of Richard G. Hewlett and Oscar E. Anderson, Jr., Leslie R. Groves, and some of the more recent books on the atomic bomb project.[9] But these works have not given the Du Pont perspective, a perspective that adds, I think, an important dimension to an otherwise fascinating story.[10]

As is well documented, Arthur Compton took the first step toward bringing Du Pont into the Manhattan Project when he grew concerned about the Stone & Webster Engineering Corporation's ability to fulfill its contract for the design, construction, and operation of the plutonium separation plant and the full-size pile project that eventually became the Hanford Engineer Works. Compton asked Groves if Du Pont could not, as a subcontractor, aid Stone & Webster in designing and constructing the separation plant and then assume responsibility for running it. Groves approached Du Pont's chief engineer, E. G. Ackart, with such a proposal on September 28, 1942. By October 7, Du Pont had agreed to something much bigger: full responsibility for design, construction, and operation of the separation plant.[11]

Groves envisioned an even greater role for Du Pont in the Manhattan Project. Later in October, he invited Du Pont representatives to Washington, where he asked them to assume sole responsibility for the design, construction, and operation of the full-scale pile project. Without more information, Du Pont was unwilling to agree. Consequently Groves arranged for eight Du Pont representatives to go to the University of Chicago to evaluate its Metallurgical Laboratory's research. Immediately Charles Stine led a delegation to Chicago to review the entire project with Compton and his staff. Interestingly, among

9 Hewlett and Anderson, *The New World,* Groves, *Now It Can Be Told,* Compton, *Atomic Quest,* Jones, *Manhattan,* Rhodes, *The Making of the Atomic Bomb.*

10 A brief discussion of Du Pont's role in the Manhattan Project appears in Hounshell and Smith, *Science and Corporate Strategy,* pp. 338–46.

11 Du Pont executive committee minutes, Oct. 7, 1942.

the eight were two men who had been intimately involved in the nylon project, Elmer Bolton and Crawford Greenewalt, and several others who had worked on pieces of it, including Roger Williams, former research director in the Ammonia Department.[12]

By November 11, Du Pont's delegation had reached a consensus that the company should undertake the project only if (1) Du Pont "goes into it wholeheartedly, viz., with all the talent the job needs," (2) Du Pont were responsible for "all phases of design and operation," (3) Du Pont were allowed to examine alternative approaches being pursued at Columbia and Berkeley, and (4) Groves and Du Pont could reach a clear understanding "regarding absolute necessities for timing."[13]

On November 12, Groves and his assistant, Colonel Kenneth D. Nichols, and Compton and his assistant, Norman Hilberry, came to Wilmington to discuss the matter. Du Pont was, according to Groves, "noncommittal."[14] The company's executives briefly chronicled Du Pont's near-perfect approach to nylon's development and contrasted it with that of plutonium, for which there was virtually no laboratory data. Representatives from Du Pont's delegation to Chicago then delivered an extensive critique of Chicago's program. Not rejecting Grove's request, Du Pont's executives asked for an opportunity to compare other approaches to the production of fissionable material being pursued by Harold Urey and Ernest Lawrence. With this request, the meeting ended.[15]

A week later Groves and James B. Conant agreed to allow Du Pont to appraise these other approaches.[16] Together with Du Pont representatives, they concocted something of a ruse to achieve Du Pont's objectives: a "representative" technical committee, headed by Warren K. Lewis, ostensibly charged with reviewing all avenues to plutonium production. In fact, the committee's sole function was to give Du Pont's Crawford Greenewalt, Roger Williams, and Thomas Gary an opportunity to look at the other approaches so that Du Pont could back what they deemed would be the winner.[17] The "findings" of the Lewis Committee did not establish a sufficient basis for Du Pont's

12 Other members of the delegation included Tom C. Gary (director, Design Division, Engineering Department), Thomas H. Chilton (director, Technical Division, Engineering Department), F. W. Pardee (Engineering Department), and Willis F. Harrington (executive committee advisor on engineering).

13 Greenewalt, Manhattan Project Diary (1942–44), Nov. 11, 1942. Manuscripts Department, Hagley Museum and Library, Wilmington, Del.

14 Groves, Now It Can Be Told, pp. 48–49.

15 Ibid., pp. 49–50; Hewlett and Anderson, The New World, p. 107.

16 Greenewalt Diary, Nov. 18, 1942.

17 Ibid. Greenewalt, interviewed by David A. Hounshell and John Kenly Smith, Jr., Dec. 15, 1982, confirmed that the Lewis Committee was established solely for the benefit of Du Pont. Manuscripts Department, Hagley Museum and Library.

representatives to recommend against acceptance of Groves's proposal.[18] On December 16, Du Pont formally agreed to undertake at once the design, construction, and operation of the plutonium production operation on top of the separation plant already agreed upon.[19]

As Hewlett and Anderson have perceptively noted, Du Pont was large enough to fit the plutonium project into its existing organizational structure.[20] The executive committee created a new division within the Explosives Department and named it TNX, a ruse that harkened back to the World War I days when Du Pont produced an explosive made from *trinitroxylene* and called TNX.[21] Roger Williams was named the division's head, and he brought with him from the Ammonia Department engineer R. Monte Evans to be responsible for the operation (in Du Pont parlance, the TNX Division's "manufacturing" operations) of what became the Hanford Engineer Works. Crawford Greenewalt, who had been a major force in nylon's development, was named the head of the research or "technical" section of the TNX Division. Greenewalt's major responsibility was to be an effective liaison between researchers at Chicago's Metallurgical Laboratory and Du Pont's Wilmington operations, including the Engineering Department, which would manage the actual design and construction of Hanford.

Almost immediately conflict erupted between the scientists at Chicago and the Du Pont Company. Metallurgical Laboratory physicists began to fear being controlled by an industrial organization. As Hewlett and Anderson stated, "they did not intend to become a field station of the Du Pont Explosives Department."[22] Greenewalt had anticipated some of this sentiment, and he sought at once to allay Chicago's fears. He convinced General Groves and Roger Williams that his proper role was to be a liaison with Chicago, conveying Du Pont's design team's needs for research information to Chicago and carrying Du Pont's work back to the physicists for review. Groves had wanted Greenewalt to be "the boss" of the physicists, but the pragmatic Greenewalt recognized that this was impossible. Only a distinguished physicist like Compton could serve that role.[23]

On his first visit to Chicago after Du Pont signed the contract, Greenewalt reviewed his role as liaison with Compton, a move that quickly won the physicist's good will. To his surprise, however, Greenewalt found that Compton and his associates held "peculiar ideas as to the difference between 'scien-

18 The conclusions of the Lewis Committee are appended to Compton to Greenewalt, Nov. 15, 1955. Manuscripts Department, Hagley Museum and Library, Accession 1814, Box 30.

19 Du Pont executive committee minutes, Dec. 9, 11, 14, and 16, 1942.

20 Hewlett and Anderson, *The New World*, p. 187.

21 Hounshell and Smith, *Science and Corporate Strategy*, p. 79.

22 Hewlett and Anderson, *The New World*, p. 191.

23 Greenewalt Diary, Dec. 17, 18, 19, and 22, 1942.

tific' and 'industrial' research."[24] Greenewalt countered that the difference was semantic rather than real and then began what he called "missionary work" to convince the Chicago physicists of Du Pont's abilities and sincere motives.

Speaking before the laboratory's technical council on December 28, 1942, Greenewalt sought to educate and assuage the many skeptics who believed that their creation was being stolen by a corporate giant. He said Du Pont was there "to do a job" rather than to "pick their brains" and "make a barrel of money out of atomic energy." Addressing the company's ability to translate pure research into full-scale production, Greenewalt held up as a model the nylon project with which he was so intimately familiar. Du Pont had special engineering know-how that Chicago's team did not possess, know-how that was critical to the project's success.[25] Following Greenewalt's presentation, some skeptics remained. But other physicists were genuinely interested in learning more about Du Pont's approach to industrial research. Robert S. Mulliken, for example, later asked Greenewalt to give a seminar on industrial research.[26]

The nylon model soon began to penetrate Du Pont's actions, not just its rhetoric. Roger Williams determined that Chicago's already-designed "semi-works" pile and separation plant planned for the Argonne Forest Preserve southwest of Chicago were inadequate. A veteran at scaling processes up, Williams believed that the facility would be too small to generate the kind of data needed for designing the full-scale plants. A semi-works of sufficient scale, Williams believed, would present too great a hazard to residents of Chicago to be built at Argonne. A bigger semi-works would have to be designed and built at a remote location—the government's Oak Ridge site intended for the full-scale operation.[27]

Unfortunately, Williams and Groves made this latter decision without consulting Compton, so the physicists at Chicago were up in arms when they heard the news.[28] However, Williams and Groves smoothed over the affair by assuring Compton that Du Pont would not only design and build the pilot

24 *Ibid.*, Dec. 28, 1942. Compton had begun his career at Westinghouse's new research laboratory in Pittsburgh, an institution that practiced industrial research and development in a manner far different from Du Pont's. Perhaps it was his experience with Westinghouse that made Compton wary of all industrial research, including Du Pont's. For more information on Compton at Westinghouse, see Kline "Engineering R&D at the Westinghouse Electric Company, 1886–1922."

25 Greenewalt interview, Dec. 15, 1982; Greenewalt Diary, Dec. 28, 1942; Hewlett and Anderson, *The New World*, pp. 190–91.

26 Greenewalt Diary, Mar. 12, 26, 1943.

27 Events leading up to this decision are detailed in Greenewalt's diary, which makes clear how Williams insisted upon getting accurate calculations on the safety of the pilot plant in the event of a worst-case disaster. See also Hewlett and Anderson, *The New World*, p. 191.

28 Greenewalt Diary, Jan. 6 and 9, 1943.

plant but operate it as well; the Chicago physicists could still build and operate their planned research facility at Argonne.[29]

Williams promised more than he could deliver. Du Pont's executive committee rejected the idea of Du Pont's operating a semi-works at Oak Ridge.[30] Most likely Charles Stine was the main factor in this decision. He adamantly believed that the principal purpose of a semi-works was to generate data for the design of full-scale facilities; a semi-works, Stine maintained, should be operated by the research group (i.e. the Metallurgical Laboratory), not the manufacturing division (i.e. Du Pont).[31] Du Pont's decision meant that the University of Chicago would have to assume operating responsibility for the semi-works that Du Pont would build at Oak Ridge.[32]

Du Pont's nylon model manifested itself in other ways as well. Early in his tenure, Greenewalt sought successfully to reorganize the management structure that Compton had created for the Metallurgical Laboratory. Greenewalt told Compton that he lacked a sufficient number of top-level research managers at Chicago and suggested that he appoint a "Laboratory Director," whose duties would be similar to those of the laboratory director in Du Pont's central research organization.[33] He also recommended that Chicago manage its research with a "plan similar to our 'steering committee' system" in central research.[34] Compton and his assistant Hilberry liked both of these recommendations and adopted them. Greenewalt also found Chicago's research reporting system lacking and suggested to the laboratory's new director that he adopt a system similar to Du Pont's.[35] Finally, concerned about Chicago's laissez-faire approach to research in nuclear physics and the problems it created for obtaining data critically needed for designing larger reactors, Greenewalt urged Compton to adopt a project system similar to Du Pont's in order to establish priorities and hence to control research.[36] Some of the Chicago physicists, especially Eugene Wigner, resented Greenewalt's reshaping of the research process at Chicago along lines familiar to Du Pont.[37]

Conflict between Du Pont and Chicago also stemmed from Du Pont's

29 *Ibid.,* Jan. 12, 1943.

30 Du Pont executive committee minutes, Jan. 15, 1943.

31 Stine's views on semi-works and their operation were stated forcefully in a memorandum to Hamilton Bradshaw, May 3, 1920, Central Research and Development Department Records, Du Pont Company, Accession 1784, Hagley Museum and Library. Greenewalt had also initially opposed Du Pont's operating the semi-works, as evidenced in his diary, Dec. 31, 1942.

32 Hewlett and Anderson, *The New World,* pp. 192–93.

33 Greenewalt Diary, Dec. 28, 1942.

34 *Ibid.,* Jan. 13, 1943.

35 *Ibid.,* Mar. 12, 1943.

36 *Ibid.,* Apr. 24 and July 29, 1943.

37 See the following entries in Greenewalt's diary for his discussion of problems with the physicists, particularly Wigner: Jan. 4, 5, 6, Mar. 20, 25, Apr. 7, May 20, July 30, 31, Aug. 3, 5, 12, 16, 19, 21, Sept. 16, Oct. 18, 28, 1943, Apr. 10, 22, 1944.

insistence that major designs be "frozen" and that subsequent research be done within the framework of these frozen designs.[38] Greenewalt encountered continual trouble from the physicists in settling the major issues and then pursuing the research necessary to complete the design. While he appreciated the propensities of some scientists to follow interesting research questions, Greenewalt needed data for Du Pont's design engineers, which could be achieved only by directing the work of the Chicago physicists—through "applied" research. Greenewalt reported that Enrico Fermi was always urging Du Pont just to build a big reactor as fast as possible, figure out why it did not work, and then build another that did.[39] Du Pont's objective was to get it right the first time, Greenewalt believed.

Physicists such as Wigner failed to appreciate the extent of the engineering problems surrounding the project and generally underestimated the importance of engineering. Here was a classic case of "science" versus "engineering." Some Chicago physicists complained of excessive red tape and charged that Du Pont was too preoccupied with safety and margins of error rather than with speed in doing the job. A workable arrangement was not achieved until Greenewalt succeeded in getting Compton to have the Chicago team review with Du Pont's designers all blueprints for the Hanford works and sign off on them. Once this process began, some of the Chicago people began to appreciate the magnitude of the engineering involved.[40]

As soon as Du Pont completed the semi-works/pilot plant at Oak Ridge (known as the Clinton Works), the Chicago physicists began to turn out data critically important for both engineers at Du Pont and scientists at Los Alamos. Du Pont had reached this stage in the road toward Hanford less than ten months after signing a letter of intent to Groves. The once-skeptical Chicago physicists deemed the Clinton complex an excellent nuclear physics research facility.[41] Yet Greenewalt soon discovered that he could not convince any of the first-class Chicago physicists to enter Du Pont's employ on even a temporary basis to serve as scientific experts for the start-up of the full-scale plant at Hanford.

In a wonderfully vain letter from Samuel K. Allison, whom Compton had named director of the Metallurgical Laboratory, to Roger Williams, the Chicago physicists explained why they rejected Du Pont's invitations. They regarded nuclear physics (especially the chain reaction of neutrons) as "the greatest achievement of the science of physics" and believed that any research in this area should be "run by physicists" having a "prominent place" in the organization. Allison wrote, "entering the Du Pont Company as individuals in

38 The Greenewalt Diary and Greenewalt interview of Dec. 15, 1982, are replete with discussions of getting major design questions frozen and the animosity this induced at Chicago. See also Hewlett, "Beginnings of Development," pp. 474–75.
39 Greenewalt interview, Dec. 15, 1982.
40 Ibid.
41 Hewlett and Anderson, The New World, pp. 210–12.

subordinate positions, the prestige of physicists in our program is greatly diminished." Work at Chicago had been directed by "physicists of world-wide reputations." Du Pont had no such men in the Hanford organization. Finally, "in contrast to the chemists," the nuclear physicists "greatly prefer an academic life to one of service to an industrial company." They perceived that their chance for such a life would be ruined if they even temporarily entered Du Pont's employ at Hanford.[42]

The Chicago Metallurgical Laboratory was a bundle of conflicts and contradictions. The physicists wanted big science (i.e. expensive, continuously funded, technologically dependent research) without really comprehending that it entailed big technology, which had been traditionally and quite successfully carried out by industrial companies such as Du Pont. Surely such attitudes as those expressed by Allison shaped postwar developments in both nuclear physics research and nuclear power development. The bleak prospect for being able to recruit physicists was one of five important reasons why Du Pont opted to stay out of the nuclear energy field in the postwar era.[43]

The Hanford project was the largest single construction project of the war. Du Pont and its subcontractors hired some 60,000 workers ranging from common laborers and skilled craftsmen to engineers and scientists. A city was created almost overnight. The scale of the entire operation was simply impressive[44] (see Fig. 9.2).

Yet, as Richard Hewlett has stressed, the Hanford works might have been one gigantic boondoggle had Du Pont's design engineers not, against strong protests from the Chicago physicists, built in Du Pont's customary margins of error and safety.[45] When the company brought the first full-scale Hanford reactor toward full power, the pile's reactivity rate began dropping. Essentially, the pile turned itself off. Greenewalt, quite independently of Fermi and John Wheeler, ran through a few calculations and hypothesized that the pile was generating a neutron-absorbing gas (xenon-135). He then informed Wheeler and Fermi, who, approaching the problem in different ways, confirmed his hypothesis.[46] The Chicago physicists had never operated the Clinton pile at full power long enough to observe this phenomenon. Had Du Pont not built extra slug channels in the Hanford piles, which allowed this phenomenon to be overcome, the piles simply would not have worked at anything close to full power; not enough plutonium would have been available for the test at Alamogordo and the detonation over Nagasaki.[47]

42 Allison to Williams, Mar. 13, 1944, photocopy in Greenewalt Diary, Mar. 15, 1944.

43 For a discussion of Du Pont's consideration of commercial activity in nuclear energy in the postwar era, see Hounshell and Smith, *Science and Corporate Strategy*, pp. 342–45.

44 See Du Pont Company, *The Du Pont Company's Part in the National Security Program*, pp. 59–64, for an accounting of Hanford's scale.

45 Hewlett, "Beginnings of Development."

46 Greenewalt Diary, Sept. 27, 28, 29, and 30, 1944.

47 This is the conclusion of Hewlett and Anderson, *The New World*, pp. 305–8.

Fig. 9.2. Aerial photograph of part of the Hanford Engineering Works under construction in 1943–44. At one time, Du Pont had approximately 45,000 workers on the construction site, from plumbers to physicists. Photo courtesy Hagley Museum and Library.

Du Pont's managers, such as Roger Williams (who in 1945 replaced the retiring Charles Stine on the executive committee) and Crawford Greenewalt (who after the start-up of Hanford was put on Du Pont's executive fast track and was named president in 1948) saw very clear parallels between the development of nylon into a commercially successful fiber and the development of Glenn T. Seaborg's newly discovered element plutonium into macroscopically useful quantities.[48] Nylon had emerged from a high-caliber fun-

48 See, e.g., Greenewalt, "Fundamental Research: Definition and Justification," Feb. 1945. Records of E. I. du Pont de Nemours and Company, ser. 2, part 2. Manuscripts Department, Hagley Museum and Library.

damental research program in polymer chemistry; it had been scaled up from milligram quantities in Carothers's laboratory to a 4-million-pound-per-year commercial plant in Seaford, Delaware, in a crash program. With plutonium, Du Pont moved from Seaborg's microscopically observable quantity to a full-scale plant capable of producing enough for several bombs in little over two years. Du Pont had sought, quite successfully though not without protest, to structure Chicago's research in the image of Du Pont's central research organization. The company followed the same principles of scale-up that it had employed with nylon, and it had been successful with both projects because of the extraordinarily sharp focus on objectives it maintained.

Finally, both projects succeeded because of the depth of industrial and engineering skills that the company possessed. The nylon project drew on the scientific skills of those in central research, the high-pressure experience of those in the Ammonia Department, the market development and manufacturing organization skills of the Rayon Department, and the deep reservoir of technical and construction skills of the Engineering Department. The TNX project relied upon not just the scientific acumen of the Chicago physicists, but also on the same organizational and technical skills embodied in the TNX team put together by Roger Williams and the same design engineering and construction skills of the Engineering Department that had made nylon go so smoothly. The depth of the Du Pont Engineering Department's organizational, design, and construction engineering skills, in particular, should be noted. Other Du Pont departments also contributed to the Hanford works, especially the Grasselli Chemicals Department, which, among other organizations, worked on the thorny problem of encasing the slugs of uranium that went into the pile.[49]

The Clinton and Hanford works were not, it should be noted, the only jobs undertaken by Du Pont during the war. The Engineering Department designed and built 53 other plants, including $500 million worth of military explosives plants, which manufactured 2.5 billion pounds of smokeless powder, 1.5 billion pounds of TNT, and over 300 million pounds of other high explosives. For the sake of comparison, Du Pont spent about $350 million on the Hanford works.[50]

Du Pont's success with the Hanford project reinforced its confidence in the correctness of the nylon model. Before nylon, the company's principal strategies for both growth and the acquisition of new technologies had been acquisitions of companies, joint ventures, and outright purchases of technologies.[51] But several factors combined to change this strategy. First, Du Pont's scientific and technological expertise deepened, as evidenced by Stine's creation of a

49 The Greenewalt Diary is an excellent source of information on the work done by Graselli on canning uranium slugs.

50 A brief summary of Du Pont's wartime activities is Du Pont Company, *The Du Pont Company's Part in the National Security Program.*

51 Hounshell and Smith, *Science and Corporate Strategy,* pp. 65–219.

fundamental research program in the central research organization and by the growth in the size and quality of the company's industrial research divisions.[52]

Growing antitrust sentiment late in the New Deal was a more important factor. The selection of Thurman Arnold as the head of the Justice Department's Antitrust Division in 1938 signaled the end of an era in which Du Pont (and most other large American firms) could grow through acquisitions.[53]

The enormous success of nylon and the fact that it had stemmed from a high-quality fundamental research program provided the third and perhaps the most important factor in Du Pont's shift in corporate strategy. Simply put, the company's new strategy was to generate "new nylons."[54] To implement this strategy, Du Pont radically expanded its research facilities throughout the company. Industrial departments were instructed to initiate fundamental research programs (a type of research that had been done almost solely by the central research department), and most of the departments built new laboratories in which to carry out this research at the campus-like Experimental Station. With a strong central research organization and with each industrial department doing its own fundamental and pioneering research, the company's leaders expected the almost continuous discovery and development of "new nylons" based on the company's deep technical and capital resources. This was Du Pont's version of big science.[55]

Delrin Acetal Resin

Delrin acetal resin was "the Manhattan Project" of Du Pont's Polychemicals Department. Commercialized in 1960, Delrin was the result of the company's most expensive research and development project up to that date. Like nylon and the Manhattan Project, it emerged from a crash program. The only problem was that it was not as successful as nylon; one reason, perhaps, was because in trying to force the project as it did the Manhattan Project, Du Pont broke some of its own rules about how such projects should be carried out.[56]

In 1950 the Polychemicals Department (a new department representing the merger of the old Plastics and Ammonia departments) was prospecting for a new polymer to develop as a plastic. The managers of the department's research division asked their counterparts in the central research organization about candidate polymers. Among several items on central research's list was

52 See chapter 15 of Hounshell and Smith, *Science and Corporate Strategy,* for more information on the growth of Du Pont's departmental research organizations in the pre–World War II period.

53 Hounshell and Smith, *Science and Corporate Strategy,* pp. 346–47.

54 Greenewalt, "Fundamental Research: Definition and Justification."

55 Hounshell and Smith, *Science and Corporate Strategy,* pp. 350–64.

56 *Ibid.,* pp. 486–91. For a discussion of another firm's development in a "Manhattan Project" mode, see Margaret B. W. Graham, *RCA and the VideoDisc: The Business of Research* (New York: Cambridge University Press, 1986), pp. 196–212.

polyformaldehyde. Here was a polymer that was intellectually attractive, even though chemists had been trying to make a good plastic from it since the 1920's. Formaldehyde was cheap and it was easy to polymerize. The only problem was that polyformaldehyde was highly unstable; it easily reverted to formaldehyde at relatively low temperatures.

Chemists in central research believed that if one could obtain a very pure formaldehyde, its polymer would be stable. In the late 1940's, they pursued this approach and obtained a solid with good strength and resilience and with improved thermal stability. But the polymer was still not good enough to commercialize. Having drawn this conclusion, central research dropped its work on polyformaldehyde until it put the polymer on the list of promising leads it supplied the Polychemicals Department in the 1950's. Polychem's research management was attracted to the polymer and authorized central research to reexamine its work and try new approaches.

Robert N. McDonald, a 33-year-old Yale Ph.D., was assigned the task, and he produced a polyformaldehyde with greatly improved properties. McDonald's work led to Polychem's research management's assigning four of its chemists to undertake additional research on polyformaldehyde in 1952.

Enter Roger Williams, nylon and Hanford veteran, former supervisor of many of the managers in Polychem, and now the executive committee's advisor on research. In conducting a review of Polychem's research program, Williams noted that the department was pursuing half a dozen new polymers and really not getting very far with any of them. He thought the organization should freeze on one polymer and devote a minimum of six months of intensive team research on it to bring about a breakthrough. If no such breakthrough came, the polymer should be dropped and another candidate pursued the same way. Williams's recommendation prevailed, and polyformaldehyde was selected as the first target.

In September 1952, Polychem beefed up its manpower on the polymer from six to 50. Interestingly, a 41-year-old chemical engineer and Manhattan Project veteran was given the leadership of the task force. The task force attacked all phases of development simultaneously. Research groups went to work on the product and the process, and members of the sales division began to formulate a marketing plan. One problem remained, however. The polymer was still too thermally unstable to survive in the market. But researchers soon learned that the polymer's internal bonds were stable; decomposition began at the ends of the chains. This finding suggested a solution to the problem: capping the ends of the chains to prevent the initiation of decomposition.

With this discovery, work on the project became more intense. More work was done on both the product and the process. Work began on a semi-works that was consciously intended to make products for market development rather than to generate data for plant design. At this point Polychem's thinking was that the new polymer (called "synthetic stone" by one research manager) would be so cheap that it could easily penetrate existing plastics markets, including that held by Du Pont's Zytel nylon resins.

But in less than a year, the task force was obliged to redefine the product. Formaldehyde could not be purified as cheaply as had been expected, and the capping process was expensive. The polymer would be very high priced unless it was made in very large quantities—in a plant with an annual capacity of at least 30 million pounds. Even then, the plastic would be expensive. Such a large plant meant that the market for polyformaldehyde would have to grow at an unprecedented rate. These findings called for rethinking the market development program. The product would have to be "a premium-priced [plastic meeting needs] that cannot be served by plastics other than nylon and hopefully not even that."

The market development team of the task force requested a delay in the decision to commercialize the new plastic (now known as Delrin) while it made its potential market calculations. Moving away from the idea of Delrin competing with other plastics, the team studied applications in which Delrin could be substituted for nonferrous metals. On the basis of 44 such applications, the team showed that at 60 cents per pound Delrin could find markets of nearly 40 million pounds per year. An expanded study raised the total to 143 million pounds and potentially to a billion pounds per year.

With these findings, the task force and Polychem's management believed it important to commercialize Delrin as rapidly as possible. The process development team was ordered to stop looking for new routes and instead to polish the most promising process. Now the major issue was just how big to build the commercial plant. In late 1955 Polychem asked the Engineering Department to provide it with estimates of investment and operating costs for plants with capacities of 2, 20, and 40 million pounds. But soon the department's management abandoned any idea of building a 2-million-pound plant; they deemed it too small for commercial purposes and unnecessary for generating design data for a large commercial plant. After considerable agonizing, the department decided to build a 20-million-pound plant that could be easily expanded to 40 million pounds. The plant would operate with a process completely different from that used in the small, 50,000-pound semi-works that had been making material for market development. On November 2, 1956, a few days after the basic Delrin patent was issued, the executive committee authorized Polychem to begin designing the plant, which went into commercial operation in January 1960 (see Fig. 9.3).

Delrin had been commercialized in only seven years, but because of the intensity of its development the price had been high. In fact, it was the most expensive research and development project in the company's history; total costs were over $50 million with 60% going to precommercial research and development expenses and the remaining 40% to the cost of the plant. Moreover, Delrin's initial operating losses were very high for two reasons. First, the

Fig. 9.3. Part of control room for Delrin acetal resin manufacture at Du Pont's plant in Parkersburg, West Virginia. Photo courtesy Hagley Museum and Library.

plant had to operate at a fraction of capacity. The first year, it ran at 15% of capacity, which meant that costs were about $4.00 per pound; Du Pont sold the new material at $0.85 per pound. Demand grew far more slowly than Du Pont hoped, so the product continued to lose money for a long time until the output of the Delrin plant approached the point where cost and price broke even. Second, the Delrin plant was plagued with operating problems. Essentially, Polychem had commercialized a big product without following the company's practice of going from laboratory to commercial operation via a semi-works and/or pilot plant in which the generation of data for design took precedence over the manufacture of material for market development. The Delrin semi-works's function had been almost exclusively to turn out product for market development.

Because of the intensive task-force approach to Delrin's development, which Roger Williams likened to the Manhattan Project, Du Pont probably commercialized Delrin faster than it would had a more "normal" course for the polymer's development been followed. Perhaps it would never have been commercialized. Although a good product, Delrin's properties and economics were such that it would never be "another nylon" and, therefore, probably should not have been pursued—certainly not by crash development. One thing is certain; the cost of commercializing Delrin was much, much higher than anything ever encountered before at Du Pont. Yet the needs to get new products into the market and to develop new processes to lower costs of existing products increasingly made the approach taken with Delrin the rule rather than the exception at Du Pont. Consequently, during the 1960's Du Pont experienced skyrocketing precommercial research and development costs on most of its new products, a trend that led in the mid-1970's to the depletion of a once-large cash reserve and to the abandonment of the policy outlined by Pierre du Pont in 1907.[57]

Conclusions

Does the experience of the Du Pont Company shed any light on our understanding of big science? In scale, at least, what Du Pont does in research and development is big enough to qualify as big science. For instance, through 1982, when the company started up its commercial-scale plant, Du Pont had spent more than $500 million on Kevlar aramid fiber without any single market guaranteeing success of the venture.[58] This is roughly comparable to getting the Space Telescope made but not launched into orbit.[59] Moving a project like Kevlar from its initial laboratory discovery to commercial man-

57 On the problems of the 1960's and 1970's, see Hounshell and Smith, *Science and Corporate Strategy*, pp. 509–40, 573–91.
58 On the history of Kevlar, see Hounshell, "Making of a New Industrial Fiber."
59 The *New York Times*, Feb. 19, 1989, pegged the telescope's cost at $1.4 billion.

ufacture is an often tortuous process in which there is a constant dialectic between scientific and technical reality (as well as expectations) and market expectations (as well as realities). Often, marketing considerations tend to mediate the process, but at Du Pont scientific and technical concerns have often had the upper hand. With Kevlar, as with Delrin, the amazing properties of the new material led managers and executives alike to place more stock in the obvious superiority of the product than in the nagging question of whether there was real market sufficiently big to sustain such a wonder material at prices necessary to cover costs. Even though ostensibly mediated by market considerations, industrial research and development projects can develop momentum fully comparable to the momentum built up in the projects typically labeled big science.

Projects like Kevlar must compete against other projects within their own industrial departments, not to mention within the company as a whole. (Kevlar competed with half a dozen other very expensive product development programs in Du Pont's Fibers Department and against dozens of projects in other departments.) Given this situation and human frailties, "politics" does enter into research and development in Du Pont. A historically strong and profitable department like Fibers can play a better game of hardball with the executive committee than can a historically weak and less profitable department. Therefore, because of the company's decentralization, radical shifts in strategy or priorities at Du Pont have been difficult to effect; departmental inertia is a real phenomenon.

Above all, however, market *realities*, not market *expectations*, have been the major mediating factors shaping the scale and kind of science and technology pursued at Du Pont. Here is where I see important differences between Du Pont's big science and that of government laboratories and projects like the Space Telescope. In the latter instances, domestic partisan and international politics have probably been the important mediating factors.[60]

Of course, within both Du Pont and the government-supported big science projects, "politics" exists at all levels—from the research scientist through the research administrator—and these need to be better understood. With the nylon project, Du Pont's research directors sought to minimize the negative effects of these politics by pushing a productive development plan that made clear all of the players' responsibility for and "stake" in the project. This scheme worked amazingly well, so well in fact that Du Pont essentially repeated it when called into the Manhattan Project. But the ideology and expectations of the Chicago physicists made the project far more challenging than the nylon project had been.

In the postwar period, Roger Williams sought to push the lessons of nylon

---

60 See, for example, the space program as interpreted by McDougall, *Heavens and Earth*.

and Hanford as hard as he could. Hence Delrin. Although formulated with
nylon as the model, the Delrin development program in fact departed significantly from the nylon model in several important ways, and the new product
encountered some extraordinarily rough sailing as it entered the stormy wa-
ters of the plastics business in the 1960's. For reasons that are well beyond the
scope of this chapter, the Delrin experience became the rule rather than the
exception at Du Pont after 1960, posing major problems for the company's
stewards of research and development.

   Although it made perfectly good sense at the time (given the internal and
external factors at work), Du Pont's adoption of a postwar strategy of "new
nylons" was problematic.[61] Furthermore, the company's strategy raises some
fundamental questions about what a research-intensive corporation intent on
operating entirely within the civilian sphere could actually achieve in the
postwar era, given the well-documented rise of the "permanent war economy"
in which the nation's research and development expenditures were dominated
by military and space programs. Du Pont was not the only large American
company to expand its basic research programs greatly in the postwar era; in
fact, most firms that had established research programs before the war took
virtually the same course as Du Pont after the war, and for the same reasons.[62]
How were these firms' goals either aided or impeded by the new order of
research and development spending, of increased federal (especially military)
support for research, including funding for what we now regard as big science
projects? Was recruitment of first-rate physicists, chemists, mathematicians,
and engineers more or less difficult? Was research, therefore, more or less
expensive? Was civilian industrial research of higher or lower quality than
government-funded research? Did the postwar "permanent war economy"
change the dynamics of the relationship between civilian industrial research
and development laboratories and academic researchers that had been forged
in the decades before World War II? Such questions as these must occupy the
agenda of historians interested in better comprehending research and development in an era of big science.[63]

   61 Both Charles Stine and Elmer Bolton, for entirely different reasons, had cautioned
Du Pont executives about being lured by the siren song of nylon. See Hounshell and Smith,
Science and Corporate Strategy, pp. 351–52, 360.
   62 These included firms in the chemical, electrical, and automotive industries that had
not previously made major commitments to basic or fundamental research as well as firms
that had engaged in such research well before the war.
   63 To begin with, we need studies of other firms, such as Dow, Monsanto, Union
Carbide, Allied, General Electric, and Westinghouse to parallel the study of Du Pont's
research and development by Hounshell and Smith, *Science and Corporate Strategy*. Beyond
such studies, we must then begin to evaluate governmental (both military and civilian)
research programs (including those carried out in academia) in essentially quantitative terms
to discern larger patterns. Some suggestive contemporary evidence appears in Clayton,
Economic Impact of the Cold War.

References Cited

Clayton, James L., ed. *The Economic Impact of the Cold War.* New York: Harcourt, Brace and World, 1970.
Compton, Arthur H. *Atomic Quest: A Personal Narrative.* Oxford: Oxford University Press, 1956.
Du Pont Company. *The Du Pont Company's Part in the National Security Program.* Wilmington, Del.: E. I. du Pont de Nemours and Company, 1946.
Dupree, A. Hunter. *Science in the Federal Government.* New York: Harper and Row, 1964.
Groves, Leslie R. *Now It Can Be Told.* New York: Harper and Row, 1962.
Hewlett, Richard G. "Beginnings of Development in Nuclear Technology." *Technology and Culture* 17 (1976): 465–78.
Hewlett, Richard G., and Oscar E. Anderson, Jr. *A History of the United States Atomic Energy Commission,* Vol. 1, *The New World, 1939–1946.* University Park: Pennsylvania State University Press, 1962.
Hounshell, David A. "The Making of a New Industrial Fiber: The Case of Du Pont's Kevlar, 1950–1980." Paper presented at the Business History Seminar, Harvard Business School, Apr. 17, 1989.
Hounshell, David A., and John Kenly Smith, Jr. *Science and Corporate Strategy: Du Pont R & D, 1902–1980.* New York: Cambridge University Press, 1988.
Jones, Vincent C. *Manhattan: The Army and the Bomb.* Washington, D.C.: Center for Military History, U.S. Army, 1985.
Kline, Ronald. "Engineering R&D at the Westinghouse Electric Company, 1886–1922." Paper presented at the Society for the History of Technology Meeting, Pittsburgh, Oct. 25, 1986.
McDougall, Walter A. *The Heavens and the Earth: A Political History of the Space Age.* New York, Basic Books, 1985.
Rhodes, Richard. *The Making of the Atomic Bomb.* New York, Simon and Schuster, 1986.

PART III

BIG SCIENCE AND NATIONAL SECURITY

Mission Change in the Large Laboratory: The Los Alamos Implosion Program, 1943–1945

Lillian Hoddeson

The characteristic feature of a "mission-directed" laboratory is that all its scientific and technological research is oriented by a larger goal, the "mission," which typically is expressed in terms of a contribution to society reaching beyond the laboratory. For example, the research during World War II at Los Alamos was directed toward building the first atomic weapons, and research at the MIT Radiation Laboratory was oriented toward developing radar. Similarly, at Bell Telephone Laboratories the mission since the mid-1920's has been to improve communications systems. At such laboratories, any research that is construed as advancing the mission is typically supported, while other research is frowned upon and eventually terminated. The problems of mission-oriented research offer many challenges for the historian of science, for example, to understand how the managements of such laboratories select and enforce their missions, how the mission orientation of a laboratory affects the nature of the research, and how the notion of a mission and institutional "success" relate.

In this chapter, I examine why and how missions change in the large-scale government laboratory, focusing on the specific case of Los Alamos during World War II, the pioneering laboratory at which the first atomic bombs were built.[1] During the summer of 1944, the central mission of the laboratory changed dramatically from developing a "gun"-assembled fission weapon to developing an implosion bomb. As I show, this change responded directly to a laboratory-wide crisis, which, peculiarly, was not brought on by a macroscopic factor (such as a political, economic, personal, or financial factor) but rather by a purely scientific finding in the realm of microscopic physics. Very few counts in a bank of electronic detectors were responsible for the reorganization of this large-scale institution. The laboratory's resistance to this change is suggested by the fact that although the unsettling physical results that brought on the crisis were evident early in April 1944, not until late July were they officially accepted. After that, the institutional change occurred within days. This change was one basis for the success of the historic Trinity test of the implosion weapon on July 16, 1945 and of the Nagasaki bomb drop on August 9, 1945.

To understand the speed with which this mission change occurred at Los Alamos, one must bear in mind that during World War II Los Alamos was a *military institution* in which civilian project leaders wielded great power. In a period of world war, at a time when large-scale research was not yet a well-established mode of doing science or technology, this military basis enabled the division and group leaders to create a very effective hierarchical research institution, in which the work of staff scientists could be strongly directed and in which tight deadlines could be enforced. It was not uncommon for a scientist to be switched overnight from one project to another having higher priority; the laboratory's director, J. Robert Oppenheimer, was empowered to function like a general in moving his scientific troops around. The various groups within the laboratory were expected by the leadership to cooperate closely; within and between groups, scientists and engineers worked together, encouraging scientists to bring their own research tools to bear on engineering problems.

In this period, Los Alamos was possibly the most introspective research organization ever to exist. Group and division leaders assessed their unit's work in biweekly or monthly meetings, and the division leaders participated in various advisory committees, such as the Governing Board and the Coordinating Council, which continuously set goals, assessed progress, and assigned research. Numerous outside consultants, advisors, and committees reviewed the work, often biweekly, making recommendations that the laboratory was obliged to take seriously. The national importance of the laboratory's mission also tended to make the institution very conservative in its approach, from its early pursuit of alternative efforts, such as Seth Neddermeyer's original implosion program or the thermonuclear bomb program at a time when the main

1 References to Los Alamos documents not in the public domain are indicated by "LA Archives." For a more extensive technical treatment of implosion, see Hoddeson et al., *Critical Assembly,* prepared with support from Los Alamos National Laboratory.

emphasis of the laboratory was on the gun method, to its overdesign of both bombs in an attempt to guarantee success. In this pressured context, and with effectively unlimited government support, a new methodology for large-scale research was proved, an approach based on a fusion of traditional methods used by engineers and craftsmen with the most up-to-date techniques of the scientists.

Gun vs. Implosion Research Between March 1943 and July 1944

When the Los Alamos laboratory opened in the spring of 1943, its technical program was organized around the problem of developing a gun-assembled fission weapon, in which two subcritical masses of fissile material— uranium or plutonium—were shot together to form a critical mass. Three research divisions—the Theoretical (T-), Chemistry and Metallurgy (CM-), and Experimental Physics (P-) divisions—examined the basic physics and chemistry of the weapon, while the Engineering and Ordnance (E-) division aimed primarily to solve the engineering problems of gun assembly. By that time, a considerable amount of experimental and theoretical work had been devoted to such a weapon. Robert Serber summarized the state of progress in a series of indoctrination lectures he delivered at Los Alamos in the first weeks of April 1943[2] to give "the people working at the separate universities [who] had no idea of the whole story . . . the picture of what it was all about."[3] Serber assessed the likelihood of achieving both a uranium and a plutonium gun-assembled bomb as probable; during the first year of the Los Alamos project the laboratory was to produce both plutonium and uranium gun weapons. There were many unresolved issues, however. For example, could enough fissile uranium for gun-assembly bombs be produced by isotope separation? In the case of plutonium, the unknowns included whether the neutron number for plutonium fission was greater than one and whether the fission neutrons were delayed on emission. Plutonium was seen as an important part of the mission because, unlike uranium, unlimited amounts could be produced in a reactor. Acceptance of the gun method as workable provided an optimistic outlook for the laboratory.[4]

In contrast to the relatively simple method of gun assembly, implosion— envisioned as a means for assembling any fissile material—relied on extremely

2 These lectures were written up by E. Condon in a document now referred to as "The Los Alamos Primer," Los Alamos Report 1 (Apr. 17, 1943).

3 Robert Serber, interviewed by Lillian Hoddeson, Mar. 26, 1979, OH-9, p. 24. All interviews and documents cited in this chapter are in the Los Alamos National Laboratory Archives.

4 Minutes of meeting of unnamed committee (soon to be called the Governing Board), Mar. 6, 1943, A-83-0013, 1-1; Planning Board meeting minutes, Mar. 30, 1943, Apr. 2, 1943, Apr. 1943, VFA-213.

complicated shock-wave phenomena that had never before been examined with precision. In this approach the sample of fissile material (plutonium-239 or uranium-235) is surrounded by high explosives, detonation of which creates shock waves traveling inward.[5] These in turn collapse the fissile material from a subcritical geometry into a supercritical mass, leading to a chain reaction. The basic notion of such a process had been brought up at Berkeley during the summer of 1942, before the start of the Los Alamos project. While theoreticians there, including J. Robert Oppenheimer, Robert Serber, Hans Bethe, Edward Teller, Emil Konopinski, Felix Bloch and John Van Vleck, were focusing on the gun weapon, Richard C. Tolman, one of the Washington associates of the Berkeley effort, visited and raised the idea of implosion, although not using the name, as an "interesting" alternative method of assembly. Serber and Tolman wrote a joint memorandum on this idea, but the suggestion was then given little notice by others.[6]

Nevertheless, Tolman continued to think about his implosion idea during the remainder of 1942 and through the early months of 1943, writing in a letter on March 27, 1943, to Oppenheimer, who was by now the director of the Los Alamos laboratory, that "[James B.] Conant and I have discussed the somewhat modified possibility of starting off by using ordinary explosive to blow the shell of active material into the center. I think that this would be an easy thing to do, dividing the shell into separate or nearly separate parts before the explosion, and making proper arrangements for 'arming' the device by completing the outer shell at a safe time before detonation."[7] Two days later, he mentioned the idea in a memorandum to General Leslie Groves, the director of the Manhattan Project: "In the case of the mechanism depending on the deformation of a shell of active material . . . it might be possible to bring this

5 The study of high explosives—materials whose detonation propels matter at supersonic speeds (miles per second) by a process involving chemical reaction and a shock wave—was a rather primitive empirical art at the start of World War II. The British had begun by that time to develop a small body of systemized knowledge on explosives, as did the U.S. from about 1941. Although "low" explosives that deflagrate or burn extremely rapidly had been studied as early as A.D. 1200, when documents reveal fireworks and black powder to have been known to the Chinese and Arabs, "high" explosives, which are characterized by much higher "brisance" (shattering power), were only recently discovered. Nitroglycerine (glyceryl trinitrate) was prepared in Italy in 1846. Twenty years later, in Sweden, Alfred Nobel stabilized nitroglycerine by adsorbing it on diatomaceous earth (kieselguhr). Trinitrotoluene (TNT) became generally available after 1902, when an economical process for its manufacture was developed in Germany. It was promptly adopted worldwide by the military.

6 Serber, personal communication, Oct. 16, 1985. Neither Bethe, Konopinski, nor McMillan, all present at the Berkeley meetings, recalled any discussion of the implosion then. And Oppenheimer's memory in the spring of 1945 was that the development of implosion at Los Alamos began in April 1943 with Neddermeyer's suggestion of the idea to the laboratory. Oppenheimer to Smith, 1945.

7 Tolman to Oppenheimer, Mar. 27, 1943, LA Archives.

about by explosive charges which would blow fragments of the shell into the interior."[8] Although never realized in this form, the early implosion idea of Tolman and Serber helped to create the context for designing implosion assemblies at Los Alamos.

Phase 1: Exploratory Work of Neddermeyer's Group, April–September 1943

The Los Alamos implosion program began soon after the opening of the laboratory in March 1943. Serber included a short discussion of his and Tolman's implosion concept in one of his indoctrination lectures during April 1943, in a section on "shooting" together fissile material. After discussing a number of gun methods, he commented, "Various other shooting arrangements have been suggested but as yet not carefully analyzed. For example, it has been suggested that the pieces might be mounted on a ring. . . . If the explosive material were distributed around the ring and fired the pieces would be blown inward to form a sphere."[9]

It is possible that Serber's presentation of implosion stimulated Seth Neddermeyer's pivotal ideas about this method. Neddermeyer developed them about a week after hearing Serber's indoctrination series during the Los Alamos conferences held between April 15 and May 6, 1943, to analyze scientific problems, define schedules, and design the experimental program. In the discussion portion of a meeting on April 28, 1943, we learn from a summary that Neddermeyer "presented some preliminary calculations on the compression of a spherical shell, indicating that it was worth investigating further."[10] However, unlike Serber and Tolman, Neddermeyer envisioned the imploding spherical shell of fissile material as being plastically deformed by the surrounding high explosives into a just-critical sphere. He gave arguments to show that such an implosion would assemble the critical mass substantially faster than would a gun. Los Alamos scientists recognized immediately that this feature might be particularly important for assembling plutonium, because with plutonium the probability of premature detonation owing to neutron emission in the system before attainment of the optimal configuration was greater than with uranium.

Neddermeyer, who at this time was virtually alone in his belief that implosion should be pursued vigorously at Los Alamos, convinced Oppenheimer to establish an exploratory implosion program consisting of a handful of researchers—besides Neddermeyer, these would be Hugh Bradner, John Streib, Felix Bloch, Charles Critchfield, and Donald Mueller. Since it was expected that the gun method would succeed in assembling both the uranium and

8 LA Archives.
9 Los Alamos Report 1, p. 22; Serber interview, pp. 14–16.
10 LA Archives.

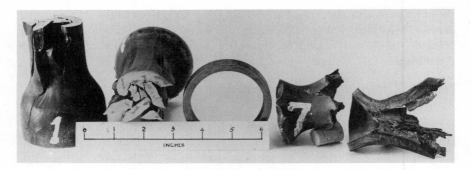

Fig. 10.1. Data from one of Seth Neddermeyer's earliest implosion tests. The center ring is an untested cross section of the carbon steel tubing used in the experiment.

plutonium weapons, this small effort was given low priority and viewed as a program to fall back on should unexpected problems arise in gun development.

One major technical difficulty in realizing an implosion weapon was that symmetrical implosion of a metal such as plutonium or uranium required precise use of high explosives. But little work this detailed had yet been done with high explosives. To become familiar with the latest research, Neddermeyer and Edwin McMillan, in May 1943, visited the site of the principal American explosives research program—the Explosives Research Laboratory at Bruceton, Pennsylvania, a National Defense Research Committee (NDRC) experiment station headed by the Harvard chemist George Kistiakowsky.[11] Together with Bruceton scientists, Neddermeyer and McMillan conducted the first tests on implosion of cylindrical pipes surrounded by explosives. They then returned to Los Alamos and set up a largely cut-and-try experimental effort on South Mesa, several miles from the main technical area. To cast the high explosives needed for the experiments, the Ordnance Division erected a small casting plant at the nearby Anchor Ranch. The basic implosion experiment that Neddermeyer had participated in at Bruceton was repeated on July 4(!), 1943, and subsequently many times with different explosive arrangements, pipe sizes, metals, and so forth (see Fig. 10.1). The results—a series of bashed-in pipes—were analyzed in hopes that they would reveal important aspects of implosion, such as symmetry and collapse rate.[12] Half a year later, this technique evolved into a more systematic procedure known as "terminal

11 Kistiakowsky, "Reminiscences of Wartime Los Alamos"; McMillan, "Early Days at Los Alamos"; McMillan, interviewed by R. Seidel, Apr. 17, 1985.

12 C. Critchfield, interviewed by L. Hoddeson and A. Kerr, Aug. 2, 1984, pp. 6–7; McMillan, "Early Days at Los Alamos," p. 17; Neddermeyer, "Collapse of Hollow Steel Cylinders by High Explosives," Los Alamos Report 18 (Aug. 9, 1943).

observations," a diagnostic focused on recovery of the imploded objects. But the naive mode of terminal observation used by Neddermeyer's initial group was not useful in studying systems having a larger ratio of explosive to metal mass, because more violent explosions would scatter the remains. Theoretical study, although extremely crude, yielded an approximate one-dimensional implosion model.

During this initial phase of the Los Alamos program, the small implosion effort was supported as Neddermeyer's back-burner project. Neddermeyer's small group of half a dozen was attempting to accomplish over a period of several months all the experimental, theoretical, and high explosives work that would later be conducted strenuously over a period of a year by several hundred researchers. Despite serious limitation of resources, this early program exposed many difficulties that would plague the Los Alamos laboratory over the next two years, for example, the problem of overcoming asymmetries of shell implosions. But it could not have succeeded within the span of the war, and possibly not at all. This informal effort's main importance was as the germination of implosion research at Los Alamos.

Phase 2: Implosion Research Is Established, September 1943–June 1944

In the second phase, the implosion program expanded into a well-organized scientific effort having moderate priority, resources, and personnel. This phase began with John von Neumann's visit to Los Alamos in late September 1943. On learning about Neddermeyer's implosion tests on cylindrical pipes, von Neumann first suggested assembling the weapon by a process based on the metallic jets produced by high-explosive "shaped-charges," like bazooka warheads, where high explosive collapses an embedded cone to form a jet. After further thought, especially in conversations with his boyhood friend Teller, von Neumann concluded that Neddermeyer's design for the implosion could be made far more efficient if one were to use a substantially greater ratio of high explosive to metal mass. That scheme would cause a still more rapid assembly of the fissionable material, with two immediate consequences: less material would be needed, and it could be less pure. These advantages would be of particular interest to Groves, because the material production and purification programs were both very costly.[13]

The enthusiastic suggestions of von Neumann, one of the most eminent mathematicians of the period, had an immediate impact on leading Los Alamos theorists, including Bethe, Oppenheimer, and Teller, who now became very excited about the possibility of such an implosion weapon. At this stage, Teller realized that one could benefit from the extremely high pressure achieved

13 Governing Board minutes, Sept. 23 and Oct. 28, 1943; minutes of conference, Oct. 1, 1943, all in LA Archives.

near the center of the implosion assembly to compress the active material beyond its normal density. This compression would increase the efficiency of the weapon further. Soon Bethe and Teller were devoting ever more time to implosion problems, while von Neumann continued to work on the problem in Tolman's office at the National Academy of Sciences in Washington, D.C. Implosion was now seen by these theorists as an extremely interesting, but highly uncertain, means of assembling a fission weapon.

Oppenheimer and Groves then increased the priority and support of the implosion program; Neddermeyer's group grew from 5 to roughly 50 individuals over the next several months. Because the laboratory was still banking on gun assembly for both plutonium and uranium weapons, and because the gun program was progressing smoothly, with no apparent obstacles, why did Oppenheimer, along with his Governing Board and Groves, decide just then to invest more heavily in the implosion program? Although the documentary evidence does not answer this question, several explanations seem pertinent. First, after von Neumann lent his vigorous support to the implosion concept, and after his suggestion of a faster and more efficient approach to implosion, this technique was recognized as an elegant approach to the fission bomb, superior to the gun because it would require less active material and less costly material purification. Second, one of Groves's and Oppenheimer's policies was to explore all approaches to the main problem of building an atomic bomb; implosion was viewed as one of several fall-back methods to be used should unforeseen problems arise in the gun method. Another alternative being examined was autocatalysis, based on increasing criticality by compression or expulsion of neutron-absorbing material. The fact that the gun program was so rapidly solving its essential problems paradoxically made it possible for Oppenheimer to feel secure that he was fulfilling the laboratory's mission, and that he could therefore spare a number of researchers from the gun program to put on implosion. Third, from a purely intellectual point of view, implosion was extremely challenging to the laboratory's leading theoreticians, who as research scientists were very much interested in pursuing a problem that went beyond any previous experience. Despite its focused wartime mission, Los Alamos remained a research laboratory that could afford to invest in the study of challenging but risky technology. This willingness and ability to make such an investment is a typical feature of successful mission-directed laboratories.

With greater commitment to implosion, the problem of using high explosives precisely loomed larger than ever. For this reason, Kistiakowsky, then considered the leading American explosives expert, was brought into the program in October 1943 as a consultant, and in February 1944 as a regular staff member. Kistiakowsky was one of the few scientists in the United States in the early part of World War II who recognized the potential of high explosives as a precision tool. He immediately organized a more systematic and advanced diagnostic effort to study the details of implosion.[14] This effort centered on three techniques: X rays, optical photography, and more advanced terminal observations. The latter two methods had been developed to a sophisticated degree at Bruceton, whereas the X-ray method had been explored in England by James Tuck and in the United States at Aberdeen Proving Ground by John Clark and Leslie Seely. As the months passed, more exotic methods—in particular the "RaLa," magnetic, electric "pin," and betatron methods—were devised and explored as implosion diagnostics. But this work did not go smoothly: all the programs revealed serious problems of asymmetry; in particular, jets of molten metal were racing ahead of the main collapsing metal envelope, causing asymmetry and turbulence, and drastically cutting down the implosion's efficiency.[15]

Meanwhile, theoretical studies of symmetrical implosion were quite promising. By March 1944, most of the pressing theoretical issues of gun development had been dealt with, and Bethe, the director of the theoretical, or T-, division, felt justified in setting up a group under Teller authorized to explore the challenging implosion problems. The group soon discovered that the differential equations expressing the hydrodynamics of implosion were insoluble by analytic means. In April, they began to use a new shipment of "International Business Machines," ordered for calculations of neutron diffusion, but immediately adopted for numerical implosion calculations with the help of an algorithm developed earlier by Rudolf Peierls for a different problem.[16]

Unfortunately, personal tension interfered with this theoretical work during the spring and summer of 1944. Teller was working less and less on implosion as his interest grew in the problem of developing a thermonuclear bomb, the "Super," which Oppenheimer and Bethe gave very low priority at this time. In June, Bethe dismissed Teller from T-Division and replaced him with Peierls, a friend and scientific colleague for over fifteen years. Oppenheimer set Teller up in a small group outside T-Division, and authorized him to begin formally organized studies on the Super there, but with little support and resources.[17] This handling of Teller's effort illustrates again how the large mission-oriented laboratory treats a low-priority effort that has a nonnegligible probability of becoming useful to the mission. Like the early implosion research, this early work on the Super made almost no progress, but it did start thermonuclear research at Los Alamos.

14 Kistiakowsky to W. S. Parsons, Nov. 24, 1943, "Program and Requirements of the Research and Development Phase of the HE Project," and Governing Board minutes, Nov. 26, 1943, both in LA Archives.
15 E-Division Progress Reports, Mar. 1, 1944, Los Alamos Manuscript 73, p. 35; Apr. 15, 1944, LAMS-80, pp. 4–5.
16 Peierls, *Bird of Passage*, p. 187.
17 R. C. Smith, "Report of Foreign Personnel at Project Y," July 5, Aug. 2, 1944, LA Archives.

By the middle of the summer of 1944, the theoretical machinery for analyzing a symmetrical ideal implosion was nearly complete; such an implosion was indeed shown to be a highly efficient method of assembling a weapon. At this point, the implosion program was not geared to any particular fissile material or weapons design; it was a research effort oriented toward understanding the novel means of assembly. Unfortunately, the experimental program was learning that the possibility of achieving spherical implosions was very remote, despite countless tricks made in an attempt to reduce the observed asymmetry. In May, G. I. Taylor from England deepened the prevailing gloom with his analysis of some of the experimental difficulties in terms of possible intrinsic Rayleigh–Taylor instability, caused when the lighter of two fluids is accelerated into the heavier one, as by gravity or, in this context, by high explosives.

Two developments at Los Alamos, both in May 1944, offered hope for overcoming the asymmetry. Among the underlying causes of the problems was that the multiple detonations of the surrounding explosive were not adequately simultaneous, and that the detonation waves diverging from the initiation points interacted to make asymmetries. The first problem was solved by realization of a suggestion of Luis Alvarez, confirmed by Lawrence Johnston within a few weeks, that the Primacord detonation system then being used be replaced by electric detonators.[18] The second problem could be dealt with by the three-dimensional explosive lens, conceived by Tuck. Such a lens would focus the diverging detonation waves into a converging spherical wave front.

But developing and producing practical explosive lens and electric detonator systems required a major research effort right up to the Trinity test in July 1945. In the summer of 1944 whether or not the implosion could work at all was highly questionable. At just this point, the laboratory had to confront a crisis stemming from an unexpected physics discovery.

The Crisis of Spontaneous Fission and the Reorganization of the Laboratory, August 1944

Until August 1944, bomb development at Los Alamos was focused on gun assembly of uranium and plutonium. Because the technical problems of building uranium gun bombs were essentially resolved during the first months of the project, most attention was paid to the plutonium gun.

This attention shifted abruptly during the summer of 1944 in response to a finding by Emilio Segrè's group in the Experimental Physics Division of the laboratory. This group, which included George Farwell, Clyde Wiegand, and Owen Chamberlain, made the startling discovery that the first samples of

18 Alvarez, *Adventures of a Physicist*, pp. 123, 132–34; Johnston, "The War Years."

"production" plutonium from the Clinton reactor at Oak Ridge underwent spontaneous fission at an unusually high rate, with a neutron emission approximately five times that of the cyclotron-produced plutonium-239 used previously in experimental tests. This finding would shortly undermine the plutonium gun bomb and make development of the plutonium implosion bomb the central laboratory mission. While implosion research still examined both uranium and plutonium, the developmental bomb mission now centered on plutonium. The gun program continued to focus on uranium.

Enrico Fermi and Glenn Seaborg, as well as Segrè and others, had for some time suspected that the neutron bath in the plutonium production piles might cause the formation of a significant quantity of the as-yet unobserved isotope plutonium-240.[19] On theoretical grounds, such an isotope, having an even number of neutrons and protons, had a high probability of undergoing spontaneous fission. But there was no way of knowing how seriously plutonium-239 was contaminated with plutonium-240 until the neutron fluxes in the plutonium-producing piles could be actually measured; the creation of plutonium-240 was proportional to the total "irradiation," the mean neutron flux per area multiplied by the total exposure time of the material in the pile.[20] The expected neutron emission rate, as Segrè explained, "would not have bothered" the plutonium gun device; the major worry about impurities in the gun was over light elements, which would absorb alpha particles emitted by the plutonium and then emit neutrons.[21] But in fact, as Segrè's group showed, neutrons spontaneously emitted by the production plutonium completely overwhelmed those from light-element interactions. The anomalously high rate of this process—a million times that with uranium-235—was totally unexpected. The rate was high enough to threaten predetonation of the gun-assembled gadget, which would result in a "fizzle."[22]

This spontaneous fission experiment is one of the important case studies in the history of physics illustrating how a purely scientific result can change the course of history. Because this experiment yielded data so slowly—initially, about one spontaneous fission was observed per month[23]—the historian of

19 E.g., Seaborg, "History of the Metallurgical Laboratory."

20 Plutonium production is based on bombarding uranium-238 with neutrons from fissionable uranium-235. Capture of neutrons by plutonium-239 would form plutonium-240.

21 Emilio Segrè, interviewed by L. Hoddeson, July 23, 1985.

22 Latest measured spontaneous fission rates in fissions per gram per hour: uranium-238, 20 (1.5×10^{16}); uranium-235, 1 (3×10^{17}); plutonium-239, 40 (7×10^{15}); plutonium-240, 1.6 × 10^6 (2×10^{11}); the values in parentheses are the neutron emission half-lives in years. Despite having a half-life greater than the age of the universe, neutron emission from plutonium-240 becomes significant because of the quantity of material present.

23 P-Division Progress Reports, Apr.–July 1944, LA Archives; George Farwell, interviewed by L. Hoddeson, July 23, 30, and Sept. 24, 25, 1985; Emilio Segrè, interviewed by L. Hoddeson, July 23 and Dec. 3, 4, 1985.

Fig. 10.2. Cabin in Pajarito Canyon used by the spontaneous fission group for their crucial experiments during World War II.

this development must grapple with an issue, raised in detail previously by Peter Galison,[24] of when and how the decision is made to accept experimental evidence and "end" an experiment. In this chapter I can only hint at the dilemmas faced by the Los Alamos physicists in ending the spontaneous fission experiment.[25]

In a sense, the experiment had already been running for over two years. In Berkeley, spontaneous fission of fissile materials was one of a number of

24 Galison, *How Experiments End*.
25 A more detailed analysis of this crucial experiment is in preparation.

nuclear physics issues being investigated from 1940 on. The Berkeley sponta-neous fission group—with the same cast of characters as the later Los Alamos group, that is, Segrè and his graduate students, including Farwell, Wiegand, and Chamberlain—moved to Los Alamos, with its apparatus, in the summer of 1943 and immediately set up there to continue the Berkeley studies.[26]

The very slow return of data required cutting-edge experimental methods as well as great care to avoid false counts. To prevent counting electrically induced signals, the sensitive electronics (based on the 6AK5 vacuum tube, the stand-by at that time) was operated entirely by battery. The experimental site near Los Alamos, Pajarito Canyon, about 14 miles from the main technical area, was chosen for its "peace and quiet from electrical and audible distur-bances, and for its shielding from cosmic rays"[27] (see Fig. 10.2). Because of increased sample size, these Pajarito Canyon experiments, although based on the earlier Berkeley studies, required new nitrogen-filled ionization chambers and improved amplifiers with greater stability and better frequency and at-tenuation characteristics.[28] To measure the spontaneous fission rate of any element, the group had not only to observe and count fission fragments, but also to determine v, the average number of neutrons emitted per fission. Wiegand and Segrè measured v in a concurrent (but separate) investigation, determining also the distribution of the fission fragments and the ionization produced by the fission of fragments of various sizes.[29]

Pile-produced plutonium in quantities sufficient for measurement of spon-taneous fission was not available at Los Alamos until April 1944. Before this time, Segrè's group studied the spontaneous fission of microscopic 20-microgram plutonium samples made in the "Crocker" 60-inch cyclotron at Berkeley. Over a five-month period—August to December 1943—in 80,000 microgram-hours of observation,[30] in five chambers running approximately 22 hours a day, seven days a week,[31] these samples had registered only six fissions. When on January 7 the group began to shield the ionization cham-bers, using an oxide of boron, B_2O_3, to absorb spurious cosmic-ray neutrons, the counting rate fell to roughly one fission every two and one-half months, a rate even more staggeringly low.[32] Using these data, they estimated that 50

26 For a summary of the Berkeley work, see Segrè's Los Alamos Notebook, June 6, 1943, Segrè's private collection.

27 Segrè interview.

28 P-Division Progress Reports, July 15, 1943, Los Alamos Manuscript 4, pp. 4–5; Clyde Wiegand, interviewed by L. Hoddeson, May 29, 1987, OH-157; Segrè Notebook covering work from May 1940 to Dec. 1944, p. 28; Segrè and Farwell interviews.

29 Segrè and Wiegand, in "Average Number of Neutrons Emitted per Spontaneous Fission by Plutonium 240," Los Alamos Report 491 (Nov. 11, 1946) reported a value for v of 2.37 ± 0.3.

30 Summary on Jan. 31, 1944, Pajarito Data Book 6.

31 Farwell and Wiegand interviews.

32 P-Division Progress Reports, Dec. 1, 1943, Los Alamos Manuscript 33; Farwell interview; Pajarito Data Book 6.

grams of production plutonium would be the minimal amount needed for testing spontaneous fission; the sample would have to be large enough to reveal the presence of plutonium-240, whose formation is second-order in pile exposure time.

Fermi, as an associate of Segrè, was in close touch with the spontaneous fission experiments. That winter, worrying about the reliability of the results, Fermi suggested a decisive experiment to measure the spontaneous fission due to plutonium-240. The experiment was based on the simple logic that if pile-produced plutonium showed more spontaneous fission than did cyclotron-produced plutonium, then pile-produced material that was "reirradiated" in the pile would undergo still more spontaneous fission. Fermi proposed re-irradiating approximately 50 milligrams of Clinton-produced plutonium in the pile before studying its spontaneous fission.[33]

The first crucial sample of ordinary pile-produced plutonium arrived at Los Alamos early in April 1944; it was placed in the chambers on April 5. On April 12, seven more samples were added. By April 15, tentative but startling results based on the first eight counts registered were out. These results indicated that the Clinton plutonium underwent spontaneous fission at five times the rate of the samples from Berkeley.[34] The painstaking experimental biases and calibrations made by the researchers allowed them to be virtually certain that each count represented a real event,[35] but they were still not 100% certain. Given this lingering experimental uncertainty and the devastating implications of the finding for the Los Alamos laboratory's mission to develop a plutonium gun weapon, the first shocking results were therefore not immediately publicized. The argument offered was experimental uncertainty and poor statistics.[36]

By May 5, the group had seen 66 counts, and by May 9, 40 more, indicating that the spontaneous fission rate of Clinton plutonium was 261 fissions per gram-hour, compared with some 40 to 50 from the Berkeley plutonium (with rather poor statistics on both).[37] Finally, in July 1944, after the arrival of the reirradiated plutonium Fermi had ordered, they carried out Fermi's test on this plutonium. Preliminary results from the reirradiated plutonium samples were available on July 11, 1944, after only two days of counting.[38] The same day Oppenheimer teletyped Conant, "the Pajarito Counting Rate of the reirradiated sample is increased by an amount corresponding to its

33 S. K. Allison to A. H. Compton, Jan. 25, 1944, A-84-019, 15-6; Governing Board minutes, Jan. 27, 1944, A-83-0013, 1-40.

34 Pajarito Data Book 6, pp. 137–41.

35 Chamberlain, Farwell, and Segrè, "Plutonium 240 and Its Spontaneous Fission," Los Alamos Manuscript 131, Sept. 8, 1944, containing data on the irradiation of the pile-produced plutonium samples. Wiegand interview, OH-157.

36 P-Division Progress Reports, Apr. 15, 1944, Los Alamos Manuscript 93, p. 15.

37 Farwell interview; Pajarito Data Book 6; P-Division Progress Reports, June 15, 1944, Los Alamos Manuscript 114.

38 Pajarito Data Book 6, pp. 128–31.

increased radiation period. . . . No conclusive proof exists that the substance giving these counts is four ten [plutonium-240], but the a priori probability is very high and the chemical operations performed on the material obviously did not separate it from four nine [plutonium-239]."[39] More reirradiated samples were added to the counting apparatus on July 11, 12, and 13. The results were confirmed beyond the shadow of a doubt.[40] As Farwell recalled, "every one of [these reirradiated samples] started off like a string of firecrackers."[41]

Los Alamos was now in crisis. Because of spontaneous fission of plutonium-240, the plutonium gun could not work; it was simply not fast enough to tolerate the added neutrons. Yet plutonium was the only fuel that could be produced in quantities sufficient for numerous bombs. Everyone concerned immediately recognized that the only hope for using the large plutonium production efforts at Clinton and Hanford was to build a plutonium implosion bomb. But the implosion at this time was a dismal prospect, in view of recent discouraging experimental studies. John Manley reflected, "The choice was to junk the whole discovery of the chain reaction that produced plutonium, and all of the investment in time and effort of the Hanford plant, unless somebody could come up with a way of assembling the plutonium material into a weapon that would explode."[42] Conant remarked in his July 4 report, "There is little doubt that an implosion method can be made to work for both '25' and '49.' The question is how efficient can such bombs be made to be and how fast can a moderately efficient bomb be developed. . . . Eventually it may be possible to design an implosion bomb with such speeds of assembly and such high compressions that very great efficiencies result (much greater than with the gun assembly). But at present one must be content with lower compressions and low efficiencies."[43] Fortunately, the uranium gun bomb was virtually certain, although insufficient quantities of available uranium meant that only one bomb could be made by early summer of 1945. On July 4 Conant noted, "Assuming one is confident of 10 kg '25' by Jan. 1 and 50 kg July 1 and 30 kg a month thereafter. We are confident that one bomb can be dropped on the evening of Aug 1 [1945] with every prospect of a success. . . . A similar bomb could be dropped every six weeks thereafter."[44]

In the heat of the crisis, gun researchers spent a good deal of time consider-

39 It was already difficult to separate uranium-235 from uranium-238, differing by three units of mass; in this case there was only one unit of mass difference. Segrè interview; Oppenheimer to the Washington (D.C.) Liaison Office, July 11, 1944.

40 P-Division Progress Reports, July 1, 1944, Los Alamos Manuscript 117. Oppenheimer to Bacher, Dodson, Segrè, and Wilson on "Shipment of Material," June 28, 1944, A-84-019, 46-3.

41 Farwell interview.

42 Manley, "A New Laboratory Is Born," p. 33.

43 "Findings of Trip to Los Alamos," July 4, 1944, RG 227, Bush–Conant Files, National Archives, Washington, D.C.

44 *Ibid.*

ing other shooting possibilities, such as faster guns, but these ideas were soon given up. The chemists and physicists pondered the problem of separating out the plutonium-240. Oppenheimer telegraphed Groves on July 14, 1944, "Have written to Lawrence . . . asking him to consider possibility of electromagnetic removal. . . . My opinion is that this is not a job which can be developed within any reasonable time scale but that it should be referred to him for more expert consideration."[45] The separation idea was considered in detail on July 17 at a meeting in Chicago that included Conant, Oppenheimer, Charles A. Thomas, Arthur Compton, Groves, Colonel Kenneth D. Nichols, and Fermi. All agreed that to separate out the plutonium-240, although possible by electromagnetic methods, "would postpone the weapon indefinitely."[46] Manley later reflected, "One could have separated out those bad plutonium isotopes from the good ones, but that would have meant duplicating everything that had been done for uranium isotope separation—all those big plants—and there was just no time to do that."[47]

At the Chicago meetings, Conant stressed authorizing Los Alamos to build low-efficiency implosion bombs based on both plutonium and uranium-235, a plan he considered "an almost certain way of utilizing some atomic energy, even if only the equivalent of a few hundred tons of TNT. Should the Los Alamos staff develop this bomb to the point where it seemed a fairly sure thing, they could set it aside as Mark II [the uranium gun being Mark I] and go to work with less nervousness on Mark III, an implosion weapon that would require less metal and be more powerful."[48]

With implosion the only possible course for utilizing the large investment made in plutonium production, Oppenheimer, on July 20, 1944, outlined his strategy: "Essentially all work on the 49 [that is, plutonium-239] gun program and the extreme purification of 49 should be stopped immediately."[49] The Governing Board ruled that same day: "All possible priority should be given to the implosion program. At the same time, nothing essential to the 25 gun program should be left undone."[50] The primary objective of Los Alamos thus changed from developing gun-assembled bombs to developing implosion bombs. But whereas gun assembly was virtually understood at this point, implosion—a phenomenon far removed from any previous experience—was a completely uncertain method. In fact, experiments in the diagnostic program

45 Teletype, Oppenheimer to Groves, July 14, 1944, A-84-019, 15-7.
46 Hewlett and Anderson, *History of the United States Atomic Energy Commission*, p. 251.
47 Manley, "A New Laboratory Is Born," p. 33.
48 Hewlett and Anderson, *History of the United States Atomic Energy Commission*, pp. 251–52.
49 Administrative Board minutes, July 20, 1944, A-83-0013, 1-52.
50 Governing Board minutes, July 20, 1944, A-83-0013, 1-52. The code names 49 and 210 were commonly used during the war to refer, respectively, to plutonium-239 and plutonium-240.

were just then indicating that spherical implosion might be impossible to achieve.

P-Division leader Robert Bacher recalled how much the spontaneous fission results "perturbed" researchers in other parts of the Manhattan Project. The Chicago Metallurgical Laboratory was spearheading physical and chemical work on pile development and other aspects of the plutonium effort, including purification of plutonium essential for the gun device. Since late 1943 Bacher had been regularly visiting Chicago as the liaison from Los Alamos. On his visit from May 31 to June 8, 1944, Bacher informed Compton that he wished to report on the recent results from Segrè's group. These results had been reported to Groves "with the request that he pass them on to the Chicago group." Bacher immediately realized that the Chicago group had not yet been informed. Bacher recalls that Compton, on hearing the news about spontaneous fission, "went just as white as that sheet of paper." After noting, "This will just cause great troubles in our laboratory," Compton added, "I'm not sure that should be reported here [Chicago]. I'm sure Groves would be very much upset."[51]

Bacher persisted: "It falls within the limits of what he told me I should report down here, and it's my intention to report it unless I'm told not to." So Bacher telephoned Groves, who asked "Do you think that needs to be reported to them?" Bacher replied, "Of course. . . . It's a fundamental fact of the material they're working on." Groves realized then that holding back the news "would impede the project," but because he was strongly concerned about secrecy, they agreed that Bacher would tell only "about half a dozen people there about it," which he did. But, he reflected later, "I'm sure it didn't take more than a half an hour to get all over the laboratory. . . . This just meant trouble ahead."[52]

At Los Alamos Oppenheimer responded to the crisis with sweeping organizational changes,[53] aimed to "throw the book" at the implosion weapon.[54] In June 1944, he had replaced Neddermeyer as implosion leader with Kistiakowsky, who he felt would be more suitable to lead a large research group.[55] On August 14, two new divisions to develop implosion were formed: G (gadget) under Robert Bacher, devoted to implosion research, and X (explosives) under Kistiakowsky, devoted to explosives, implosion gadget components, and further implosion research.[56] Many groups in these new divisions had simply been moved out of the earlier physics or engineering divisions, for nuclear

51 Robert Bacher, interviewed by L. Hoddeson, July 30, 1984, OH-45.
52 *Ibid.*
53 Administrative Board minutes, July 20, 1944, A-83-0013, 1-52.
54 Oppenheimer to Bacher and Kistiakowsky, Aug. 14, 1944, A-84-019, 36-10; Administrative Board minutes, A-83-0013, 1-52; quote from Hawkins, *Project Y*, p. 74.
55 Oppenheimer to Neddermeyer, June 15, 1944, LA Archives.
56 Oppenheimer to members of the steering committee for gun assembly, Aug. 7, 1944; Bacher interview.

physics and gun assembly were seen as programs sufficiently advanced to survive a reduction of staff. The other research divisions—the Theoretical Division under Bethe, and the Chemistry and Metallurgy Division under Cyril Stanley Smith and Joseph Kennedy—as well as Oppenheimer's administrative division, underwent little change in personnel, although their overall orientation was now aimed at implosion. A small number of counts in a physics experiment had thus caused major reorganization associated with mission change at Los Alamos.

Completion of the Implosion Weapon

Between August and July 1945, the implosion developments again divide into two phases: from mid-August 1944 through the end of February 1945, the aim was to settle the design for the bomb, at least provisionally; from March through July 1945 the aim was to produce and test the weapon. In both phases, a multidisciplinary coordinated army of more than a dozen groups operating within the new G- and X-divisions or in T-Division conducted implosion research, now the laboratory's first priority. Right up to Trinity, uncertainties about the feasibility of an implosion weapon lingered.

Phase 3: Freezing of the Design, August 1944–February 1945

By mid-fall, implosion looked more promising than it had only several months earlier. In late October, Conant assessed the chance that a lensed implosion device would work on schedule if all went smoothly as "50-50 for a test at Trinity on May 1, 1945," and "3:1 for a test on July 1."[57] Three crucial strands were converging: research and development on the explosive lens, on the electric detonator, and on the suggestion made in September by theoretician Robert Christy of a conservative design of the core of the gadget that avoided asymmetry at the expense of efficiency but required for adequate efficiency the use of an initiator to begin the nuclear explosion at the optimal moment.[58]

The diagnostic program, consisting in this period of the RaLa, betatron, magnetic, and electric "pin" methods, in addition to the original three diagnostics, was yielding excellent data on all aspects of the implosion. The RaLa method, developed by Bruno Rossi and Hans Staub, examined implosion by measuring the intensity of strong gamma rays passing through the imploding system. This method showed clearly that compression and reasonable symmetry could be achieved when both electric detonators and Christy's suggested design were used. Under Darol Froman, the pin method, an electrostatic diagnostic program, in which the collapsing metal sphere hits straight pins erected in the surrounded space, closing electrical circuits, was particularly

57 Conant handwritten notes.
58 Robert Christy, interviewed by L. Hoddeson, Apr. 14, 1986.

powerful in determining implosion timing. The betatron method, analogous to the X-ray method, but more powerful because gamma rays replaced the less energetic X rays, provided important data, especially on compression. Developed by Donald Kerst, the inventor of the betatron, together with Neddermeyer, the betatron method took months to begin operating because of the practical problem of locating and bringing to Los Alamos an appropriate 20-million-electron-volt betatron. The magnetic method, developed by Joseph Fowler and others, registered motion of the collapsing metal through a static magnetic field by an electromagnetic signal in a pick-up coil.

Other major efforts centered on developing the explosive lens and the electric detonators. T-Division provided extensive support; among the important calculations were those showing that the Christy device would require an initiator. Developing this initiator added yet another thorny problem to the implosion program, for it was impossible to test an initiator short of an actual nuclear explosion. Overall, the work was becoming increasingly dictated by detailed design questions such as how to ensure that multipoint detonation is simultaneous, whether an explosive or electronic switch should fire the detonator circuits, what explosives the lenses should be made of, and the design of the initiator. All of these questions required close cooperation by scientists, engineers, technicians, machinists, and support workers. Outside manufacturers were also of vital importance.

Phase 4: Production, March–July 1945

As the time approached when sizable quantities of plutonium would become available, the design had to be fixed in order to begin final bomb production. On February 28, 1945, Oppenheimer and Groves decided provisionally on Christy's core design, using electric detonators and explosive lenses made of the explosives "Comp B" and Baratol. The practicability of this design hinged on the initiator, which had not yet been developed. Furthermore, neither usable lenses nor reliable electric detonator systems were yet available.

After March 1, the emphasis was on production of the implosion weapon; the research phase was nearing its end. Kistiakowsky stated in his monthly report for May that X-Division's activities "have lost all semblance to research and have become so largely production and inspection and testing that their brief summary here seems impractical."[59] Most of the work consisted of constructing and testing particular device components, including explosive lenses, detonators, and initiators, and on shaping plutonium for the core. Schedules were controlled by the "Cowpuncher Committee," appointed to "ride herd" on the implosion program.

Yet many crucial components remained problematic. For example, short-

59 LA Archives.

Fig. 10.3. A view of the Trinity site with tower in the background. The garbage cans were used to protect equipment from the elements.

circuiting in the detonators, which caused a certain fraction of them to fail regularly, was traced to the fact that the cores of the coaxial detonator cables were made of plastic, rather than molded nylon. Nylon was a synthetic product recently developed by the Du Pont Company; it emerged between 1927 and 1940 out of the fundamental studies conducted by a small department under Charles Stine (see Chapter 9). As David Hounshell explains, Groves and others on the Manhattan Project viewed Du Pont's development of nylon as a model for effective translation of basic research into production, a view that led Groves in 1942 to ask Du Pont to assume responsibility for plutonium separation and for building the pile that became the Hanford Engineer Works.

In a desperate letter in mid-June, Kenneth Greisen, who at this time heroically led the detonator production, asked Oppenheimer whether or not he could bring his influence to bear on procuring some of the essential molded nylon, a product then being manufactured by one small company in Great Neck, Long Island. Although meeting the needs of Los Alamos would require adding only one person to the night shift, the company was reluctant to do this, having by then already closed down its war effort. Apparently something was done soon after Greisen's letter, because subsequent documents refer to a limited number of the nylon cores being used at Los Alamos.

The firing circuits for the detonators offer another example of the last-minute problems. These circuits were being manufactured by the Raytheon Company in Massachusetts, but this company, which was never informed of the critical use to which the circuits would be put, was much too slowly and carefully switching its assembly line over from an earlier model. Shockingly few firing units arrived at Los Alamos for pre-Trinity testing.

Explosive lens-making provided further opportunities for eleventh-hour alarm. Theory proved incapable of predicting accurately the velocity of detonation waves passing through lens components. Consequently the lens molds ordered for Trinity lenses were slightly wrong in size. At the last minute, the formula of one of the explosives had to be adjusted so that the only available full-scale lens molds could be used. On the eve of the test, as several hundred researchers engaged in final activities, one question stood in the minds of all involved: Would the gadget work? (See Fig. 10.3.) Bethe recalled in an interview that he was particularly nervous about the initiator because he had opposed Fermi in selecting the design, and "that was very hazardous."[60] But the implosion device did work, both at Alamogordo and at Nagasaki.

Mission Change in the Large Laboratory and a New Approach to Research

That the implosion problem proved soluble is insufficient explanation for the huge technical success of the implosion bomb tested at Trinity and dropped on Nagasaki, for had the work proceeded as in phase 1, or even phase 2, the goal could not have been met. If the army of researchers needed to solve the problem was to be assembled, supported, and coordinated, the implosion program required the laboratory's highest priority. This priority was not granted until after the spontaneous fission crisis, whose main significance was to motivate the mission change that assigned the needed priority to implosion research.

A second factor essential to the success of Trinity was Los Alamos's cautious investment in implosion research in the period when the gun weapon was the principal mission of the laboratory. Very little technical progress was made during that period—most of the work done on imploding cylinders merely showed how not to arrange an implosion assembly. But institutionally, the mobilization of an effective group of scientists to work on the problem made it possible for the laboratory to change its mission very rapidly when the need to do so arose. In addition, the failures of implosion research during the first half of 1944 challenged several of the involved scientists to invent new conceptions that later enabled the device to be completed, such as Alvarez's

60 Hans Bethe, interviewed by L. Hoddeson, Oct. 3, 1986.

inventions regarding simultaneous electric detonators, Tuck's invention of the three-dimensional explosive lens for focusing shock waves, and Christy's core design.

Because building the implosion bomb was primarily a technological, rather than scientific, task, we may ask the question: Could not good engineers alone have carried the project through? The answer is no, for in no sense was building this bomb an ordinary engineering task. Not only was the needed technology far beyond "state of the art," requiring understanding of a broad range of underlying physics phenomena, from nuclear physics to hydrodynamics, but it was unknown whether one could in fact make such a weapon. Top-level scientists—including Bethe, Peierls, Christy, Rossi, Teller, Tuck, Neddermeyer, von Neumann, Alvarez, Segrè, Kistiakowsky, and Serber— were crucial to the success of the program; their theoretical and experimental tools had been developed for the very purpose of probing the unknown. Theoretical models played guiding roles at almost every stage to bridge the gaps in knowledge of nuclear physics, explosives behavior, realistic hydrodynamics, etc. Unlike typical scientific problems, theory had to be tied constantly to practical issues such as fitting bombs into the B-29's bomb bay or building components that would withstand the severe conditions of high-altitude drops. Similarly, the experimental tools of physicists—such as electronic counters, detectors, and particle accelerators—were employed extensively in studying the phenomena on which the designs were based. Both theorists and experimentalists had to push their tools far beyond their usual capabilities; thus, for example, theorists developed methods to carry out numerical hydrodynamics on a scale never before attempted, and experimentalists pushed the sensitivity of their detectors into qualitatively new regimes.

Under the pressure of war such scientists eagerly (with some exceptions) joined in a group project whose intellectual excitement matched the military importance of the problem. Intriguingly, it appears from interviews as well as written sources that the scientists felt generally fulfilled in their scientific study of the implosion. While working on this strongly mission-directed problem, they experienced the joy of research and the sense that they were working on their own problem! The issue for historians to unravel is how it is possible for a large laboratory to create an environment in which many or most of its scientists can experience such a sense of free inquiry while in fact they are working directly in line with the mission.

To solve the difficult and complex implosion problem before the end of World War II required developing a potent new approach to research in which scientists, engineers, metallurgists, and craftsmen worked together closely, borrowing extensively from each others' tool kits. While the scientists' training and interests prepared them for exploring the unknown, the engineers and craftsmen supplied techniques for using and expanding the understanding. In the new multidisciplinary approach their efforts and styles of work joined together; theory and experiment were intertwined and firmly tied to concrete phenomena and technologies. Advances were made through a scientific generalization of trial and error, rather than through a step-by-step scientific program to understand underlying physical phenomena. This general approach enabled many of the implosion problems to be solved with unprecedented speed; the entire implosion project, from its beginnings in Los Alamos to Trinity, lasted a scant 27 months.

Among the empirical methodologies that physicists and chemists at Los Alamos used frequently in combination with traditional scientific approaches were the *Edison approach* of trying, in the absence of good theoretical guidance, one system or material after another; the *shotgun approach*, in which all experimental techniques available and everything known about a particular issue are fired at the problem to be solved, in hopes that one or more techniques hit on a piece of the problem and reveal a facet; *overlapping approaches,* or redundancy, in which multiple approaches to a specific problem are taken simultaneously in recognition that any one could be incomplete and uncertain, but together they could be used to build up a consistent picture; the *small-scale model* study, to save time and precious materials; *iteration,* a systematic generalization of "tinkering," or cut-and-try empiricism, long characteristic of American science,[61] in which an approach is taken and tested, then repeatedly modified to bring the results closer to the desired outcome; and *numerical analysis,* at Los Alamos for the first time done extensively by computing machines. Although messy, such numerical methods were more far-reaching than analytical models alone, which were simply too incomplete and idealized to handle concrete problems. But when combined with analytic methods, they became a tool of striking power.

The Edison approach was a guiding factor in the countless implosion shots fired. The shotgun technique was combined with redundancy in the many-stranded implosion diagnostic program, in which seven complementary types of experiments—X-ray, photographic, terminal observation, magnetic, electromagnetic, betatron, and RaLa—were oriented toward gathering as much data as possible about implosion. Scale models were used in every implosion diagnostic program. Iteration was used extensively in the explosive lens program: theorists made educated guesses of the index of refraction, on the basis of which were cast lenses of approximately correct geometry, whose actual index of refraction and focusing properties were then determined and used by the theorists in making improved guesses for the next iteration toward good experimental lenses. Numerical methods, carried out, for example, on the group of International Business Machines, were used extensively in the implosion program.

Although the roots of this approach began to form in America during the 1930's, for example, in Ernest Lawrence's laboratory at Berkeley and in

61 Holton, "Formation of the American Physics Community."

certain of the early industrial research institutions like Bell Telephone Laboratories and the General Electric Research Laboratory, the dramatically successful work of Los Alamos in World War II was one of the strongest forces solidifying this trend. The military control of Los Alamos during World War II contributed in several ways to solidification of the new methodology. In addition to supporting the hierarchical organization that fostered multidisciplinary collaboration, it imposed rigorous time constraints on the research, while at the same time providing essentially unlimited funding and material support. Indeed, the military priority of the project often allowed strings to be pulled when scientists needed supplies, equipment, or personnel in a hurry. The combination of strict deadlines and lavish support encouraged the scientists to employ research approaches that emphasized an abundance of systematic experimental trials in the interest of rapid progress.

The special conditions at Los Alamos could remain favorable only under the wartime pressures to get the job done. After the war most of the Los Alamos scientists, including the director and all the division leaders, chose to return to academia and basic research. But on their return they brought with them the new approach to large-scale research. Transplanted to universities and other government laboratories, this approach was applied in many areas of pure science, from subatomic elementary particle physics to numerical studies of astrophysics. It has become part of the fabric of American big science.[62]

62 This topic was touched on at the Los Alamos meeting, "Transfer of Technology from Wartime Los Alamos to the Postwar Period," held in May 1987 and organized by Robert Seidel.

References Cited

Alvarez, Luis W. *Alvarez: Adventures of a Physicist.* New York: Basic Books, 1987.
Galison, Peter. *How Experiments End.* Chicago: University of Chicago Press, 1987.
Hawkins, David. *Project Y: The Los Alamos Story.* Los Angeles: Tomash, 1983.
Hewlett, Richard G., and Oscar E. Anderson, Jr. *A History of the United States Atomic Energy Commission,* Vol. 1, *The New World, 1939–1946.* University Park: Pennsylvania State University Press, 1962.
Hoddeson, L., P. Henriksen, R. Meade, and C. Westfall. *Critical Assembly: A Technical History of Los Alamos, 1943–45.* Los Alamos, N.M.: Los Alamos National Laboratory, 1990.
Holton, Gerald. "The Formation of the American Physics Community in the 1920s and the Coming of Albert Einstein." *Minerva* 19 (1981): 569–81.
Johnston, L. "The War Years." In W. P. Trower, ed., *Discovering Alvarez: Selected Works of Luis W. Alvarez,* pp. 55–68. Chicago: University of Chicago Press, 1987.
Kistiakowsky, G. "Reminiscences of Wartime Los Alamos." In L. Badash, J. Hirschfelder, and H. P. Broida, eds., *Reminiscences of Los Alamos, 1943–45,* pp. 49–65. Boston: Reidel, 1980.

Manley, John H. "A New Laboratory Is Born." In L. Badash, J. Hirschfelder, and H. P. Broida, eds., *Reminiscences of Los Alamos, 1943–45,* pp. 21–40. Boston: Reidel, 1980.

McMillan, E. "Early Days at Los Alamos." In L. Badash, J. Hirschfelder, and H. P. Broida, eds., *Reminiscences of Los Alamos, 1943–45,* pp. 13–19. Boston: Reidel, 1980.

Neddermeyer, S. "Collapse of Hollow Steel Cylinders by High Explosives." *Los Alamos Report* 18 (Aug. 9, 1943).

Peierls, Rudolf. *Bird of Passage.* Princeton, N.J.: Princeton University Press, 1985.

Seaborg, Glenn T. "History of the Metallurgical Laboratory, Sec. c-1, April 1942 to April 1943." *Lawrence Berkeley Laboratory Publication* 112 (Feb. 1977).

CHAPTER 11

From Military Research to Big Science: Lloyd Berkner and Science-Statesmanship in the Postwar Era

Allan A. Needell

American science has produced generations of leaders: scientists who have served as spokesmen, as advocates, and as brokers between science and other segments of society. Following World War I men like Robert A. Millikan and George Ellery Hale, and later Karl Compton and Isaiah Bowman, assumed highly visible and influential positions in national life. These "statesmen of science" helped shape American science and the relations of science to society.[1]

Since 1945 leadership of American science has undergone important changes. Quite naturally, the growth of large-scale research and the increasing dependence of science on federal patronage have been associated with significant alterations in the ways in which scientific projects are promoted. But, in addition, new administrative and planning roles have been created. The scientists who have defined and filled these new leadership positions have been extremely effective advocates for the support of science. But in the process they have involved themselves in military and government affairs to a far greater extent than did the leaders of earlier periods.

---

1 Kargon, *The Maturing of American Science*, pp. 1–23. Kargon and Hodes used the term "statesmen of science" in "Karl Compton, Isaiah Bowman," p. 305. The spokesmen and leaders of American physical science were invariably men, and this has not changed.

Increasingly close involvement with the government and the "growth of large-scale research" are closely related.[2] And a surprisingly small number of individuals led the way. Lloyd V. Berkner (1905–67), although not exceedingly well known outside the inner circles of science administration, stands in the first rank of these postwar leaders of science. His career illustrates both the roots of postwar science-statesmanship in earlier eras and some of the most important changes that have occurred in recent years.

This chapter examines Berkner's career, concentrating on how he came to a position of influence at the crucial interface of science and the military and on the circumstances through which that influence was turned toward obtaining increased government support for various big science endeavors. It traces Berkner's first-hand experience with the contributions scientists could make to national strength and the vision of science and the roles of private and public institutions that grew out of that experience. It concludes with some very brief remarks on the reasons for the general, if somewhat ambivalent, acceptance that Berkner's leadership has received within the scientific community.

To establish Berkner's postwar leadership credentials, one need only list his major accomplishments during the 1950's. In 1950 Berkner was instrumental in initiating what later became the International Geophysical Year (IGY) (1957–58), a cooperative international undertaking that eventually involved 67 countries. Berkner served through 1958 as vice-president of the IGY's international organizing committee. From 1951 through the 1950's Berkner served as president of Associated Universities, Inc. (AUI), the organization that had previously created Brookhaven National Laboratory (home of the world's first nuclear reactor dedicated to basic research, and soon the world's first multibillion-electron-volt particle accelerator). At AUI, Berkner led a successful struggle to convince the National Science Foundation to contract with AUI to establish America's first federally funded big science facility for astronomy. And finally, in the aftermath of Sputnik, Berkner was appointed first chairman of the Space Science Board of the National Academy of Sciences. In that position he represented the needs and opinions of American scientists to the managers of a new American civilian space agency.[3]

What then made Berkner different from men like Millikan and Compton?

2 Beginning in the 1960's, books critical of the politicization of postwar science have appeared in growing numbers. For example, see Lapp, *The New Priesthood* (1965), Greenberg, *The Politics of Pure Science* (1967), Nelkin, *The University and Military Research* (1972), and Dickson, *The New Politics of Science* (1984).

3 On Berkner and the IGY, see Sullivan, *Assault on the Unknown*, pp. 20–27, and Newell, *Beyond the Atmosphere*, pp. 50–57; on Berkner's role in establishing the National Radio Astronomy Observatory in Green Bank, West Virginia, see Needell, "Berkner, Tuve and the Federal Role"; on the Space Science Board, see Newell, *Beyond the Atmosphere*, pp. 205–13. This list consists of only the largest and most visible of Berkner's efforts during this period. I am presently preparing a book-length study of Berkner and his impact on American science.

The lessons drawn from the World War II experience were not very different for Berkner from those drawn by those who had assumed leadership roles in the 1930's. Indeed, the great increase in the perceived importance of science and scientists for national security and the concomitant growth of federal support of science drew heavily upon the views of science articulated by science-statesmen of earlier eras, especially the enormous faith they placed in the power of cooperative research.[4]

For example, in the 1930's Compton—then president of the Massachusetts Institute of Technology (MIT)—argued that cooperative efforts involving various specialties promised the most significant advances for science. Testifying before Congress in 1937, he asserted that federal support for cooperative research efforts "would do more than anything else which I can conceive to bring about the desirable situation in which the scientific forces of the country would be actively engaged in a coordinated effort to improve the national welfare."[5] Organized science as a vehicle for benefiting society became the central theme of almost all of Berkner's postwar efforts.

Thus, the transformation of postwar leadership is not to be found in the rhetoric of social utility, military or otherwise. Much more, the transformation of science-statesmanship that Berkner represents is to be found in the vastly altered institutional and political context within which desirable social goals came to be defined, and in the organizational and management tools employed in their pursuit.

In 1939, when scientists and engineers began to face the problem of mobilizing America's scientific and technical resources for the coming war, their leaders stressed the temporary, emergency character of the organizations they created. Influential men like former MIT vice-president and newly installed president of the Carnegie Institution of Washington, Vannevar Bush, and the industrial physicist and National Academy of Sciences president, Frank Jewett, successfully built a largely voluntary coalition of private institutions and individuals to work with the government and military planners. In doing so, they were permitted to dispense an unprecedented amount of public money, and they were given direct authority to contract with industrial and academic organizations for research deemed important for the war effort.

But men like Bush and Jewett also took great care to preserve, as far as possible, the institutional relations that had existed prior to the outbreak of hostilities. To them it was important to avoid the creation of permanent governmental agencies that might later usurp power from the more traditional private academic, philanthropic, and honorary/advisory institutions at the

4 On prewar emphasis on cooperative research, see Kevles, *The Physicists*, pp. 185–99, 252–86, Dupree, *Science in the Federal Government*, pp. 323–68, Kohler, "Science, Foundations, and American Universities," pp. 135–64, and Genuth, "Groping Towards Science Policy," pp. 246–52.

5 On Compton, see Hewlett, "Compton, Karl Taylor," and Schweber, Chapter 6, this volume. The citation is from Pursell, "Preface to Government Support," pp. 154–55.

pinnacle of the American scientific establishment. In their minds politics and government bureaucracy could only be disruptive to the integrity and quality of scientific research.[6] And, most of all, they were extremely skeptical that, outside of a national emergency, government could attract and keep competent scientists in numbers sufficient to manage government-directed research programs effectively.

In contrast, Berkner and several of his postwar colleagues approved of a greatly expanded, long-term role for government in initiating and managing research. Consequently, they sought to expand formally and permanently the scope of influence of statesmen of science within the institutions of national defense, foreign policy, and other governmental activities. Whereas prewar scientific leaders were conservative and generally distrustful of political reforms, Berkner is an example of what have been called the "big operators," men who saw opportunities and advantages in the creation of new, powerful political alliances and institutions.[7]

For Berkner, making appropriate institutional and political changes to improve coordination and planning of research came to be seen more and more as an exciting technical challenge in its own right. "As the barber-surgeon of the Middle Ages has given place to the medical man of today, with his elaborate scientific training, so," predicted Berkner in 1951, "the essentially amateur politician and administrator of today will have been replaced by a new type of professional man, with specialized training. Life will go on against a background of social science. Society will have begun to develop a brain."[8]

Unlike leaders from earlier periods, whose rise to prominence generally stemmed from personal scientific accomplishment combined with long professional association with one or more of the elite institutions of American science,[9] Berkner's rise and effectiveness derived from the roles he assumed by mediating between science and the government. Indeed, Berkner was a central figure within the network of organizations that forged the postwar government-science relationship. During the 1940's and early 1950's, he vigorously advocated technocratic management of defense research and development.

6 As Carroll Pursell has noted ("Science Agencies in World War II," p. 375), the science leaders of the war effort could "muster little enthusiasm for pulling down the mighty and raising up the weak . . . and saw little to blame and much to praise in the way the nation's scientific and technical resources were distributed and used."

7 Reingold, "Vannevar Bush's New Deal," pp. 301–11, especially 307–8. The term "big operator" is from Walter McDougall, *The Heavens and the Earth*, p. 361.

8 Address to the Institute of Public Affairs, University of Virginia, Lloyd V. Berkner Papers, Box 10, Manuscript Division, Library of Congress, Washington, D.C. The language is reminiscent of New Deal social planners, but it was quite new for a leader of physical scientists or engineers. See Dupree, *Science in the Federal Government*, p. 349, and Kevles, *The Physicists*, pp. 254–55.

9 For example, their own universities, the great philanthropic foundations, the National Academy of Sciences, and/or the National Research Council.

But, just as significant, as he did so Berkner continued to work closely with and maintain the support of many of his more conservative colleagues. In the 1950's and beyond, Berkner turned those associations and the influence they provided toward promoting and managing nonmilitary big science endeavors. How he did this provides a revealing glimpse into the administrative side of the growth of large-scale research.

Berkner to 1945

Born in Milwaukee in 1905, Berkner earned a bachelor of science degree in electrical engineering in 1927 from the University of Minnesota.[10] He was an active radio amateur and worked under C. Moreau Jansky with an experimental radio station at the University of Minnesota and for several commercial stations in the Midwest. Following graduation Berkner enrolled in, but did not complete, a graduate program in physics. Later in 1927 he accepted a job with the Bureau of Lighthouses, where he worked on the installation of a radio ranging system for air navigation. A large and vigorous man at six feet, two inches, 190 pounds, Berkner also began a lifelong association with the U.S. Navy as an aviator in the Naval Reserves. In 1928 Berkner joined the National Bureau of Standards in Washington, D.C. At the Bureau he helped Amelia Earhart plan her first transatlantic flight. He also engineered short-wave communications and navigation systems for Richard Byrd's first Antarctic expedition, which he joined as a radio engineer.[11]

When he returned from Antarctica in 1930, Berkner began an ambitious and relatively costly series of studies of radio wave propagation in the ionosphere. For this work he adopted the radio pulse techniques developed by Gregory Breit and Merle Tuve at the Carnegie Institution of Washington's Department of Terrestrial Magnetism (DTM). The ambitiousness and cost of the project stand out as an early example of Berkner's promotional ability. With the depression deepening, however, government money for these studies disappeared, and Berkner left the National Bureau of Standards (and government service) to join the ionospheric radio researchers at the DTM. There, at the beautiful facility financed by the Carnegie Institution of Washington near Rock Creek Park in Washington, D.C., and at a DTM field station in Kensington, Maryland, he continued ionospheric research studies for the rest of the decade.

While at the DTM Berkner briefly returned to the classroom, studying for a Ph.D. in physics at George Washington University. But again he was distracted by the projects he undertook, this time by the opportunity to travel and help

---

10 Portions of this section are excerpted from Needell, "Berkner, Tuve and the Federal Role," pp. 262–64.

11 Merle A. Tuve, "Lloyd Viel Berkner: 1905–1967," draft of memorial memoir for the American Philosophical Society, Leland J. Haworth Papers, Manuscript Division, Library of Congress, Washington, D.C., and biographical fragments, Berkner Papers.

establish ionospheric observatories around the world. An equally important distraction was his continuing association as a reserve officer with the Navy Bureau of Ships (radio communications) and as a naval aviator with the Bureau of Aeronautics. His military experience gradually focused his attention on the technical problems facing the Navy as it prepared for the increasingly likely entrance of the United States into the growing European conflict.

In 1939 Berkner took part in discussions led by Vannevar Bush, the newly appointed president of the Carnegie Institution of Washington, on organizing science for war. In 1940, anticipating a growing need for the military to communicate over the pole to the Far East, Berkner proposed a survey, using privately purchased DTM equipment, of radio propagation conditions in Alaska.[12] Also, like many members of the DTM staff, Berkner worked as a consultant and as an "Official Investigator" on a number of projects sponsored by the National Defense Research Committee, including Tuve's effort to develop a radio proximity fuse for antiaircraft shells.[13]

In August 1941, shortly before the United States entered the war, Berkner was called to active duty in the U.S. Navy's Bureau of Aeronautics. There he organized and then led the bureau's Radar Section. His job was to direct the procurement of radar and other electronic systems and their integration into naval aircraft and supporting facilities. In that capacity he served as the bureau's principal technical contact with the various radar development efforts, including the Radiation Laboratory at MIT, sponsored by the Office of Scientific Research and Development (OSRD). In a telegram to mark Berkner's retirement from the Navy in October 1945, Milton G. White, head of the airborne radar division at the Radiation Laboratory, declared that without Berkner's "informed and vigorous championship of microwave radar . . . many of our most important weapons would never have seen battle."[14]

White's remark is indicative of the profound respect won by Berkner during the war from many of the leaders of the American scientific war effort. Berkner—who eventually assumed responsibility for the Bureau of Aeronautics's entire Electronic Materiel Division and attained the rank of captain— emerged from the war with enormous confidence in the ability of scientists to

12 Berkner to Fleming, "Memorandum Concerning Defense-Research Problem Using Available Facilities of the Department of Terrestrial Magnetism: Radio-Wave Propagation Conditions in the Alaskan Area," Oct. 16, 1940, folder "DTM—Projects Ionospheric Program 1940–41," Carnegie Institution of Washington Papers, Carnegie Institution of Washington, Washington, D.C. Bush maintained his position as president of the Carnegie Institution of Washington (DTM's parent organization) while serving as chairman of the National Defense Research Committee and later as director of the Office of Scientific Research and Development.

13 "War Activities of the Trustees and Staff: CIW 1939–46," pp. 3–4, Carnegie Institution of Washington Papers. See also Van Allen, *Origins of Magnetospheric Physics*, p. 16; Van Allen, interviewed by David DeVorkin and Allan Needell, Feb. 18, 1981, and other dates, National Air and Space Museum Oral History Collection, pp. 86–106.

14 M. G. White, telegram to Berkner, Oct. 19, 1945, Berkner Papers, Box 156.

contribute effectively toward the solution of complex technical and operational problems.

Demobilization and the Role of Science

Berkner, like many of his colleagues, came out of World War II convinced that new mechanisms and organizations were required to institutionalize the partnership between science and government forged during that conflict. That partnership was seen as something radically new; its preservation was seen as necessary if America was to retain its position of dominance among nations and if scientists were to retain the status, influence, and level of support they had achieved (or had come to expect) during the war years. But it took some time to sort out the institutional structure within which that partnership could best be effected.[15]

Early in 1946 Berkner returned to the DTM. Like many scientists, he found appealing the prospect of applying to scientific research the technology (especially the electronic devices) that had been developed during the war. He planned a research program that would make use of new electronic tools to simplify and enhance the ability to obtain and analyze radio signals reflected from or propagated through the ionosphere.[16]

Although Vannevar Bush quickly sought to dismantle the wartime OSRD, seeing it as a threat to the more traditional institutions of American science, he, like Berkner, was convinced that the armed services had to reorganize to promote the continued development and integration of new weapons. Military leaders were in general receptive. They too wanted to be sure that weapons innovation would continue after the fighting stopped. As a result, by early 1946, Bush (a civilian) was asked by the Secretaries of War and the Navy (Robert P. Patterson and James V. Forrestal) to establish and chair an unprecedented peacetime organization that would evaluate and coordinate the research and development activities of the armed services. This so-called Joint Research and Development Board (JRDB) would take over for the wartime Joint Committee for New Weapons and Equipment, which Bush had also chaired from its inception in 1942.[17] The JRDB was to be composed of Bush, two military officers from the Army, and two from the Navy.

When asked in early 1946 by Patterson and Forrestal to consider chairing the new board, Bush at first requested that Berkner be appointed deputy chairman. When the Army and the Air Corps objected because of Berkner's Navy associations, Bush circumvented the objections by proposing that the board's supporting administrative apparatus be strengthened and that Berkner

15 See Bush's statement before the Select Committee of Post War Military Policy, Jan. 26, 1945. A draft copy of these remarks was provided by Bush's wartime assistant, Ms. Lee Anna Embrey Blick, from her personal papers.

16 On postwar ionospheric research using technological advances made during the war, see Hevly, *Basic Research Within a Military Context*, pp. 93–139.

17 Baxter, *Scientists Against Time*, pp. 29–31.

be appointed to the position of executive secretary. The Army, the Air Corps, and Berkner agreed.[18]

The JRDB, as envisioned by Bush, would "bring together the Army and Navy programs of research and development, to remove unnecessary duplication, and to produce an integrated result, which can properly be considered the national program." To accomplish these goals Bush saw the board acting at various levels, both authoritative and advisory. To prevent unwarranted duplication of effort, Bush sought to rely on a complex system of committees and panels, each consisting of Army and Navy officers together with recognized civilian experts. The board itself, he expected, would generally go along with the judgments of its committees on technical matters. It would, however, exercise its own judgment in advising the Secretary of War and the Secretary of the Navy on the relative emphasis to be placed on various fields of research and development. It was to be Berkner's job, as executive secretary, to set up the various committees and panels and provide each with the staff assistance they needed to conduct reviews, gather information, and prepare reports and recommendations for the board to consider and act upon.[19]

Beginning in July 1946, following the issuance of the JRDB's formal charter, Berkner began his organizational and recruiting tasks. With general guidance from Bush, he worked tirelessly to establish the many committees, panels, and subpanels. He quickly initiated what he hoped would be a comprehensive review of all existing military research and development contracts as well as a review of all research areas deemed potentially important for the security of the nation. He created committees and panels to pursue actively, among other areas, the nuclear propulsion of ships and aircraft, guided missile development, chemical and biological warfare, communications, psychology, geography, and geophysics. The membership lists constituted a virtual who's who of American academic and industrial science and engineering. Of particular importance in the minds of both Bush and Berkner was the organization of a policy council "responsible for critical analysis of the trends of research and development and the vital planning associated with the utilization of new weapons." Berkner was particularly interested in radar and the possibility of developing a comprehensive, integrated system for air navigation and control (civilian and military). Such a system, Berkner believed, would be an essential component of any early-warning system for detecting air or missile attacks on the United States. It would also promote the redirection of the enormous aircraft manufacturing capacity that had grown up during the war toward the grand civilian air transportation system that many saw as necessary for maintaining the postwar national economy.[20]

18 Bush to W. John Kenney, June 21, 1946, Vannevar Bush Papers, File 1403, Box 59, Manuscript Division, Library of Congress, Washington, D.C.

19 Bush to Donald David Kirk, Oct. 23, 1946, Bush Papers, Folder 1403, Box 59.

20 Berkner to J. A. Stratton, Sept. 12, 1946, Bush Papers, Folder 1403, Box 59. The citation is from Berkner to Walter Dyke, Oct. 31, 1946, folder "Personal L.V.B. 1946–47,"

Berkner remained with the JRDB for only a year. Yet it was a pivotal year in his career, as it was a pivotal year in establishing the direction military research efforts would take for years to follow. It has been suggested that the JRDB's most important accomplishment may have been as a training ground "where a number of the future leaders, managers, and explicators of defense research and development received an education in national security affairs."[21] While this assessment probably understates the value to the postwar military of having a comprehensive inventory of existing efforts and authoritative evaluations of future areas of promise, in the case of Lloyd Berkner it is certainly correct that the JRDB experience was instrumental in shaping his understanding of what needed to be done in the area of national defense, and how best to do it.[22]

Berkner's return to the DTM during the summer of 1947 was brief. Once again his departure was orchestrated by Vannevar Bush. In September 1947 a new Department of Defense was created to oversee the "National Military Establishment." The JRDB was reconstituted as the Research and Development Board with Bush as its first chairman. Early in 1948, Bush began to push for an additional organization to provide technical evaluations of programs developing specific weapons systems directly to the new office of the Secretary of Defense. Bush was able to convince the new Secretary of Defense, James Forrestal, to ask Berkner to lead a group to evaluate and propose methods of providing the Secretary of Defense and Joint Chiefs of Staff with expert

---

Berkner Papers, Box 3. The two largest and most complex committees were those on electronics and guided missiles. The electronics committee is illustrative. As formed in October 1946, this committee consisted of J. A. Stratton (MIT) as chairman, D. A. Quarles (Bell Laboratories) and W. L. Everitt (University of Illinois) as civilian members. The Army had three representatives, one of which represented the Army Air Force; the Navy had one representative each from the Bureau of Ships, the Bureau of Ordnance, and the Bureau of Aeronautics. Associate members of the committee included representatives of the Army Security Agency and Naval Operations and, in addition, E. R. Piore from the Office of Naval Research. By November 1946, the committee announced plans to establish a dozen technical panels. Each would have from one to five representatives each from the Army and Navy and a civilian chairman. The panels created and civilian assignments completed by the November meeting of the electronics committee included a panel on basic research to be chaired by J. B. Fisk (Bell Laboratories), a panel on electron tubes to be chaired by R. G. McCurdy (also from Bell Labs), a panel on radiating systems to be chaired by L. C. Van Atta (Naval Research Laboratory), a panel on communications to be chaired by H. Pratt (MacKay Radio Corp.), a panel on navigation and warning to be chaired by A. E. Cullem (former assistant director of the Harvard Radio Research Lab), and a panel on interference reduction to be chaired by K. C. Black (Aircraft Radio Corp.). Panels on radar, electronic countermeasures, infrared, electronic guidance, and sonar were also being formed, but chairmen had not yet been recruited. Research and Development Board Papers, Boxes 18 and 83, Record Group 330, Entry 341, National Archives and Records Agency, Washington, D.C.

21 York and Greb, "Military Research and Development," p. 194.

22 These remarks are based in part on discussions held with Stephen P. Rosen of the Naval War College, who is currently preparing a book on the history of innovation in weapons development.

scientific and technical analysis of the weapons systems proposed by the individual services. An eight-month study led to establishment of the so-called Weapons System Evaluation Group.

Speaking before the U.S. Naval Postgraduate School in Annapolis, Maryland, in January 1949, Berkner cited Secretary Forrestal as describing the creation of the Weapons System Evaluation Group as "one of the most interesting and significant accomplishments in the work of unification. . . . This is not a supplanting of the military judgment by scientists, but rather a marriage between the two professional capacities and abilities."[23] Use of the marriage metaphor was apt. For, as do marriages generally, the science-military partnership faced difficult questions. How, given the closeness of the relationship, could the parties maintain those distinctive qualities that attracted them to each other in the first place? And how was responsibility for controlling the products of the union to be shared? Although rarely addressed explicitly through the 1950's, such questions increasingly occupied science-statesmen and others as the impact on science and society of the Cold War expansion of federal support of research became more and more apparent.

Nevertheless, the main topic of Berkner's speech in January 1949 remained modern weapons and how best to obtain the indispensable expert contributions of the nation's scientific community in their development and use. Echoing Bush and other spokesmen of science and the military, Berkner asserted that "in order to defend this country adequately, it is imperative that we think not in terms of weapons of the last war, which even now are largely obsolescent, but in terms of the weapons of the next war." But going further than many in the Navy, he stated that the serious threat posed by a new generation of enemy submarines required a restructuring of the Navy with the creation of a new research organization headed by a civilian. As to what kind of man should lead the new unit, he insisted that "to effectuate the partnership between the Navy and science, the administrator must have insight into and the confidence of the scientific profession. He must know the leaders of science, and he must enjoy their full personal confidence. He himself must comprehend the advances of knowledge, so that he can exercise the kind of leadership that his position would owe to the Navy and to the nation. He must certainly be a scientist of demonstrated ability, rank, and creative instinct."[24]

It is not clear if Berkner was actively seeking such a position, or even if he believed his own scientific accomplishments were sufficient to qualify him. Significantly, he was at the same time again attempting, in vain it turned out, to establish a productive research program for himself at the DTM.[25] Clearly his

23 Folder "Speeches pre 1951," Berkner Papers, Box 10. In fact, in his private diary Forrestal credited Bush with the accomplishment: "The idea began to germinate in his [Bush's] mind a year ago. All I had to do was back it." Millis, *The Forrestal Diaries*, p. 541.

24 Folder "Speeches pre 1951," Berkner Papers, Box 10.

25 That scientific accomplishments remained at the center of his professional self-image can be seen from a January response to a questionnaire that asked what he considered to be

ideal was that leadership and perspective in matters of policy involving complex technical issues stemmed from the same characteristics—such as creativity, dedication to truth, rigor, and adherence to rational methods—he believed were responsible for scientific accomplishment.

Also entering into deliberations over the path his career might take, in 1949, while he continued working at the DTM, Berkner began to receive offers from universities, primarily in engineering programs. In February he declined an offer to become chairman of the electrical engineering department at the University of Illinois; in March he declined to become dean of engineering at the University of West Virginia. His expressed reason for turning down the Illinois position was the "outstanding opportunity offered by [the Carnegie Institution of Washington] for research and service in the field of science and by the belief that the Carnegie Institute, as an independent, private, scientific organization, exerts a distinctive and essential influence on the relation of science to national and international affairs." Attached to a copy of this letter, which he sent to Bush, is a note from Bush agreeing that "we will have some interesting times together in the next few years."[26] Ironically, the note was written at a time when Berkner was about to step out, once and for all, from under Bush's shadow.

Expanding the Vision

Lloyd Berkner was an old friend of James E. Webb, fellow aviator in the Naval Reserve and the future Apollo-era head of the U.S. civilian space agency. Webb, as President Truman's director of the Bureau of the Budget, had become an important figure in Washington.[27] In February 1949, in response to rapidly increasing international tensions and the perceived threat of Soviet political or military advances in Europe, Truman asked Webb to leave his Bureau of the Budget post to go over to the State Department as under secretary. In May, Webb convinced Berkner to take another leave of absence from the DTM and join the State Department as head of an interdepartmental government committee to plan, coordinate, and obtain congressional approval for the administration's Military Assistance Program for the countries of the new North Atlantic Treaty Organization.

---

his most important work. He responded, neglecting his war service or his work for national security, that it was his "research work related to the experimental definition of the distribution of ion density in the outer atmosphere under solar and terrestrial influences, and the consequences of this ionization and its variations on geomagnetism, radio wave propagation, and meteorology of the high atmosphere." For the questionnaire response, see folder "L.V.B. Personal Correspondence 1949," Berkner Papers, Box 3.

26 Folder "L.V.B. Personal Correspondence 1949," Berkner Papers, Box 3.

27 James Webb, interviewed by Martin Collins and Allan Needell, National Air and Space Museum Oral History Collection.

"I found myself catapulted into my present position rather suddenly as a result of a request from my old friend Jim Webb," Berkner explained to former JRDB consultant William Shockley. Somewhat uneasy among scientists about his growing public stature, he continued, "I fear that there has been a certain amount of notoriety attached to my appointment here but I hope my friends will overlook this."[28]

His Military Assistance Program assignment was completed in October. "I have now completed my work with the State Department," he wrote, "having planned the general program for arms aid to Europe and having received favorable consideration from Congress on this program. I therefore look forward with pleasure to the continuance of my research here at the Department during the next few months. Unfortunately, I am not entirely free of my State Department connection. . . . In these troubled times it seems necessary that one give part of his time to the Government in the endeavor to achieve a more stable world."[29]

These concluding remarks reflect the fading remnants, in Berkner, of the more traditional vision that the proper relationship of scientists to government is temporary, in emergencies. With relations between the United States and the Soviet Union rapidly deteriorating and the prospect, voiced by many, that the tensions were likely to last for a decade or longer, the idea that a permanent mobilization of science was called for became commonplace. Berkner's remark also reflects the marked broadening of the purview of national security concerns that had taken place over the previous half-decade. One of Berkner's continuing State Department assignments will be discussed shortly. It was highly classified, involving technical issues of communications (overcoming the jamming of American propaganda broadcasts) and other aspects of psychological warfare. Another involved leading a new project, supported by Webb, a study of the impact of science on foreign policy. That study led to an influential report "Science and Foreign Relations," which, among other proposals, called for a *permanent* science advisor for the Secretary of State and the creation of posts for science attachés at various overseas missions. Although all these topics—radio wave propagation, psychological warfare, and science in foreign relations—had been discussed by the JRDB during Berkner's tenure as executive secretary, they extended far beyond providing technical solutions to specific technical problems and, indeed, far beyond the traditional concerns of the military.

During the summer of 1950, Berkner began to devote more time to participation in groups studying important national security issues. He was an active participant in the Navy-sponsored, MIT-managed Project HARTWELL. Proj-

28 Berkner to William Shockley, May 12, 1949, folder "State Department," Berkner Papers, Box 3.

29 Berkner to V. A. Bailey, Oct. 4, 1949, folder "L.V.B. Personal Correspondence 1949," Berkner Papers, Box 3.

ect HARTWELL, led by Jerrold Zacharias, involved 33 full-time members and focused on the technical problem of preserving America's ability to transport supplies overseas in the face of improved enemy submarines.[30] By the fall of 1950 Berkner expanded his involvement in the State Department's Project TROY, which evolved from his own earlier studies of radio propagation, communication behind the Iron Curtain, and psychological warfare. Project TROY, also managed by MIT, involved many of the scientists who had taken part in HARTWELL, plus experts in psychology, anthropology, economics, and foreign relations. Berkner's participation built upon his earlier interests in radio propagation and in the broad problem of how to compete with the Soviet Union and defend the United States without resorting to the use or threat of all-out nuclear attack.[31]

Especially after the rise of mobilization fever following the November 1950 entry of Chinese troops into the Korean War, "summer studies" like HARTWELL and the less well-known TROY were seized upon as model arrangements for providing expert civilian advice on complex national se-curity problems.[32] Nevertheless, especially at MIT, several issues plagued scientists and administrators. Among them were the questions of whether MIT's relations with individual government agencies might compromise its independence and whether the undertaking of special studies for one agency (especially the State Department, then facing political problems) might alien-ate agencies not involved. MIT's leaders began to expect and to advocate that a new organization be created to oversee such studies and isolate the university from interservice and intragovernmental rivalries.[33]

30 Berkner had previously taken part in Navy-sponsored symposia organized in coop-eration with the National Academy of Sciences on technical issues associated with undersea warfare. On the earlier Navy studies, see D. Bronk to Berkner, "Navy Desires Continued Advice of Civilian Scientists in the Solution of Technical Problems in Undersea Warfare," Aug. 5, 1946, folder "Personal L.V.B. 1946–47," Berkner Papers, Box 3. On Project HART-WELL, see Zacharias to Berkner with attachments, May 19, 1950, Berkner Papers, Box 156. See also Kevles, Chapter 12, this volume.

31 The State Department's records of Project TROY remain classified. I am in the process of having them reviewed for possible release. The nature of the project and Berkner's involvement were cited by L. Haworth in a draft of a posthumous tribute to Berkner titled "Berkner and Associated Universities, Inc.," Haworth Papers. The subject of Project TROY can be inferred from various unclassified letters and comments, such as a January 1951 letter from Bush to Conant on the subject of "unconventional warfare," which reads in part as follows: "The background is that there is quite a stir on this subject now. The State Department has, as you undoubtedly know, a contract at MIT on a project called TROY, on which some of your people are collaborating. This is concerned with various aspects of unconventional methods, not merely with the Voice of America or merely with the subject of propaganda. It is quite a job, I understand, and the ruffles I hear from it are reassuring, for they seem to be getting down to brass tacks." Bush Papers, Folder 614, Box 27. See also Tuve to Bush, Dec. 22, 1950, folder "CIW General, July–Dec. 1950," Department of Terrestrial Magnetism Papers, Washington, D.C.

32 Marvin and Weyl, "The Summer Study."

33 Stratton to Killian, Dec. 12, 1950, MIT President's Papers, Institute Archives and Special Collections, MIT, Cambridge, Mass.

All of this activity left Berkner anxious to establish for himself a position from which he could exert some leadership and explore alternative ways of facilitating scientist participation in the emergency efforts and in planning for the future defense of the nation. Reacting to the growing interservice conflicts and to perceived resistance within the military to the advanced systems for control of air navigation and continental defense that he had long favored,[34] Berkner now felt that new weapons and other advanced defense research must be independent from the military if large and sophisticated projects were to be carried out effectively. In addition, with others, Berkner was convinced that the United States had at most only a few years to develop a defense against airborne atomic warfare. Without such a system he believed that the country would soon find itself in the unacceptable position of finding its cities held hostage in any future showdown with the Soviet Union.

It was under such grave assumptions that in January 1951 Berkner was appointed president of AUI. He accepted the job even though he was then the leading candidate to become the first director of the newly created National Science Foundation.[35] Berkner was guaranteed by AUI's trustees that as president he would be free to explore AUI's accepting management of appropriate projects. With this guarantee, he discussed with Ivan Getting and Louis Ridenour, who were acting in behalf of the Air Force, the need to establish a permanent laboratory to conduct research and development on information processing, communications, and various other components of a future continental defense system. Berkner believed that AUI was a promising vehicle for providing expert civilian management of this or other such laboratories. Apparently, his efforts notwithstanding, Berkner had become convinced that the Carnegie Institution of Washington was not about to take on such a role.[36]

On the problem of air-defense technology, the Air Force soon decided to set up Project CHARLES and later the LINCOLN Laboratory at MIT. Nevertheless, Berkner continued to search for defense projects for AUI to undertake. For example, in May 1951 he proposed that Brookhaven follow up the important Caltech-directed VISTA Project.[37] Instead, in July the AUI board of

34 See Berkner to Stratton, Sept. 12, 1946, Bush Papers, Folder 1403, Box 59.

35 See England, *A Patron for Pure Science,* pp. 123–27.

36 Lee Anna Embrey Blick, interviewed by Allan Needell, July 14, 1987, National Air and Space Museum Oral History Collection. The proper role to be played by the Carnegie Institution of Washington and especially its Department of Terrestrial Magnetism in conducting or managing government-sponsored projects was an active issue that led to several disagreements. Most vocal in advocating that DTM avoid government contracts was Merle Tuve, its director since his return from directing the wartime Applied Physics Laboratory.

37 Berkner requested approval from the AUI board for Brookhaven to participate in a national defense program related to Project VISTA. VISTA had addressed the problem of developing tactical uses for nuclear weapons. He also discussed an Air Force social science program described in the formal AUI minutes simply "as related to operations research." AUI executive committee minutes, May 18, 1951, AUI Papers, Associated Universities, Inc., Washington, D.C. On Project CHARLES, see Marvin and Weyl, "The Summer Study," p. 3; on Project VISTA, see Gilpin, *American Scientists and Nuclear Weapons Policy,* pp. 113–15.

trustees voted, at Berkner's request, to have AUI manage Project EAST RIVER for the Federal Civil Defense Administration, the National Security Resources Board, and the Department of Defense. EAST RIVER, a comprehensive look into the problems of civil defense, had been turned down by MIT, which was gearing up for LINCOLN. The study required about two dozen full-time staff members and many consultants. It resulted in a partially classified report that stirred considerable controversy.[38] Berkner also personally played an active role in projects CHARLES, LINCOLN, and SUMMER LINCOLN.

Berkner supported the existing, primary mission of AUI—the management for the nation's scientists of the advanced research tools being built at Brookhaven National Laboratory. As he wrote in a letter to his long-time assistant in Washington shortly after accepting the new job, "I have some hard study ahead to master the fundamentals of the new job, but I cannot help but feel that the development of huge research facilities with Government support in the interests of our society presents a challenge of the first order."[39] But, even so, given the international situation, Berkner's experiences during the immediate postwar period, and his own areas of technical expertise, it is clear that Berkner joined AUI to facilitate the continued use of American science to solve urgent national security problems rather than specifically to promote the special interests of the basic research community. What is remarkable is just how easily, as Berkner's vision of the proper relations of science to society continued to mature, he became convinced that the two goals were not in conflict and that the presidency of AUI would allow him to reach for both with considerable effectiveness (see Fig. 11.1).

Berkner, Society, and Nonmilitary Big Science

Once he assumed the AUI presidency, Berkner began to devote much more thought to the broader relations of science and society. He had long believed that science and technology contributed much to mankind besides military might. In May 1951 he delivered a speech, "The Impact of Science on Society," to the Institute of Public Affairs of the University of Virginia. It was the first of many far-reaching talks that Berkner would make over the coming years. In it he paused to review all of human history from the perspective of the relations between science, technology, and society. Berkner described three major phases of western history, the first two having been brought to their ends by the eighteenth-century "industrial" revolution and the twentieth-century "communications" revolution, respectively. To him, both of these periods had been characterized by individual efforts. The third great age, in his view, had been ushered in by the atomic bomb. He called it the "nuclear age." As to what

38 AUI executive committee minutes, July 20, 1951, AUI Papers. For a contemporary account and evaluation of the EAST RIVER study, see the special Project EAST RIVER issue of the *Bulletin of the Atomic Scientists* 9, no. 7 (Sept. 1953).

39 Berkner to Embrey, Feb. 12, 1951, Embrey personal papers, in her possession.

Fig. 11.1. Control room for the Cosmotron at the Brookhaven National Laboratory. Through the window can be seen the 220-ton magnet, covered by a white plastic "cocoon." Service equipment lies on the floor inside this ring-shaped magnet, which has an inside diameter of 65 feet.

characterized this new age, "Perhaps the real revolution of this century is the *organization of science* and the acceptance by society of *its capacity for producing new and radical solutions to old problems, both social and military.*"[40]

In an April 1952 address Berkner emphasized a different point: "The government has become a major element in the support of research efforts. In providing this support, it has *of course* greatly influenced the direction of the

40 Berkner, speech text, July 11, 1951, folder "Speeches pre 1951," Berkner Papers, Box 10 (emphasis added).

effort and to a certain extent instituted a control of the results. Before, free markets, profit motive, and occasional government regulation guided technology to socially useful ends. With increased government support that guidance must come through political pressure based on informed public debate." Military research, with its requirement for secrecy, was an essential, special case—a special case with its own special problems. "It is interesting to note," wrote Berkner,

> that scientists have from time to time been accused of endeavoring to form a priesthood in which they would interpret for the public the best course of action in the light of the development of specific technology. Scientists have generally disclaimed any such idea. Nevertheless, it cannot be denied that scientists since the war have taken extraordinary interest as a group in the formation of our national and international policy as it depends on the emergence of new technologies. There is a very important reason why this is so. Of the entire group forming the present oligarchy who control secret information, the scientists are the only group having homogeneous interests within the oligarchy. . . .
>
> They [scientists] have come to sense that they, in fact, bear the responsibility for developing either the moral or immoral aspects of their creations.[41]

Apparently, by "homogeneous" Berkner meant to imply, at the very least, that as a result of their training and their devotion to careful research and objective methods, scientists shared a common purpose. In contrast, military men tended to maintain primary loyalty to one or another branch of the armed forces. That scientists themselves sometimes acted as a special interest that needed to be balanced by other scientists or by other interests in society was an issue that Berkner never acknowledged or discussed.

By 1952, Berkner had become concerned that the nation was providing the military with inordinate power. Reflecting on some of his recent State Department work, Berkner maintained that "the present international situation may very well depend on more intelligent understanding and application of the political and social implications of scientific progress. Somehow we should learn to use and to develop these ideas as an international force to ease the tensions and to contribute to the creation of world peace."[42]

These musings on the role of science in furthering the broadly defined goals of our society are just one indication that, with his move to AUI, Berkner took an increasingly expansive view of the postwar role of science-statesmen and of science-government relations, far more expansive than when he labored primarily for the military. He also adopted and expanded upon an extraordinary vision of the special abilities that scientific training and experience afford. His perspective was influenced in part by the scale of the basic research tools he saw first-hand being operated and proposed by scientists for their own pur-

41 Draft of "Cooperative Forum" speech, Apr. 23, 1952, Berkner Papers, Box 10.
42 Folder "L.V.B. Speeches and Papers," Berkner Papers, Box 10.

poses, and in part by the grand strategic issues that had been raised in discussions of continental air defense and unconventional warfare.

In 1952, defense concerns were still paramount. And Berkner was increasingly insistent that the existing form of the science-military partnership was inadequate to the tasks before the nation. In a September 1952 speech, "The Influence of Science and Technology on Military Factors in Foreign Policy," given at the Minnesota World Affairs Center at the University of Minnesota, Berkner assessed the organizational requirements of the Cold War and especially the problem of continental defense.

> I believe that the time has come when science should be temporarily organized under a new "OSRD" to exploit to the fullest the possibilities of the new technological "break-throughs." Most scientists wanted to be "in reserve" until some vital deficiency appeared, requiring bold, new, and very general military concepts that depended wholly on a major scientific effort. These conditions now seem fulfilled; there is positive and bold action that can be taken with regard to matters of the gravest national importance. The communications [between science and the military] associated with OSRD must be restored.[43]

The need to reactivate the OSRD was a recurrent theme in popular and professional speeches and articles after 1950.[44] Significantly, many now attributed the wartime triumphs in weapons development to the organizational structure that had been set up rather than to the voluntary personal relationships that had been built between scientists and government and military leaders. Many felt that perceived deficiencies in the existing relations between civilian experts and the military in weapons development could be rectified by adopting the wartime organizational precedent. As the previous quotation

43 Berkner Papers, Box 10.

44 Already in August 1948 (after the Czech coup and Berlin crisis) Bush had requested that Irvin Stewart chair a committee to study the general question of "mobilization of the civilian scientific effort in the event of an emergency." The Stewart committee reported to the Research and Development Board (Compton was then chairman) in December 1949. The report called for a new OSRD-like organization that, like the World War II version, would report directly to the President. After the Korean War began, the problem was passed on to William T. Golden, a special consultant to the Bureau of the Budget. On Dec. 18, 1950, Golden submitted a report to the President recommending "the prompt appointment of an outstanding scientific leader as Scientific Advisor to the President." Among other things, the scientific advisor was "to plan for and stand ready to initiate a civilian Scientific Research Agency, roughly comparable to the Office of Scientific Research and Development of World War II." The result of Golden's study was the creation in April 1951 of a Science Advisory Committee reporting to the Office of Defense Mobilization (SAC/ODM), an agency within the White House hierarchy. The first SAC/ODM chairman was Oliver Buckley, former president of Bell Laboratories. It was not immediately clear to Berkner or to others what role Buckley or the SAC/ODM would plan in mobilizing American scientists for the current emergency or, especially, for the long-term development projects that would become necessary if the U.S. was to seriously consider developing the means to counter a nuclear surprise attack. See York and Greb, "Military Research and Development," pp. 198–99.

indicates, Berkner became one of the more vocal of the proponents of a new OSRD.

Berkner's views were not universally shared among defense-oriented scientists. Lee DuBridge, president of the California Institute of Technology, no doubt echoing the concerns of many of the old-guard science-statesmen, responded to a draft copy of remarks Berkner planned to make before the spring 1953 meeting of the American Physical Society. DuBridge expressed doubt that the existing relationship with the armed services was the chief obstacle to the implementation of grandiose plans for continental defense urged by Berkner.

> I confess that I fail to see how, from the material that goes before, it follows that an independent research and development organization is needed. I realize that many administrative headaches would be solved if enterprises such as Project Lincoln could be reporting to someone like Van Bush rather than to a military agency. But it has yet to be proved to me that Project Lincoln has been really stymied in its efforts to carry out the development of new techniques of air defense through the fact it operates under contract with a military agency. Naturally, the best technique for providing adequate air defense is still a matter for debate and for further investigation, and no agency, civilian or military, is going to bet a billion dollars until the technological situation is more clear, and I do not think it takes a billion dollars to do additional research and development work. I have the feeling that a good group of scientists and engineers, operating under contract with an institution like MIT and having good personal contacts with officers of all three military services, can accomplish any job that could be accomplished by a similar group under contract with an independent civilian agency.[45]

Fearing that once a bureaucracy was created it would take on a life of its own, others besides DuBridge objected to Berkner's call for a new agency. The effectiveness of such an agency was not guaranteed, and it could easily grow to threaten the hard-won prerogatives of existing organizations both inside and outside of the military and government.

Berkner's view did not prevail on the issue of continental defense. He soon came to realize that his managerial and organizational aspirations were more fruitfully applied in areas where preexisting interests did not conflict so directly. The International Geophysical Year was an excellent model. The international organization that was set up was designed to fill an organizational vacuum even as it advanced the goal (supported by the JRDB and the State Department) of promoting science in foreign counties and cementing the relationship between the international and American scientific communities. The development of advanced big science facilities for basic research offered similar potential. By the time the launch of Sputnik I spawned a national consensus that the United States should vigorously develop a capacity to

45 Folder "L.V.B. Speeches and Papers," Berkner Papers, Box 9.

operate in and explore space, Berkner and his allies had placed themselves in a position to push successfully for a civilian agency to manage the bulk of those efforts.[46]

Conclusion

Lloyd Berkner developed an extremely optimistic vision of the prospects for coordinated efforts and social progress reminiscent of that of the science-statesmen of the 1930's. But he went far beyond them in his enthusiasm and in his taste for proposing institutional change. New leaders like Berkner and his close friend and confidant James Webb believed strongly that the technical virtuosity displayed by American scientists and engineers during World War II, with sufficient support and proper administrative framework, could be vitalized and channeled to accomplish almost anything (from continental defense to the banishment of hunger and social unrest). Basic scientific research became one important vehicle for demonstrating the power of organized interdisciplinary efforts and for developing the organizational tools for effectively managing large-scale technical projects in the national interest.

I have described elsewhere Berkner's role in creating a government-financed large-scale facility for radio astronomy.[47] Much of the appeal of that project was that it could serve as a prototype for development of national research facilities serving many constituencies. The National Radio Astronomy Observatory met the needs of astronomers, even if some were slow to recognize that fact. It met the needs of the National Science Foundation in allowing it to expand the scope of its activities into big science. It met the needs of the military in that it fostered the rapid development of a technology deemed essential for national security. As just mentioned, following Sputnik, the civilian space program provided similar opportunities.

As this chapter indicates, along with the shift from the great philanthropic foundations to the federal government as the major source of scientific patronage, the process by which scientific leaders sought to argue the social value of science has undergone important changes. Men like Berkner, who stressed the need to plan, organize, and channel the scientific and technical resources of the nation, replaced those who—in an era that valued the ideal of voluntary, cooperative efforts—sought primarily to inspire cooperation among scientific technological specialists and thereby to attract private and public support for science. Where the earlier statesmen of science shared backgrounds and assumptions with the industrial and foundation supporters they courted, the postwar leaders began to associate themselves with a growing professional cadre of planners and public administrators inside government.

Although there has been considerable conservative opposition to the ex-

---

46 See McDougall, *The Heavens and the Earth*, pp. 157–76.
47 Needell, "Berkner, Tuve and the Federal Role."

panded role of government, sufficient political support has been developed to allow various centralized efforts to go forward. That support has been powerfully augmented by the Cold War and various other competitive challenges from abroad. From their perspective, working scientists, by and large, did not object to Berkner's far-reaching vision, especially the part that equated the flourishing of science with the ultimate good of mankind. The big science facilities that Berkner proved so successful in organizing and in administering rapidly became indispensable tools within many scientific specialties. In the end, that more than anything may account for the acceptance by scientists of Berkner's leadership.

Objections, like those raised most vociferously by Merle Tuve[48] that the real value of science (which in his view remained in essence an individual intellectual activity) would be destroyed by such emphasis on organizations and on tools, have gone largely unheeded. Such objections have been overwhelmed, on the one hand, by the sheer magnitude of support that has been made available for large-scale scientific research and, on the other, by the impressive results achieved by scientists as a result of the access provided by big science equipment to previously inaccessible phenomena.

Concern that these gains are, in the end, to be balanced against hidden or longer-term losses, I suspect, underlies, at least in part, the production of this volume. It is apparent, however, that such concerns were not given great weight by Berkner as he rose to his position as a statesman of American science. That point, in itself, helps to illuminate an important aspect of the dramatic postwar growth of large-scale research.

48 *Ibid.*

References Cited

Baxter, James Phinney. *Scientists Against Time*. Boston: Little, Brown, 1946; Cambridge, Mass.: MIT Press, 1968.
Dickson, David. *The New Politics of Science*. New York: Pantheon, 1984.
Dupree, A. Hunter. *Science in the Federal Government: A History of Policies and Activities*. 2nd ed. Baltimore: Johns Hopkins University Press, 1986.
England, J. Merton. *A Patron for Pure Science: The National Science Foundation's Formative Years, 1945–1957*. Washington, D.C.: National Science Foundation, 1982.
Genuth, Joel. "Groping Towards Science Policy in the United States in the 1930s." *Minerva* 25 (1987): 238–68.
Gilpin, Robert. *American Scientists and Nuclear Weapons Policy*. Princeton: Princeton University Press, 1962.
Greenberg, Daniel S. *The Politics of Pure Science*. New York: New American Library, 1967.
Hevly, Bruce W. "Basic Research Within a Military Context: The Naval Research

Laboratory and the Foundations of Extreme Ultraviolet and X-Ray Astronomy." Ph.D. diss., Johns Hopkins University, 1987.

Hewlett, Richard G. "Compton, Karl Taylor." In Charles Gillispie, ed., *Dictionary of Scientific Biography*, 3: 372–73. New York: Charles Scribner's Sons, 1970.

Kargon, Robert H., ed. *The Maturing of American Science: A Portrait of Science in Public Life Drawn from the Presidential Addresses of the American Association for the Advancement of Science, 1920–1970*. Washington, D.C.: American Association for the Advancement of Science, 1974.

Kargon, Robert, and Elizabeth Hodes. "Karl Compton, Isaiah Bowman, and the Politics of Science in the Great Depression." *Isis* 76 (1985): 301–18.

Kevles, Daniel J. *The Physicists: The History of a Scientific Community in Modern America*. 2nd ed. Cambridge, Mass.: Harvard University Press, 1987.

Kohler, Robert E. "Science, Foundations, and American Universities in the 1920s." *Osiris* 3 (1987): 135–64.

Lapp, Ralph E. *The New Priesthood: The Scientific Elite and the Uses of Power*. New York: Harper and Row, 1965.

Marvin, J. R., and F. J. Weyl. "The Summer Study." *Naval Research Reviews* 8 (1966): cover–28.

McDougall, Walter A. *The Heavens and the Earth: A Political History of the Space Age*. New York: Basic Books, 1986.

Millis, Walter, ed. *The Forrestal Diaries*. New York: Viking Press, 1951.

Needell, Allan A. "Berkner, Tuve and the Federal Role in Radio Astronomy." *Osiris* 3 (1987): 261–88.

Nelkin, Dorothy. *The University and Military Research: Moral Politics at M.I.T.* Ithaca, N.Y.: Cornell University Press, 1972.

Newell, Homer E. *Beyond the Atmosphere: Early Years of Space Science*. NASA SP-4211, Washington, D.C.: NASA, 1980.

Pursell, Carroll. "Preface to Government Support of Research and Development: Research Legislation and the National Bureau of Standards, 1935–1941." *Technology and Culture* 9 (1968): 145–64.

———. "Science Agencies in World War II." In Nathan Reingold, ed., *The Sciences in the American Context: New Perspectives*, pp. 359–78. Washington, D.C.: Smithsonian Press, 1979.

Reingold, Nathan. "Vannevar Bush's New Deal for Research: Or the Triumph of the Old Order." *Historical Studies in the Physical and Biological Sciences* 17 (1987): 299–344.

Sullivan, Walter. *Assault on the Unknown: The International Geophysical Year*. New York: McGraw-Hill, 1961.

Van Allen, James. *Origins of Magnetospheric Physics*. Washington, D.C.: Smithsonian Institution Press, 1983.

York, Herbert F., and Allen G. Greb. "Military Research & Development: A Postwar History." *Bulletin of the Atomic Scientists* 33 (1977): 12–26. Reprinted in Thomas Kuehn and Alan L. Porter, *Science, Technology and National Policy*, pp. 190–215. Ithaca, N.Y.: Cornell University Press, 1981.

CHAPTER 12

The cold war has become, in large measure, a
technological race for military advantage.
—David Z. Beckler, Executive Secretary,
Science Advisory Committee, 1955[1]

K₁S₂: Korea, Science, and the State

Daniel J. Kevles

In 1945, scientists and policymakers in the United States were well aware
that the Allied victory in World War II had drawn heavily upon a variety
of wartime technological miracles. The armed forces of the victors had
been strengthened decisively by devices such as proximity fuses, solid-fuel
rockets, and microwave radar, and the war itself had been brought to a sudden
end by the atomic bomb. Now nuclear weapons and other technological
means promised to offset the Soviet manpower advantage in Europe. To
scientists and policymakers in 1945, it was evident that the United States'
national security in the postwar era depended upon the maintenance of technological superiority.

Technological superiority during the war had been achieved largely by
civilian scientists working under the auspices of the Office of Scientific Research and Development (OSRD). OSRD had operated not by establishing
laboratories of its own but by letting contracts to academic and industrial
institutions. Even though it had been engaged in defense research and develop-

1 Beckler, "Notes on Science Organization and National Policy," Karl T. Compton/
James R. Killian Papers, MIT Archives, Box 257, Folder 21 (hereafter C/K Papers). For
support during my research for this chapter, I am grateful for a fellowship year at the Center
for Advanced Study of the Behavioral Sciences, Stanford, California, and for a grant from
the Alfred P. Sloan Foundation.

ment, it had been independent of the military, a civilian-dominated agency with its own congressional appropriation and direct authority from the President. Its most gigantic offspring—the atomic-bomb effort—had been spun off to the Manhattan District of the U.S. Army Corps of Engineers, but it had nurtured and harbored several big science defense research projects of its own. The biggest had been the Radiation Laboratory at MIT, whose staff, in 1945, comprised some 4,000 people and whose wartime OSRD contracts totaled about $80 million.[2]

The achievements of OSRD and the Manhattan Project demonstrated dramatically that technological superiority demanded a transformation in scope and scale of the relationship between civilian science and the American state. Peacetime research was needed in two broad areas: first, in subjects clearly related to military technology (for example, the behavior of electromagnetic radiation at the frequencies of microwave radar), and second, in topics falling under the rubric of pure science, often defined by a logic internal to the field and commonly exemplified, in the discussions of the late 1940's, by the prewar nuclear explorations that had made possible the invention of the atomic bomb. The first would contribute directly to the development of military technology; either could yield radically new weapons in the future.

Thus, though demobilization was slimming down or eliminating some defense research projects—for example, the Radiation Laboratory at MIT was going out of business—postwar national-security policy compelled an ongoing commitment to big science. There would have to be major defense research installations, both military and civilian, big federally supported programs of scientific research, and pressure-cooker efforts to overcome the acute wartime shortages of expert personnel by steadily enlarging the nation's pool of trained scientists and engineers.

Some of the research could be conducted in government laboratories, but the OSRD model suggested that a good deal of it ought to exploit the nongovernmental sector of civilian science, the laboratories of both industry and academia, the main source of fresh thinking and activity on the frontiers of science. Moreover, in the mode of OSRD, such research ought to be as independent of the military's control as possible, so as to tap the civilian scientific capacity to generate ideas for radical new weapons and weapons systems, yet its practitioners should be kept involved in the forging of national strategic policy. As Vannevar Bush, the head of OSRD, had argued as early as 1941, only by drawing upon scientific experts familiar with the latest laboratory products could military planners know the best way to exploit new weapons. Only by having access to the military's strategic requirements could defense scientists best understand the kinds of weapons that needed developing.[3]

2 Kevles, *The Physicists*, pp. 307–8.
3 *Ibid.*

After 1945, a series of policy initiatives and political compromises did transform relationships between science and the American state. The Korean War, which broke out in June 1950, transformed them further, yet with effects on national security policy that went beyond merely enlarging the already big defense research and development establishment.

In fiscal 1950, the federal government spent some $1 billion for research and development, almost $300 million more than it had spent for the purpose in 1946, the year of demobilization. No single federal agency managed American science; OSRD had been disbanded. Yet most of the research and development funds—90%—came from the Atomic Energy Commission (AEC), which had been created in 1946, and the Department of Defense, which had been established by the National Security Act of 1947. The department's research and development budget totaled somewhat more than $500 million, which supported at least 15,000 different projects. Some 54% of these allocations was for work in industry, about 9% was for research in universities and other non-profit institutions, and the rest was for work in the government's own laboratories, mainly military installations. In 1950 the Defense Department's role in American science was an intensified version of what it had already started to become in the immediate postwar period, when the director of the Research and Development Division of the Army General Staff had declared that "the publicly owned laboratories and drafting rooms, as well as the research and engineering staffs of our educational institutions, industries, and foundations, are being put to work in as orderly a manner as possible by the research and engineering agencies of the War and Navy Departments."[4]

At the end of the 1940's, the military supplied about 15% of the Bell Telephone Laboratory's budget. It spent $350 million on research in industrial laboratories, accounting for about 25% of all funds devoted to research and development in industry. About two-thirds of the budget of the National Bureau of Standards came from other government agencies, mainly the military. The nominally civilian National Advisory Committee for Aeronautics had been reallocated in the U.S. Code from Title 49, "Transportation," to Title 50, "War," partly in recognition that its budgetary growth had been based "entirely on military considerations."[5] The Army Signal Corps sustained the MIT

4 Forman, "Behind Quantum Electronics," p. 180; Forrestal to Compton, Sept. 30, 1948; chart, "Research and Development Obligations of the Department of Defense," fig. 2, attached to "Science Advisory Committee, Summary, Mtg. No. 3," Sept. 18, 1951, C/K Papers, Box 245, Folder 16; Box 256, Folder 10.

5 Golden, memo to file, "Conversation with E. U. Condon, Director, National Bureau of Standards, and Messrs. Hugh Odishaw and N. E. Golovin, Assistants to the Director," Oct. 31, 1950, p. 3, William T. Golden Papers, "Government Military-Scientific Research: Review for the President of the United States, 1950–51," Niels Bohr Library, American Institute of Physics, New York; "Research and Development in the United States, 1941–1952," table attached to Buckley to Killian, Oct. 26, 1951, C/K Papers, Box 256, Folder 10; Forman, "Behind Quantum Electronics," p. 211; Roland, *Model Research*, vol. 1, pp. 260–61.

Research Laboratory in Electronics—85% of MIT's research budget came from the military and the AEC—the Radiation Laboratory at Columbia, and the Croft Laboratory at Harvard. The Atomic Energy Commission funded the big particle accelerators at the MIT Radiation Laboratory, Berkeley, and Brookhaven. The AEC was also supporting some 800 fellowships a year in the physical and biomedical sciences, while the Office of Naval Research (ONR)—by far the principal military patron of academic science and currently the sponsor of some 1,200 research projects in almost 200 universities—was assisting some 2,500 science students towards their doctorates. In 1949, the Defense Department and AEC together accounted for 96% of all federal dollars spent on the campuses for research in the physical sciences. For every two of those dollars spent by the AEC, the military spent at least three.[6]

Each of the armed services had extended into peacetime the wartime arrangements that permitted leading universities to manage major weapons research facilities for defense agencies in a semi-autonomous fashion. Perhaps the best known was the Los Alamos Weapons Laboratory, which the University of California operated, first for the Manhattan Project, then for its successor, the Atomic Energy Commission. (In 1949, J. Robert Oppenheimer remarked with irony that "it is a great liberal university that is the only place in the world, as far as I know, that manufactures, under contract with the United States government, atomic bombs." He added, "I have sometimes asked myself whether we can find any analogy to this situation in the practice of the monastic orders that devote a part of their attention and derive part of their sustenance from the making of their private liqueurs.")[7] Operating in the shadow of Los Alamos but also products of the war were several university-connected laboratories sponsored by the Department of Defense. Typical of them were the Jet Propulsion Laboratory at the California Institute of Technology and the Applied Physics Laboratory of the Johns Hopkins University, the former a ward of Army Ordnance, the latter of Navy Ordnance. Both were devoted to basic research related to the development of guided missiles.[8]

6 Forman, "Behind Quantum Electronics," pp. 156, 204, 186–87; chart, "Research and Development Obligations of the Department of Defense," fig. 2, attached to "Science Advisory Committee, Summary, Mtg. No. 3," Sept. 18, 1951, C/K Papers, Box 256, Folder 10; Kevles, *The Physicists*, pp. 355, 359; Golden, memos to file, "Conversation with Kenneth Pitzer, Director, Research Division, AEC," Oct. 31, 1950, p. 1, "Conversation with Rear Admiral T. Solberg, Director of Office of Naval Research," Jan. 15, 1951, as of Jan. 10, 1951, p. 1, Golden Papers (in Golden's dating system, the "as of" date refers to the day of the conversation, the other date to the day of the memo).

7 Oppenheimer, *Uncommon Sense*, p. 30.

8 Koppes, *JPL and the American Space Program*, pp. 18–34; Michael Aaron Dennis, "No Fixed Position: University Laboratories and Military Patronage at Johns Hopkins and MIT, 1944–46," unpublished paper. Army Ordnance's sponsorship of JPL sharply expressed the change in the military's attitude toward civilian science. The foot soldier's Army had long been the most backward of the services with respect to scientific research. Ordnance, which received about two-thirds of the Army's research and development funds, had traditionally been prone to rely on its own laboratories, such as the Aberdeen Proving

The power of military patronage of academic science worried a number of the nation's scientific leaders. In 1949, Lee DuBridge, the head of the Radiation Laboratory at MIT during the war and now the president of the California Institute of Technology, declared, "When science is allowed to exist merely from the crumbs that fall from the table of a weapons development program then science is headed into the stifling atmosphere of 'mobilized secrecy' and it is surely doomed—even though the crumbs themselves should provide more than adequate nourishment." University scientists were constantly—and rightly—apprehensive that the military might impose security restrictions on their research. Some worried that the military's overwhelming presence in university science would distort its intellectual direction.[9] However, the Department of Defense not only supported basic research recognized, to quote a later Defense Department directive, "as an integral part of programmed research committed to specific military aims"; it also provided a good deal of money for projects in pure science free of most restrictions, security or otherwise. In any case, in March 1950 President Truman signed into law the bill establishing the National Science Foundation (NSF), which was intended to be the flagship of fundamental science in the United States and was expected in many quarters to take over much of the military's sponsorship of pure research.[10]

Though all this patronage gave the military leverage over the course of civilian science, in the postwar period civilian scientists also gained influence in the shaping of national security policy and technology. Some of the influence arose from consultantships and summer studies, like that begun in late 1949 by MIT physicist Jerrold R. Zacharias, who agreed to head an investigation for the ONR of ocean transport and antisubmarine warfare. (The study, conducted during the summer of 1950, was dubbed Project HARTWELL, because the civilian scientists who carried it out dined frequently at the Hartwell Farms Restaurant, near the MIT field station in Lexington, Massachusetts, where they did the work.)[11] Some of the influence also derived from participation in cadres planning and evaluating weapons systems. The

Ground, and to distrust civilian establishments. Golden, memo to file, "Meeting with Roger W. Jones, Assistant Director in Charge of Legislative Reference, Bureau of the Budget," Oct. 11, 1950, Golden Papers. See the comments on contract-operated government laboratories in Buckley to Truman, May 1, 1952, attached to Science Advisory Committee, "Summary, Meeting No. 11," May 9, 1952, C/K Papers, Box 256, Folder 12.

9 Forman, "Behind Quantum Electronics," p. 185; Kevles, *The Physicists*, pp. 378–79.

10 Department of Defense directive, "Policy on Basic Research," June 19, 1952, C/K Papers, Box 256, Folder 13; Kevles, *The Physicists*, p. 356; Golden, memo to files, "Conversation with Dr. Vannevar Bush," Dec. 5, 1950, Golden Papers.

11 Project HARTWELL ran formally from March through December 1950 and cost $124,000, much of which went to pay the summer salaries of the 21 civilian scientists responsible for the study. T. J. Crane to Killian, July 23, 1954, C/K Papers, Box 257, Folder 18; Zacharias, manuscript of an unpublished autobiography.

Army had its Operational Research Office; the Navy, its Operational Evaluation Group. The Air Force had several groups of such experts attached to its various commands and also the Rand Corporation, in Santa Monica, California. At the top of the armed services, attached to the Joint Chiefs of Staff, was the Weapons Systems Evaluation Group, comprising some 25 civilian scientists and an equal number of military officers. Participation in key standing scientific advisory committees afforded civilians more general policy influence. In the most portentous area, there was the General Advisory Committee of the AEC, which was loaded with world-class physicists. In the workaday areas of practical military postures, there were, notably, the Air Force Scientific Advisory Committee, the Naval Research Advisory Committee, and the Army Scientific Advisory Panel, each populated by prominent scientists and engineers from industry as well as academia.[12]

The most wide-ranging and, at least nominally, powerful defense-science advisory group was the Research and Development Board (RDB), which had been established by the National Security Act of 1947 to advise the Secretary of Defense on the progress and needs of scientific research and development as they related to national security. Although the RDB included representatives of each of the armed services, it was by law headed by a civilian. It was empowered, among other things, to advise the Joint Chiefs of Staff on the interaction of research and development with strategy. It was, in short, designed to institutionalize Bush's vision of a coequal interplay between civilian scientists and professional military officers forming policies for the development and use of new weapons.[13] Indeed, Bush had been its first chairman, and he was succeeded, in 1948, by Karl T. Compton, the president of MIT, a prominent physicist, veteran of the wartime OSRD, and Bush's good friend. When Compton took office, Secretary of Defense James Forrestal told him that, in his view, the chairman of the RDB was "the center in the National Military Establishment of the application of science to war," his principal

12 Kevles, *The Physicists,* p. 355; York and Greb, "Military Research and Development," pp. 16–17; William C. Foster to John Stennis, Apr. 23, 1952, C/K Papers, Box 256, Folder 12. William T. Golden, who was surveying defense research, noted, "Advisory committees are becoming increasingly fashionable." Golden, memos to file, "Conversation with Brigadier of Feb. 28, 1951," p. 3; "Conversation with H. P. Robertson, Deputy Director, WSEG, Dr. Louis Ridenour, Special Adviser to the Secretary of the Air Force and to the Director of Research and Development of the Air Force, and Professor Marshall Stone," Dec. 8, 1950, pp. 1–2; "Conversation with Lt. General Hull and Dr. Robertson, Director and Deputy Director of the Weapons System Evaluation Group," Nov. 21, 1950, as of Nov. 15, 1950, p. 1, Golden Papers.

13 *U.S. Statutes at Large,* vol. 61 (1947), pt. 1, pp. 506–7. The revision of the National Security Act, in 1949, left the duties of the RDB virtually unchanged. *U.S. Statutes at Large,* vol. 63 (1949), pt. 1, pp. 584–85. The RDB replaced the Joint Research and Development Board, which had been established in 1946 and which was, in turn, an outgrowth of the wartime Joint Committee on New Weapons and Equipment. York and Greb, "Military Research and Development," pp. 14–15.

advisor in that area, and essential to the Joint Chiefs of Staff for introducing into war planning adequate consideration of the evolution of weapons.[14]

By 1949, as a result of directives from the Secretary of Defense, the RDB was charged with drawing up and putting into effect a "complete and integrated program of research and development for military purposes." It was also to keep tabs on the activities and budgets of the various individual service agencies, and to force shifts in their programs if necessary. To carry out these considerable duties, the RDB had a full-time staff of about 250 people, distributed over numerous committees, which called upon some 2,500 civilian and military individuals for advice.[15]

In early November 1949, Compton, who was about to leave the chairmanship of the RDB because of ill health, summarized the defense research situation to President Truman and pronounced it good. In the preceding year, not only had the RDB reported to the Joint Chiefs of Staff on the status of every project that might impinge on future military strategy but it had prepared a systematic plan for military research and development "based on the strategic thinking of the Joint Chiefs," a plan that the departments and the RDB had used in preparing their budget estimates. Particularly exciting to Compton, the RDB was able to recommend a military research and development program for the next year that was not significantly affected by shortages in technical personnel. The postwar shortage had eased considerably. Henceforth, Compton hoped, the military research and development budget could be "determined on the basis of military value in the light of national policy, rather than by the more arbitrary standards which of necessity had to be applied previously."[16]

About two months before Compton wrote his summary, the President announced that the Soviet Union had detonated its first atomic bomb. Later in 1949, China was declared to have "fallen" to the control of the communists under Mao Tse-tung. The turn of events prompted Paul Nitze, the head of the State Department's policy planning staff, to argue in National Security Council Memorandum Number 68 (NSC-68), in the spring of 1950, that the United States was headed for a period of maximum danger and that the ensurance of

14 Forrestal to Compton, Sept. 30, 1948, C/K Papers, Box 245, Folder 16.

15 Secretary of Defense [Louis Johnson], "Directive Research and Development Board," Sept. 14, 1949, C/K Papers, Box 245, Folder 17; Golden, memo to file, "RDB—Conversations with Messrs. Loomis, Walker, and Cornell," Nov. 13, 1950, as of Nov. 10, 1950, Golden Papers.

16 Compton to Truman, Nov. 2, 1949, C/K Papers, Box 245, Folder 17. Even Vannevar Bush thought that defense research was in pretty good shape, certainly in far better shape than it had been in 1940. Golden, memo to file, "Conversation with Vannevar Bush," Oct. 24, 1950, p. 3, Golden Papers. In the view of insiders, the RDB was thought actually to control all of the Defense Department's research and development funds. See Golden, "Notes of Conversations re Study of Military and Scientific Research," [Sept./Oct. 1950], especially the conversations with Willis Shapley and John Manley, Golden Papers.

its safety required full-scale rearmament.[17] However, while the budget of the AEC was expanded considerably and the agency was committed to crash development of a hydrogen bomb, there was no overall increase in funding or activity in nonnuclear defense research. Quite to the contrary, the general defense research and development budget had already fallen from $530 million in fiscal 1949 to $510 million in fiscal 1950. The Truman administration recommended for fiscal 1951 its lowest overall military budget since the end of the war. In the spring of 1950, Congress approved the budget virtually unchanged, including funds for defense research and development about the same as in the previous year, meaning a level lower absolutely than in fiscal 1949 and, in constant dollars, lower still. Beneficiaries of ONR support of basic research were apprehensive, and rightly so. The ample patronage that ONR was providing academic science had its critics at the highest levels of the Navy; indeed, the Navy's General Board expressed the opinion that "expenditures for this purpose should be assigned a relatively lower priority if further curtailment of the total research and development budget is necessary."[18]

Then, too, all was not well at the key point of contact between civilian scientists and the military, the RDB. In January 1949, the Committee on Organization of the Executive Branch—the Hoover Commission—reported that the RDB had been "handicapped" in meeting its statutory duties, especially in bringing civilian scientific expertise to bear upon strategic weapons planning. The difficulties of the RDB derived partly from the immensity of the job it had been trying to do: policing the entire defense research and development budget, which many of its civilian scientific members and consultants found daunting and which earned it the enmity of some branches of the armed services. Moreover, the RDB had suffered from lack of leadership between Compton's resignation and the appointment of his successor, William Webster, a 1920 graduate of the Naval Academy and a 1924 alumnus of MIT, who had spent his post-Navy days mainly in the electrical utilities industry, and had joined the OSRD during World War II. Still, even after Webster took office, early in 1950, he was only rarely invited to sit with the Joint Chiefs of Staff during their deliberations on research and development, and he felt himself very much an outsider.[19]

17 Herken, *Counsels of War,* pp. 49–51.

18 York and Greb, "Military Research and Development," p. 17; Forman, "Behind Quantum Electronics," pp. 157–58 and n.13; Compton, "The Research and Development Budget of the Department of Defense," Oct. 30, 1950, C/K Papers, Box 245, Folder 19; Sapolsky, "Academic Science and the Military," pp. 387–88.

19 Compton to Truman, Nov. 2, 1949, R. F. Rinehart to Hanson W. Baldwin, Feb. 4, 1950, C/K Papers, Box 245, Folders 17, 19; Golden, memo to file, "Conversation with Mr. William Webster, Chairman, Research and Development Board, Department of Defense," Nov. 1, 1950, Golden Papers; Committee on Organization of the Executive Branch of the Government, "Task Force Report on National Security Organization," Appendix G, Jan. 1949, pp. 6, 18–21, 97–98. The dissatisfaction with the participation of civilian scientists in strategic planning is evident in Bush, *Modern Arms and Free Men,* pp. 251–53, 261.

However, on the eve of the Korean War the military's involvement in civilian science—and vice versa—remained substantial. In the Atomic Energy Commission, the Applied Physics Laboratory, the Jet Propulsion Laboratory, and wherever else civilian science was semi-autonomously tied to the military, radical new weapons were being born, including the hydrogen bomb, certain types of guided missiles, and a variety of other hardware innovations. Although analysts like Nitze thought that budgetary constraints were keeping the machinery of defense-related big science running too slowly, that machinery was firmly in place, ready, if necessary, to be speeded up.

The outbreak of the Korean War, in June 1950, provoked a mood of grim-faced preparedness among policymakers in the United States. If the Soviets had previously seemed to rely on subversion to achieve their aims, now they were perceived as threatening the West with armed aggression—a challenge that demanded not only a major and immediate increase in military strength but, perhaps, an even larger boost in defense research and development. Karl Compton, reflecting in October 1950 on the defense research budget, noted the "danger of military aggression, like Korea, in other quarters, which could lead to piecemeal defeat or all-out war" and added, "The United States cannot match its potential adversary in numbers. . . . Our main source of military superiority is in those technological developments which multiply the per capita fighting effectiveness of our forces."[20]

In short order, the defense research and development budget followed the overall defense budget into the stratosphere, doubling to slightly more than $1.3 billion in fiscal 1951, and rising still higher, to about $1.6 billion, in fiscal 1952. By late 1951, it was estimated that Department of Defense and AEC contracts accounted for nearly 40% of all money spent on industrial and academic research. Defense research was estimated to be occupying some two-thirds of the nation's scientists and engineers. At the American Physical Society meeting earlier that year, perhaps the principal nontechnical topic of conversation was the wholesale and high-powered recruiting of scientists by defense agencies, especially the Air Force. Planners were once again concerned with shortages of technical manpower, and the draft status of young scientists, particularly in such critical fields as nuclear physics and electronics, was once again a matter of policy debate.[21]

20 Compton, "The Research and Development Budget of the Department of Defense," Oct. 30, 1950, attached to Compton to E. O. Lawrence, Oct. 31, 1950, C/K Papers, Box 245, Folder 19.

21 Buckley, "An Appraisal of Some Indicated Needs of Defense Research," Dec. 31, 1951, attached to "Science Advisory Committee, Summary of Meeting No. 6," Dec. 11, 1951; Compton, "The Research and Development Budget of the Department of Defense," Oct. 30, 1950, attached to Compton to Lawrence, Oct. 31, 1950, C/K Papers, Box 256, Folder 11, Box 245, Folder 19; Golden, memo to file, "Conversation with Dr. Robert F. Bacher," Feb. 6, 1951, as of Feb. 3, 1951, p. 2, Golden Papers; Forman, "Behind Quantum Electronics," p. 167, n.32.

A series of administrative moves inside the Defense Department expressed the sense of technological emergency. In mid-1950, Secretary of Defense Louis Johnson attempted to beef up the RDB by allocating $25 million in the board's fiscal 1952 budget for distribution to departmental research and development programs. In February 1951, Secretary of Defense George C. Marshall formally enlarged the RDB's powers in a directive authorizing it to "originate research work" of military value for which the various armed services had no projects.[22]

In 1950, Marshall established an Office of the Director of Guided Missiles in the Defense Department and appointed as head of it the industrialist K. T. Keller, who quickly became known as the "missile czar." Civilian scientists were brought in and given authority at the top of the Air Force, and an independent Research and Development Command was created at Wright Field, the Air Force's principal research and development facility, in Dayton, Ohio. In March 1950, the Air Force was given exclusive jurisdiction over the development of long-range strategic missiles. In the meantime, the Army and Navy accelerated their short-range missile programs. The Army transferred a team of missile engineers to the Huntsville Arsenal, in Huntsville, Alabama, where, under Wernher von Braun, work commenced on the development of a tactical ballistic missile. In Pasadena, California, the Jet Propulsion Laboratory obtained authorization from Army Ordnance to move beyond basic research into the development of the Corporal guided missile, which would be designed to carry atomic warheads for use in Europe. Between 1950 and 1953, the Jet Propulsion Laboratory's budget more than doubled, to $11 million a year, and its staff multiplied similarly.[23]

The expansion in defense research and development prompted the Truman administration to come to grips with a variety of issues in the mobilization and management of civilian science, some of them predating the outbreak of the Korean War. There was the approaching activation of the National Science Foundation. There was the recommendation to create a new OSRD in the event of another war emergency, a move that had been urged in a June 1950 report from a committee of the RDB chaired by Irvin Stewart, a high-ranking aide to Vannevar Bush during World War II. There was the idea, suggested by George F. Hines, a lobbyist for the state of Massachusetts, and brought to Truman's attention by Congressman John McCormack, majority leader of the House of Representatives, that all military research and development should be under the direction of civilians and independent of the armed services. In

22 Webster to Robert E. Wilson, July 6, 1950, "Directive Research and Development Board," Feb. 1, 1951, C/K Papers, Box 245, Folder 19; Box 246, Folder 4.

23 York and Greb, "Military Research and Development," pp. 17–18; Armacost, *The Politics of Weapons Innovation*, pp. 26–27; Yanarella, *The Missile Defense Controversy*, pp. 37–38; Golden, memos to file, "Conversation with Mr. William A. Burden and Henry Loomis," Jan. 30, 1951; "Conversation with . . . Burden," Feb. 27, 1951, as of Feb. 18, 1951, Golden Papers; Koppes, *JPL and the American Space Program*, pp. 43–48.

mid-October 1950, the director of the Bureau of the Budget reminded Truman of all these issues, pointing out in addition "the emphasis which the increasing responsibilities of the U.S.A. in world affairs places on the relationship between strategic plans and scientific research and development" and urging a review of all activities related to defense science. The review was to be conducted by William T. Golden, an investment banker in New York City and devotee of science. Truman approved the review on October 20, 1950, and Golden went promptly to his task.[24]

Golden worked assiduously, discussing the intricacies of defense research and development with dozens of people, including officers in all the armed services as well as academic, industrial, and governmental scientists. He found a number of difficulties in the relationship between defense and civilian science. His informants told him that the military laboratories tended to be uncomfortable places for civilian scientists. While pay scales were said to be competitive for junior, less distinguished personnel, at the senior level they were thought to be noncompetitive with those in industry and academia.[25] Then, too, at a number of military laboratories, civilian scientists had to work under the control of military officers and to submit to their judgment in technical matters. Among the worst offenders in the management of civilian scientists was Wright Field, where slights against civilians included prohibiting them from using the Officers' Club. The Air Force, having long relied for technical advances on industrial contractors and the National Advisory Committee for Aeronautics, had no tradition of managing civilian scientists; it was in the process of building up its research and development capacities virtually from scratch. And the military's traditional jealousy of its prerogatives pervaded the Army and Navy as well. Not only at Wright Field but at several Army and Navy laboratories it was difficult to get and hold first-class civilian scientists.[26]

24 Golden, memos to file, "Meeting with Deputy Secretary of Defense Robert A. Lovett," Oct. 17, 1950, "Meeting with George F. Hines," Oct. 10, 1950; F. J. Lawton [Director, Bureau of the Budget], "Memorandum for the President: Scientific Research and Development of Military Significance," Oct. 19, 1950, Golden Papers. The report of the Stewart Committee was "Report of the Committee on Plans for Mobilizing Science," June 26, 1950, C/K Papers, Box 256, Folder 8.
25 Chart, "Research and Development Obligations of the Department of Defense," fig. 2, attached to "Science Advisory Committee, Summary, Mtg. No. 3," Sept. 18, 1951, C/K Papers, Box 245, Folder 16; Box 256, Folder 10; Golden, memo to file, "Conversation with Robert F. Bacher," Nov. 6, 1950, p. 2, Golden Papers.
26 Golden, memos to file, "Conversation with Brigadier General L. E. Simon and Major General A. C. McAuliffe," Mar. 1, 1951, as of Feb. 28, 1951, p. 1; "Conversation with Lt. General Hull and Dr. Robertson, Director and Deputy Director of the Weapons System Evaluation Group," Nov. 21, 1950, as of Nov. 15, 1950, p. 1; "Meeting with Roger W. Jones, Assistant Director in Charge of Legislative Reference, Bureau of the Budget," Oct. 11, 1950, p. 1; "Conversation with Dr. Ellis Johnson and George Shortley, Director and Deputy Director, Operational Research Organization, U.S. Army (Johns Hopkins contract)," Nov. 21, 1950; "Conversation with Mr. William A. M. Burden," Feb. 27,

The armed services on the whole remained committed to their traditional insistence upon controlling defense research and development and their equally traditional reluctance to cooperate with civilian scientists in strategic planning.[27] The physicist Lawrence Hafstad, a civilian scientific insider as head of the Reactor Development Division of the AEC, judged that the Navy was generally disinclined to admit scientific outsiders to its high councils. In Hafstad's view, both Army and Navy Ordnance were still ruled by tight, exclusionary cliques. The Air Force, reportedly, kept trying to have the WSEG eliminated.[28] And the RDB was in worse trouble.

The enormous increase in the defense program had further overwhelmed the oversight capacities of the RDB. To cope, Webster concluded that, "instead of striving to achieve the soundest possible balance within a total research and development program bounded by a fixed over-all dollar limit, we must now seek to insure that we recognize the major challenges to research and development, that no stone is left unturned to meet these challenges." In his view, the RDB committees ought no longer to engage in "routine scrutiny" but to focus their attention on programs of "greatest consequence."[29] Still, Golden's military and civilian confidants stressed that the RDB commanded little respect among the professional military, accomplished little of significance, and was not much involved in deliberations on the relationship of technological development and strategic policy.[30]

As a result of his investigation, Golden concluded that there was no need at the moment for a new OSRD—defense research was generally vast and well in

---

1951, as of Feb. 18, 1951, pp. 1–2; Golden Papers. John Manley, assistant to the director at Los Alamos, thought that the military had learned to use scientists since the war and was managing to get and keep good ones. Golden, "Notes of Conversations re Study of Military and Scientific Research and Scientific Mobilization," [Sept./Oct. 1950: conversation with Manley, Sept. 21, 1950], Golden Papers.

27 Golden, memo to files, "Conversation with Dr. Lawrence Hafstad, Director, Reactor Development Division, Atomic Energy Commission," Nov. 8, 1950, p. 2, Golden Papers. For the difficulties that scientists faced in the strategic planning area during World War II, see Kevles, *The Physicists,* pp. 309–23.

28 Golden, memos to files, "Conversation with Dr. Lawrence Hafstad, Director, Reactor Development Division, Atomic Energy Commission," Nov. 8, 1950, p. 2; "Telephone conversation with Dr. H. P. Robertson," Jan. 25, 1951, Golden Papers.

29 Golden, memo to file, "Conversation with Mr. William Webster," Dec. 20, 1950, as of Dec. 18, 1950, Golden Papers; Compton to Robert P. Russell, Dec. 26, 1950; Webster, "Memorandum for Chairmen, RDB Committees," Draft 143, Jan. 9, 1951, C/K Papers, Box 246, Folder 2, Folder 3.

30 Golden, memo to file, "Conversation with Mr. William Webster, Chairman, Research and Development Board, Department of Defense," Nov. 1, 1950, Golden Papers. According to Admiral Arthur C. Davis, the director of staff for the Joint Chiefs, the chiefs did not as a group concern themselves with the details of new or improved weapons, nor with their implications for war plans. Golden, memo to file, "Notes of Conversations re Study of Military and Scientific Research and Scientific Mobilization," [Sept./Oct. 1950], Golden Papers.

hand—though, in the event of another war emergency, there might be need for a new one, to provide a place, he reported to the President in December 1950, for "the successful wildcats of science" who might devise radically new weapons yet feel uncomfortable in a military organization.[31] But he did think that something was required to bring civilian scientific expertise better to bear upon the problems of national defense. In his report to Truman, Golden urged that what was in order, given the vast diversity of defense research and development, was a Science Advisor to the President—someone informed about all the research of military relevance going on in and out of the government, someone who could initiate a new OSRD if and when its creation was required.[32]

Golden's idea of a presidential science advisor had been endorsed by a number of his confidants, but not by several members of the board of the new National Science Foundation, weakly funded and thus fragile. By its authorizing act, the NSF was supposed, in part, to secure the national defense; the dubious board members, including James B. Conant, the president of Harvard University, feared that the creation of a presidential science advisor would tend to diminish the NSF. Golden argued to the NSF's board, citing his numerous conversations, that the consensus of defense-research officials was that the NSF could best serve the country if it left military matters to other agencies and concentrated on fostering the advancement of basic science—a position that the board adopted at a meeting in February 1951.[33] Golden's idea ran into a different type of opposition from General Lucius Clay, assistant director of the Office of Defense Mobilization, who freely conceded to Golden that his vision of scientific possibilities of interest to the military had in the past been limited. In Clay's view, any science advisor would deal with issues of mobilization; therefore, the post should be located in the Office of Defense Mobilization, with its occupant appointed as assistant to the director.[34]

31 Golden, "Memorandum for the President. Mobilizing Science for War: A Scientific Adviser to the President," Dec. 18, 1950, Golden Papers.
32 Golden, memos to files, "Conversations with Drs. Oppenheimer, Robert Bacher, and Charles Lauritsen," Dec. 21, 1950; "Conversation with Dr. Ellis Johnson and George Shortley, Director and Deputy Director, Operational Research Organization, U.S. Army," Nov. 21, 1950; "Conversation with Dr. Ellis A. Johnson," Oct. 31, 1950; "Conversation with General Maris' Staff and General McAuliffe, Chief of the Chemical Corps," Feb. 19, 1951; "Memorandum for the President. Mobilizing Science for War: A Scientific Adviser to the President," Dec. 18, 1950, Golden Papers. It is interesting to note that in April 1951, Webster suggested as an individual that the RDB needed to be reshaped, mainly by absolving it of responsibility for detailed oversight of the different military branches, making it into a high council on defense technology policy, and adding to it more civilian scientists. Webster, "Memorandum for General Marshall," Apr. 24, 1951, C/K Papers, Box 246, Folder 4.
33 Golden, memos to file, "Meeting with Conant, Stauffacher and Staats and Carey and Levi at Bureau of Budget," Jan. 5, 1951; "Telephone Conversation with William Webster," Jan. 4, 1951; "Conversation with I. I. Rabi," Jan. 5, 1951, Golden Papers; Bronk, "Science Advice in the White House," pp. 248–49.
34 Golden, memos to file, "Conversation with General Lucius Clay," Jan. 19, 1951, Jan. 26, 1951, Golden Papers; Bronk, "Science Advice in the White House," p. 250.

In the end, Golden prevailed, though so did Clay, to an extent. On April 19, 1951, President Truman established, in the Office of Defense Mobilization, a Science Advisory Committee to provide advice not only to the director of the office but to himself on scientific matters, particularly in connection with national defense. The advisory group comprised eleven leading scientists, including, as chairman, Oliver E. Buckley, who had just stepped down as president of the Bell Telephone Laboratories, and DuBridge, Conant, Oppenheimer, Webster, Alan Waterman (the head of NSF), James R. Killian (the president of MIT), and Detlev W. Bronk (the president of the Johns Hopkins University and head of the National Academy of Sciences). Taken together, the group represented key veterans—many of them physicists—of the mobilization of science during World War II and key players in postwar national security policymaking.[35]

Sometime in April, Buckley saw the President, who assured him that he could have access to the Oval Office at any time and applauded the set of operating principles for the committee that Buckley had drawn up, particularly the principle that the group would "avoid fanfare" and "minimize public appearances." In truth, the principles were on the whole a recipe for passivity. Not surprisingly, Buckley, a self-effacing man, wrote to the membership that the committee would be "limited largely to policy and other general matters," adding, "It cannot be relied on as the principal source of imaginative, technical leadership in the government."[36] The committee met roughly once a month, carrying on with no staff other than an executive secretary and a clerical assistant. In Buckley's view, the committee was in no position even to think about coming to grips with the nation's defense research program.

In its first year, the group expressed several unexceptional opinions on issues concerning the mobilization of science—for example, that universities best served the national defense by training scientists and advancing knowledge—and various observations on the difficulty of getting scientists comparable in stature to the leaders of OSRD to work in the Defense Department. Such matters occupied the committee's first report to the President, which Buckley hand-delivered to Truman on May 5, 1952, and which Truman said, in a perfunctory note a few days later, that he had read with interest. DuBridge recalled, "Buckley didn't want the committee to do anything except figure out what scientists might do in another war emergency. The rest of us were frustrated. We didn't see much point in just writing reports for a file drawer."[37]

35 Truman to Buckley, Apr. 19, 1951, C/K Papers, Box 256, Folder 8; press release, Apr. 20, 1951, Golden Papers.

36 "Proposed Principles for Committee," Apr. 5, 1951, attached to Buckley to Killian, Apr. 25, 1951, C/K Papers, Box 256, Folder 8; Bronk, "Science Advice in the White House," p. 251.

37 Science Advisory Committee, "Summary, Meeting No. 1," May 12, 1951; "Summary, Meeting No. 2," June 23, 1951; "Summary, Meeting No. 3," Sept. 8, 1951, and attached "Scientists and Mobilization, Some Views of the Science Advisory Committee"; Buckley, "An Appraisal of Some Indicated Needs of Defense Research, A Memorandum for

The tenor of the committee's deliberations changed dramatically after June 1952, when Buckley resigned from the chairmanship because of ill health and was succeeded by DuBridge. After the first two meetings over which DuBridge presided, in mid-June and mid-September 1952, the committee resolved to deal with key issues of science and the state—how to increase the effectiveness of defense science and how to get science and technology more involved with policy-making. By the time of the committee's next meeting, in early November, Dwight Eisenhower had been elected president. Toward the end of a three-day conclave at the Institute of Advanced Study, in Princeton, New Jersey, the group summarized its conclusions with the aim of somehow getting them to the President-elect. In the view of the Princeton gathering, there was no point in continuing the committee as currently conceived. The committee stressed, however, that there was an acute need to bring scientific expertise to bear upon national security planning, and it proposed mechanisms to illustrate how that end might be achieved.[38]

In the following weeks, DuBridge pressed the committee's views on Arthur S. Flemming, who would become the new director of the Office of Defense Mobilization, and, on December 17, DuBridge and Oppenheimer spent an hour and a half discussing them with an attentive Nelson Rockefeller, who was looking into the organization of the executive branch of the government for the President-elect. At the end of the month, Rockefeller conveyed the committee's views directly to Eisenhower. Eisenhower responded favorably to the ideas; so did Robert Cutler, a special assistant to the President, who was handling matters concerning the National Security Council.[39] Neither Eisenhower nor Cutler seemed particularly interested in the mechanisms that the committee proposed for establishing high-level scientific advice, but they did apparently care about obtaining that advice for national-security policy-

Discussion," attached to "Summary, Meeting No. 6," Dec. 3, 1951; Buckley to Truman, May 1, 1952, attached to "Summary, Meeting No. 11," May 9, 1952; Buckley to Killian, July 24, 1951, C/K Papers, Box 256, Folders 8, 9, 10, 11, 12; DuBridge, interviewed by Daniel J. Kevles, July 15, 1988.

38 DuBridge, "Memorandum to Members and Consultants, Science Advisory Committee," Sept. 16, 1952; Science Advisory Committee, "Summary, Meeting No. 14," Nov. 7, 8, 9, 1952, and attached "Draft Conclusion," Nov. 9, 1952, C/K Papers, Box 256, Folder 13. See also Bronk, "Science Advice in the White House," pp. 252–53. Bronk here recounted that at the November meeting the committee sought to relocate itself more closely to the President, specifically in the National Security Council. However, one of the mechanisms proposed involved the Secretary of Defense; the other, participation in a new high council on foreign and defense policy. Bronk seems to have confused the outcome of the Princeton conclave with that of a later one, in 1955. See DuBridge to Killian, Dec. 16, 1955; "Summary of Meeting of an Ad Hoc Group on Science Organization, Sponsored by the SAC," Nov. 25, 1955, attached to Beckler, "Notes on Science Organization and National Policy," C/K Papers, Box 257, Folder 21.

39 DuBridge to members and consultants, Science Advisory Committee, Jan. 5, 1953, Apr. 20, 1953, C/K Papers, Box 256, Folder 14.

making. While nothing in the institutional arrangement of the Science Advisory Committee was modified, a distinct change in the scope and level of duties given it seemed likely.

During the election, the Republican Party had hammered the Democrats on the issues of Korea, communism, and corruption—K_1C_2, in the shorthand of the campaign. But if frustration with the protractedness of K_1 influenced the outcome of the election, the war also fostered a series of subtle—and not so subtle—changes in S_2, the relationship between science and the American state.

Unlike that during World War II, the scientific mobilization during the Korean War had produced no miraculous new weapons. Combined with the Soviet Union's arrival as a nuclear power, however, it had generated a pervasive NSC-68 mentality, a devotion to "the ability to convert swiftly from partial to all-out mobilization," to quote Eisenhower's 1954 state of the union address, a commitment to an expansive technological readiness and to whatever big science that achieving such an end might require. The military's change in outlook since the advent of the atomic bomb had struck James B. Conant, as he told the National War College, as "something like the old religious phenomenon of conversion." Conant continued, "The military, if anything, have become vastly too much impressed with the abilities of research and development. They are no longer the conservatives . . . at times they seem to be fanatics in their belief of what the scientists and the technologists can do."[40]

On the side of civilian science, the psychological change was exemplified by the conclusions of Project HARTWELL. Though the conflict in Korea had no direct bearing on the content of the project, Zacharias recalled, the conflict "heightened our sense of purpose and underlined the relevance and the urgency of the task—what it takes to fight half way around the world." The thick two-volume HARTWELL report dealt with what the Navy should do to protect shipping from Soviet forces in a war spreading from Europe and Latin America to India, Southeast Asia, and Japan. It assumed that the Soviets would be well armed and prepared to use all their weapons.[41]

40 "Public Papers of the Presidents of the United States: Dwight D. Eisenhower, 1954," p. 11; Conant, "The Problem of Evaluation of Scientific Research and Development for Military Planning," speech to the National War College, Feb. 1, 1952, quoted in Hershberg, "Over My Dead Body," p. 416. Conant suggested to a meeting of the Science Advisory Committee that, in order to get better control of military research, at key levels every proposal for a new defense project should have at least one designated naysayer to make a case against it. Science Advisory Committee, "Summary, Meeting No. 7," Jan. 11, 1952, C/K Papers, Box 256, Folder 12. Louis Ridenour, a physicist who was special advisor to the Secretary of the Air Force, told William Golden that any kind of project, no matter how far-fetched, could count on finding support in some branch of the military. Golden, memo to file, "Conversation with H. P. Robertson . . . Louis Ridenour," Dec. 8, 1950, Golden Papers.

41 Zacharias, manuscript of an unpublished autobiography.

The HARTWELL analyses, which covered technologies for the destruction as well as the detection of submarines, paid particular attention to nuclear weapons. Zacharias recalled, "We wanted the military to start thinking about how to integrate atomic weapons into the battle plan of 'a conventional war,' a protracted affair, in which both sides would have ample opportunity and time to gear up, get prepared, and deploy forces—*without devastating destruction on both sides.*" The report sought to destroy certain myths about nuclear weapons, starting with the myth that all were big bombs deliverable only from big high-flying aircraft. HARTWELL stressed that they could be built small, in both size and explosive power, and that they could be released for use against submarines and their bases by a variety of small aircraft, including helicopters. The report concluded that it was not unreasonable for the United States to seek to equip itself soon with 10,000 such atomic weapons.[42] HARTWELL influenced the Navy decidedly: according to one account, the report had "an electrifying influence on several segments of its research and development program." It shaped the Navy's strategy for combating submarines, though the extent of this influence has been difficult to measure because of security restrictions. Suffice it to say that years later Naval officers treasured the HARTWELL report as the bible of antisubmarine warfare.[43]

The change in administration—and, for the first time in twenty years, the change in parties—brought fresh players, fresh arrangements, and fresh doctrines into the defense policy game. A key rearrangement was mandated by the Defense Reorganization Act of 1953, which abolished the RDB and created two new assistant secretaries of defense, one for research and development, the other for applications engineering. The salient fresh doctrine was the "New Look," which emphasized economies of dollar cost and troop commitments in national defense in favor of relying on technological advantage to counter the perceived Soviet threat. In short order, civilian enthusiasts of technological advantage, newly arrived in the office of the Secretary of Defense, began prevailing on the Air Force to step up its development of intercontinental ballistic missiles; such missiles seemed all the more feasible as a result of the early hydrogen bomb tests, which suggested that a megaton of explosive could be delivered to the Soviet Union via a missile less powerful than had previously been assumed.[44]

While at times the insistent economizing threatened to curtail defense research and development, the demands of the new arsenal—nuclear warheads, rockets and missiles, antisubmarine warfare and continental defense

42 *Ibid.*

43 *Ibid.;* Marvin and Weyl, "The Summer Study," p. 2.

44 See, for example, York and Greb, "Military Research and Development," pp. 20–21; Armacost, *The Politics of Weapons Innovation,* pp. 28–31, 56–58. Insightful observations on the Air Force's reluctance to move rapidly into an intercontinental ballistic missile program are advanced in Robert L. Perry, "Commentary," pp. 119–21.

systems, and the like—prevented military research expenditures from falling after the war; indeed, in areas related to these major military systems, they kept rising at a moderate rate.[45] Defense-related agencies provided between 80 and 90% of federal research and development monies. They made industrial research into sophisticated technology increasingly a ward of the military, with defense projects supplying an ever-larger fraction—the portion crossed the 50% mark in 1956—of total expenditures for industrial research. The Defense Department and the AEC were pervasive presences on the nation's campuses, the source of funding for the vast majority of research in physics, electronics, aeronautics, computers, and myriad other branches of the physical sciences and engineering.[46]

The situation left academic scientists well supported and comfortable. The Korean War had put a hold on any serious move to transfer support for pure science out of the military and into the National Science Foundation. When the Eisenhower administration took office, it ventured such a transfer. The Office of Naval Research had already turned against any such idea. The attitudes of many university scientists were no doubt represented by Du-Bridge, who opposed the move, stressing to Flemming that the ill-funded NSF would have to be granted appropriations "*ten times* their present level" to do the job properly, an amount of money that Congress would surely decline to provide. The NSF, DuBridge added, was "wholly unsuitable for the support of large research projects at large research centers. The California Institute of Technology, for example, would go broke very promptly if all of its basic research support were suddenly transferred to the National Science Foundation."[47]

DuBridge's viewpoint prevailed. The nation's scientific leadership breathed a collective sigh of relief when it became clear that very little responsibility for basic research would be transferred to the NSF and that most such research would continue to be supported by the pluralistic system that had grown up since 1945 under the military's generous and predominant patronage. Yet perhaps more important than the victory itself was what the process by which

45 A *bête noir* of the basic research community was Secretary of Defense Charles E. Wilson, who, having spent his career at General Motors, where there was no significant tradition of scientific research, tried to cut the defense research and development budget more than once during the Eisenhower administration. He opined while at the Pentagon that "basic research is when you don't know what you are doing." See Killian to DuBridge, June 25, 1953, C/K Papers, Box 256, Folder 14; Kevles, *The Physicists,* p. 383; Armacost, *The Politics of Weapons Innovation,* pp. 32–33, 267.

46 See Kranzberg, "Science, Technology, and Warfare," p. 162; Forman, "Behind Quantum Electronics," pp. 161–64, 191–94, 220–21; Kevles, *The Physicists,* pp. 374–75.

47 Golden, memos to file, "Conversation with Mr. Charles Stauffacher re National Science Foundation," Dec. 6, 1950; "Conversation with Rear Admiral T. Solberg, Director, Office of Naval Research," Jan. 15, 1951, Golden Papers; DuBridge to Flemming, Aug. 12, 1953, C/K Papers, Box 256, Folder 15; DuBridge interview.

the victory had been achieved indicated, that scientists like DuBridge were now exercising considerable influence at the levels of high policy-making in a way that they had not been, save perhaps for nuclear weapons, under Truman.

The establishment of the Science Advisory Committee had put scientists institutionally within reach of the White House; Eisenhower took them inside of it. In August 1953, a month after the end of the Korean War, Cutler and Flemming, now in place as heads of the National Security Council (NSC) and the Office of Defense Mobilization (ODM), respectively, arranged for the committee to meet in the Executive Office Building, next to the White House, to be briefed by National Security Council staff, and to provide advice on matters pertaining to air defense. DuBridge wrote to the committee members, "You will all recognize what an important assignment this is. It is the first assignment to our Committee under the new administration and this meeting will give us all a chance to become acquainted with the members of the ODM and NSC staffs with whom we may possibly be working during coming years."[48]

The President was naturally skeptical about the claims of the military that he knew so well and eager for alternative yet informed opinion on issues of technology and national security. The Science Advisory Committee was kept apprised of relevant discussions in the National Security Council by Cutler and, eventually, by its own executive secretary, David Beckler, who sat in on the council's meetings. For its part, the committee was constantly active even outside of its regular meetings, with its members in New York, Cambridge, and Pasadena constituting themselves as local sections for discussion.[49]

At a combined meeting of the Cambridge and New York groups, on March 10, 1954, a strong push for a study to evaluate the broad implications of new weapons came from Isidor I. Rabi. His reasons, passionately advanced, were that thermonuclear weapons could not be thought of solely as military weapons, as nuclear weapons might have been construed in the late 1940's. Use of hydrogen bombs would risk political and psychological upheaval, and their role in strategic policy had to be assessed with regard to such implications. In Rabi's view, disarmament negotiations were imperative. American democratic institutions could not survive an indefinite arms build-up.[50]

Reaction in the gathering was mixed. Buckley, worried that Rabi's ideas might be taken as implied criticism of the New Look, proposed an alternative, and narrower, purpose for the study, "to examine strategic plans and policies in light of new weapons," with reference above all to assessment and "public

48 DuBridge to Science Advisory Committee members, Aug. 7, 1953, C/K Papers, Box 256, Folder 14.

49 DuBridge interview; I. I. Rabi, "The President and His Scientific Advisers," pp. 21–22; DuBridge to Science Advisory Committee members, Feb. 15, 1954, C/K Papers, Box 257, Folder 2.

50 York and Greb, "Military Research and Development," p. 13; "Meeting of the Cambridge–New York Group of the Science Advisory Committee," Mar. 10, 1954, attached to Killian to Beckler, Mar. 17, 1954, C/K Papers, Box 257.

indoctrination of the urgency implicit in our present danger."[51] The committee was much impressed by Project HARTWELL's attempts to integrate new weapons into the strategy of antisubmarine warfare; it was attracted to the idea of seeking a similar integration across the whole range of strategic policy planning. To that end, at the urging of Jerrold Zacharias, the group decided to seek a meeting with the President and the National Security Council to urge the creation of a special group to study the overall problem of science and national defense.[52]

On March 27, 1954, the committee met with Eisenhower, who focused attention on the problem of surprise attack and asked that his science advisors conduct a study of the matter. The request led to the formation under Killian of the Technological Capabilities Panel, which interpreted its charge broadly and set about investigating not only the gathering of intelligence to guard against surprise attack but also several other topics, including what technology might do for the retaliatory power of American deterrence.[53] In February 1955, delivering its report in an extended discussion with the National Security Council, the panel stressed, in a tone of foreboding, that the United States was vulnerable to surprise attack and urged, among other things, that the country establish overflight surveillance of the Soviet Union and give highest priority to the development of both long-range and intermediate-range ballistic missiles.[54] Cutler recalled the session as the high point of his tenure as the President's special assistant for national security. Indeed, the panel's recommendations helped not only to obtain the highest national priority for the intercontinental ballistic missile program but also to precipitate what became the Thor, Jupiter, and Polaris rocket programs[55] (see Fig. 12.1).

If the Korean War had made pervasive the attitudes of NSC-68, it had also provided those attitudes with new or strengthened institutional means to make themselves felt. The bigger that the installations of defense-related science grew, the greater their propensity to call for—and ability to create— new weapons systems. The closer civilian scientists came to the center of

51 "Meeting of the Cambridge–New York Group of the Science Advisory Committee," Mar. 10, 1954, attached to Killian to Beckler, Mar. 17, 1954, C/K Papers, Box 257.

52 *Ibid.;* Beckler to Killian, Mar. 19, 1954, and attached "Scope of Proposed Examination of New Weapons and National Strategy," draft, Mar. 19, 1954, C/K Papers, Box 257, Folders 2, 18. Enthusiasm for HARTWELL-type projects was manifest at the meeting and also earlier in Buckley, "Notes on Report of the Committee on Plans for Mobilizing Science," draft, June 8, 1951, attached to Buckley to Killian, June 15, 1951, C/K Papers, Box 256, Folder 9.

53 Killian, *Sputnik, Scientists, and Eisenhower,* pp. 70–71; DuBridge to Flemming, July 21, 1954, C/K Papers, Box 257, Folder 18.

54 Armacost, *The Politics of Weapons Innovation,* pp. 50–53; Killian, *Sputnik, Scientists, and Eisenhower,* pp. 71–86, "The Origin and Uses of Scientific Presence in the White House," p. 29.

55 York and Greb, "Military Research and Development," ⌐p. 21–22. This account of the panel's origins, like Killian's, misses the role of Rabi's concer: is and, therefore, the irony in the outcome. See Killian, *Sputnik, Scientists, and Eisenhower,* pp. 67–68.

Fig. 12.1. Eisenhower and the Science Advisory Committee, December 1960. Having established a close working relationship with the committee, Eisenhower here enjoys a moment with Presidential Science Advisor James R. Killian, Jr., at the final meeting of the advisory panel. Photo courtesy MIT Museum.

executive power, the better positioned they were to influence overall defense policy. But while they might exercise that influence to check the ambitions of the defense laboratories, they might equally well use it to represent the civilian defense-science enterprise, pressing the continuing pursuit of technological superiority as the key to national security. It had been, of course, Buckley's version of a weapons review, not Rabi's, that eventually formed the basis for the establishment and recommendations of the Technological Capabilities Panel. The Korean War, along with making big civilian science bigger, tied its laboratories and advisory apparatus closer to the state in ways that, at least in the mid-1950's, amplified the opportunities and, in some respects, the incentives to intensify the arms race.

References Cited

Armacost, Michael. *The Politics of Weapons Innovation.* New York: Columbia University Press, 1969.

Bronk, Detlev W. "Science Advice in the White House: The Genesis of the President's Science Advisors and the National Science Foundation." In William T. Golden, ed., *Science Advice to the President*, pp. 245–56. New York: Pergamon Press, 1980.

Bush, Vannevar. *Modern Arms and Free Men*. New York: Simon and Schuster, 1949.

Forman, Paul. "Behind Quantum Electronics: National Security as Basis for Physical Research in the United States, 1940–1960." *Historical Studies in the Physical and Biological Sciences* 18 (1987): 149–229.

Herken, Gregg. *Counsels of War*. Expanded ed. New York: Oxford University Press, 1987.

Hershberg, James G. " 'Over My Dead Body': James B. Conant and the Hydrogen Bomb." In Everett Mendelsohn and Merritt Roe Smith, eds., *Science, Technology, and the Military*, pp. 379–430. Sociology of the Sciences Yearbook, Vol. 12, 1988. Dordrecht: Kluwer Academic Publishers, 1988.

Kevles, Daniel J. *The Physicists: The History of a Scientific Community in Modern America*. Cambridge, Mass.: Harvard University Press, 1987.

Killian, James R. *Sputnik, Scientists, and Eisenhower: A Memoir of the First Special Assistant to the President for Science and Technology*. Cambridge, Mass.: MIT Press, 1977.

——. "The Origin and Uses of a Scientific Presence in the White House." In William T. Golden, ed., *Science Advice to the President*, pp. 27–31. New York: Pergamon Press, 1980.

Koppes, Clayton R. *JPL and the American Space Program: A History of the Jet Propulsion Laboratory*. New Haven: Yale University Press, 1982.

Kranzberg, Melvin. "Science, Technology, and Warfare: Action, Reaction, and Interaction in the Post–World War II Era." In Monte D. Wright and Lawrence J. Paszek, eds., *Science, Technology, and Warfare*, pp. 123–70. Washington, D.C.: Office of Air Force History, Headquarters USAF and United States Air Force Academy, 1969.

Marvin, J. R., and F. J. Weyl. "The Summer Study." *Naval Research Reviews* 8 (1966): 1–28.

Oppenheimer, J. Robert. *Uncommon Sense*. Boston: Birkhauser, 1984.

Perry, Robert L. "Commentary." In Monte D. Wright and Lawrence J. Paszek, eds., *Science, Technology, and Warfare*, pp. 110–21. Washington, D.C.: Office of Air Force History, Headquarters USAF and United States Air Force Academy, 1969.

Rabi, I. I. "The President and His Scientific Advisers." In William T. Golden, ed., *Science Advice to the President*, pp. 15–26. New York: Pergamon Press, 1980.

Roland, Alex. *Model Research: The National Advisory Committee for Aeronautics, 1915–1958*. Washington, D.C.: NASA, Scientific and Technical Branch, 1985.

Sapolsky, Harvey. "Academic Science and the Military: The Years Since the Second World War." In Nathan Reingold, ed., *The Sciences in the American Context*, pp. 379–99. Washington, D.C.: Smithsonian Institution Press, 1979.

Yanarella, Ernest J. *The Missile Defense Controversy: Strategy, Technology, and Politics, 1955–1972*. Lexington: University Press of Kentucky, 1977.

York, Herbert F., and Allen G. Greb. "Military Research and Development: A Postwar History." *Bulletin of the Atomic Scientists* 33 (1977): 13–76.

CHAPTER 13

Far Beyond Big Science: Science Regions and the Organization of Research and Development

Robert Kargon, Stuart W. Leslie, and Erica Schoenberger

T he journal *Nature* reported in the March 17, 1988, issue that the Japanese and the Australians are planning what they term "an international high-technology city" somewhere in Australia. The new city, with a projected population of a quarter of a million people, will be organized around research institutes, both governmental and private, and high-technology industry.

The initiative for this "multi-function polis" comes from Japan's Ministry of International Trade and Industry and projects an initial investment of about a billion dollars. The new city is intended "to provide researchers and their families with a lifestyle integrating work and leisure." It would attract, according to plan, researchers from Japan, Europe, and the United States to work in internationally sponsored facilities and, presumably, provide a creative mix to launch science and industry into the twenty-first century.[1]

One may look upon this rather dramatic plan as just another "techno-Utopia" along the lines of Walt Disney's Experimental Prototype Community of Tomorrow (EPCOT) in Florida. Or, as we will argue, one may see in it the latest, and most socially ambitious, attempt to mobilize society's resources for the advancement of science, technology, and industry. It is the most recent in a

1 *Nature* 332 (Mar. 17, 1988): 195.

long line of efforts to harness social energies for research, efforts that are intended to repay society many times for its investment.

Toward Big Science: Horizontal and Vertical Integration

When Alvin Weinberg, almost thirty years ago, examined the phenomenon he labeled "big science," it was, in part, this investment that concerned him. He warned that big science could attenuate science itself: "The big scientific community tends to acquire more and more bosses. The Indians with bellies to the bench are hard to discern for all the chiefs with bellies to the mahogany desks. . . . Science dominated by administrators is science understood by administrators, and such science quickly becomes attenuated, if not meaningless."[2]

But Weinberg was also concerned about the social costs of big science. He was concerned that what he termed the big science "Olympics" was diverting science's attention from endeavors yielding a high social return to those low-return efforts he disparagingly called "fragile monuments of Big Science."[3]

Big science, however, is not only a matter of *scale,* and the *money* needed to support that scale of effort. Big science involves a pattern of organization that informs the scientific endeavor and its relation to the larger society. Big science is marked, as is well known, by the hierarchically organized *team,* led by a principal investigator-manager, with co-principal investigators, senior researchers, junior researchers, graduate students, technicians, administrative assistants, and secretaries. We can call this kind of organization a *vertical integration* within the scientific enterprise. This team is plugged into a *facility,* such as Stanford's linear accelerator, with its own hierarchically organized structure. The facility, in turn, connects with the larger society, nowadays in the United States through an umbilicus to the federal government.

The nature of the scientific instruments demanded by big science ensures that only the federal government has pockets deep enough and that only big industry commands the technology elaborate enough to accomplish what is necessary. Two recent examples come to mind: the Hubble Space Telescope, and the recently approved Superconducting Supercollider. Both enterprises already illustrate the interpenetration of politics, management, and economics so characteristic of the recent big science endeavors; both illuminate their interdisciplinary character, demanding the cooperation of government, industry, and academia. We can term this the *horizontal* association or cooperation of sectors of society, the main goal of which is the *production of research.*

The planned Japanese-Australian science city can be seen, as can the less-planned Silicon Valley and Route 128 complexes, as an attempt to drive horizontal association or cooperation toward *horizontal integration* in part

2 Weinberg, "Impact of Large-Scale Science," p. 162.
3 *Ibid.,* p. 164.

via geographical agglomeration. This spatial concentration is intended to encourage frequent interaction and rapid feedback among the sectors of society (government, industry, and academia) and among the elements of the technical system, research, development, and industry. These interactions, in turn, are supposed to stimulate creative endeavors that will lead to new products and even to whole new industries.

In this way, the production of research is associated with the production of very particular kinds of places, frequently, as in the case of Silicon Valley, in areas lacking a significant history of prior industrialization. If all goes well, the resulting "science regions" develop with great rapidity, buoyed by the often explosive growth of the new, "high-tech" industries generated by the research complex. Thus, if geographical agglomeration contributes to the success of the research endeavor, this success in turn helps transform the region in question. In other words, the history of organized research and the history of particular places frequently go hand in hand, each influencing the other.

The goal is no longer merely the production of research but, as Weinberg has urged, the enhancement of the *technical system* that relates research to industrial production. Such a goal has a long history. At the birth of modern science, during the scientific revolution of the seventeenth century, philosophers and visionaries such as Tommaso Campanella and Francis Bacon wrote about the social organization of natural philosophy for the accomplishment of human goals. In his *City of the Sun* Campanella attempted to create, literally, a city of knowledge: on the twelve concentric walls of the city was inscribed what he understood to be all knowledge. As the Solarians went about their daily lives, they imbibed the knowledge of both the ancients and the moderns. Francis Bacon's Saloman's House, on the other hand, was organized not only to instruct but to *advance* learning. It was an institution devised by its author to increase the light of learning as well as its fruit. Natural philosophy and technology would, together, create the New Atlantis, a new and better world. In the City of the Sun, there are no laboratories; the city itself is a museum. On the island which holds Saloman's House, the goals are the discovery and application of new knowledge. It may be noted that even in these early conceptualizations the pursuit of knowledge was organized in rather precise geographical terms.

The scientific societies of the seventeenth century, whether influenced by these "techno-Utopias" or not, were in fact designed to socialize the costs of doing natural philosophy and to an extent to socialize the practice of science as well. The Royal Society of London, the Academie de Science of Paris, and the Accademia del Cimento of Florence, to suggest a few, were organizations dedicated to the advancement of natural knowledge according to the social exigencies of the time. The Industrial Revolution added new kinds of organizations such as the Royal Institution of Great Britain, which provided a home for the work of Humphry Davy and Michael Faraday, and the provincial societies of England, which did more than ape their metropolitan counterpart. But all these organizations adhered to the same concept of the scientific enterprise: science was a gift from God, and the scientist a sport of nature. The best they could aspire to was to harness the energies of the geniuses given them and to maximize the awards of God and nature.

This concept, and many others concerning science and technology, changed radically in the late nineteenth century. This series of changes can be called "the Research Revolution" for it is at this point that the notion of "research," especially in the natural sciences, began to transform society itself. First, science—especially physics and chemistry—became directly useful. Directed scientific endeavor—goal-directed research—became an *economic* factor to be reckoned with. Electromagnetism and organic chemistry, especially, were the foundations of new science-based industries and of communications systems. Understanding scientific theory became a practical necessity in a modernizing nation. Second, it was for the first time becoming understood that science could be an organized enterprise. If before the Research Revolution the production of science and scientists was (like lightning) an act of God, after it recognition was widespread that they could be produced like hats or pins.

Scientific research became, in due course, a national asset, both economic and military. The consequences of the rise of goal-directed research, applied science, and the concept of science as an organized enterprise were significant for both society and science. Relatively rapidly, an infrastructure for the production of science appeared on the scene in America and in other scientific nations such as Germany and Great Britain. In the United States, for instance, we see the beginnings of university laboratories turning out Ph.D.'s on a regular basis; we find the organization of industrial laboratories devoted to mission-oriented research and of institutes devoted to "pure" research such as the Carnegie Institution of Washington and the Rockefeller Institute in New York.

One of the results of the Research Revolution was that doing science required a strong institutional base and, increasingly, large amounts of money. As early as 1883, one of America's leading physicists, Henry Rowland, recognized some of these changes: "The fact remains, that one can only be free to investigate in all departments of chemistry and physics, when he not only has a complete laboratory at his command, but a fund to draw on for the expenses of each experiment."[4]

For Rowland, the answer was simple: private philanthropy. The gifts and bequests of wealthy patrons were to be the source for funds for research; physicists needed only make sure that they were worthy of receiving such largesse. "Generosity," he wrote, "is a prominent feature of the American people; [physicists must] live lives of such pure devotion to our science that all

4 Rowland, "A Plea for Pure Science," p. 604.

shall see that we ask for money not that we may live in indolent ease at the expense of charity but that we may work for that which . . . will advance the world more than any other subject, both intellectually and physically."[5]

As scientific laboratories both academic and industrial began to explore the implications of the new discoveries in physics—the electron, X rays, and radioactivity—and as scientific research in such laboratories became more and more specialized, the old idea of research as an enterprise carried out in the attic or in the basement with string and sealing wax became more and more untenable. As Rowland recognized, the day of the genius in the garret was over.

Rowland's model, the philanthropic funding of basic science so that applied science could follow in its trail, was short-lived. Science-based corporations such as A.T.&T. and General Electric established their own in-house organs for the production of research.[6] Universities, not unmindful of these developments and despite traditional inhibitions, began tentative links with industry.[7]

One of the most interesting developments aimed at capitalizing on the evolving relationship between theory and practice, and between university and industry, was the Trafford Park Industrial Estate near Manchester, England. Established in 1894, it appears to be one of the earliest efforts to organize an entire geographic region toward the goal of scientific–technical integration. Electrical engineering, mechanical engineering, nascent automobile and aircraft industries, and other innovating, science-based industries located there. What is particularly interesting about Trafford Park is the close relationship established between the region and the Victoria University of Manchester and the convergence of many of the ingredients that later commentators have suggested are the necessary conditions for a "Silicon Valley": the existence of a major university, a climate of encouragement for new enterprises, and "agglomeration externalities," a term expressing the benefits of clustering like-minded enterprises in one geographic location. Indeed, a puff piece from the early 1920's described Trafford Park as "an 'Americanised' corner of old jog-trot England."[8]

But the archetype of the modern university-centered high-technology complex is, of course, Silicon Valley. The transformation of Santa Clara County from a "peaceful agricultural valley" into "the capital of the semiconductor industry and the densest concentration of 'high-technology' enterprises in the world" has been one of the most intensively studied, and frequently emulated,

5 *Ibid.*, p. 605.
6 See the recent books by Reich, *The Making of American Industrial Research,* and Wise, *Willis R. Whitney.*
7 This is an area that requires more systematic study. A preliminary survey of the British scene is Sanderson, *The Universities and British Industry, 1850–1970.*
8 Trafford Park Estates, *The Story of Trafford Park,* p. 5.

models of technology-driven regional development in the world.[9] No plan for regional development seems complete nowadays without some version of "silicon mountain," "silicon plain," "silicon beach," or, as someone at Michigan Technological Institute recently quipped, "wood chip valley." Yet, as the promoters of these enterprises have often discovered, identifying the critical variables in the Silicon Valley equation—from strong university science and engineering programs and entrepreneurial vision to plentiful sunshine and even more plentiful government money—has been far easier than synthesizing them in a place where they can reproduce themselves. We still lack a precise understanding of how a place such as Silicon Valley comes to be.[10]

As the most visible and arguably most successful of today's research regions, and as a model for later imitators such as the Research Triangle, Silicon Valley offers a particularly valuable perspective on the integration of intellectual and financial resources—academic, governmental, and industrial—characteristic of big science on a regional scale. Tracing the history of the institutional relationships underlying the development of Silicon Valley will, we believe, cast valuable light on three related issues: the changing organization of the production of research, the character of the university-industry-government nexus at the heart of the research endeavor, and the production of new territorial complexes—science regions—based on the reciprocal elaboration of these relationships. Many current plans for the replication of Silicon Valley concentrate, to their detriment, on supplying ingredients and providing an appropriate environment, without paying sufficient attention to the *structural relationships* that lie at the heart of the process. As we shall see, Silicon Valley's history includes microwaves and aeronautics as importantly as solid-state physics and electronics.

Building Silicon Valley: The Production of a Science Region

If anyone deserves the title "father of Silicon Valley," it is Stanford's famous electrical engineering professor, dean, and later provost, Frederick Terman. He first envisioned its mutually reinforcing climate of academic, government, and industrial science, and he trained the first generation of students who made it happen.[11] As the son of the celebrated Stanford psychologist Lewis Terman, he had virtually grown up on campus, and through his studies there in electrical engineering he gained real appreciation for the industrial applications of academic engineering, lessons reinforced by his graduate studies at MIT.

Terman returned to Stanford in 1926 with the ambitious goal of remaking

9 Saxenian, "The Genesis of Silicon Valley."

10 Scott, *New Industrial Spaces.*

11 For Terman's role in creating Silicon Valley, see Malone, *The Big Score,* and Leslie and Hevly, "Steeple Building at Stanford."

Stanford in MIT's image, starting with his own graduate program in communications. To keep his students up to date, he arranged field trips to local electronics companies (a few, like Heintz and Kaufman, founded by Stanford graduates) and invited their engineers to give campus seminars. David Packard, then a graduate student in the radio laboratory, recalled these tours as a highlight of the course: "Here, for the first time, I saw young entrepreneurs working on new devices in firms which they themselves had established. One day Professor Terman remarked to me that many of the firms we had visited, and many other firms throughout the country, had been founded by men who had little formal education. He suggested that perhaps someone with a formal engineering education and a little business training might be even more successful."[12] Shortly thereafter, Terman got an opportunity to prove his point by helping Packard go into business with another graduate student, William Hewlett. In 1939 they started their own company to build resistance-tuned oscillators (an idea they'd heard about from Terman) and began their climb to the top of the electronics industry. Even Terman's textbooks reflected his commercial bent. His *Radio Engineering* became an immediate best-seller, primarily because, like his courses, it placed real-world problems at the center, with an elegance and simplicity that especially appealed to working engineers.

Terman spent World War II directing the Radio Research Laboratory, a spinoff of MIT's famous Radiation Laboratory housed upriver at Harvard and devoted to radar countermeasures.[13] As director, Terman had responsibility not only for developing new radar-jamming devices and other countermeasures but also for teaching industrial contractors like RCA, General Electric, and Bell Laboratories how to manufacture them. To smooth the always bumpy road from laboratory to the field, he invited corporate engineers to work with his design teams in Cambridge and sent some of his people back to the production plants. Such experiences convinced him that the emerging partnership of universities, industry, and government that was helping to win the war would transform the postwar world.

The Forging of the University-Government-Industry Nexus: From Microwaves to Solid State

Terman returned to Stanford as dean of engineering in 1946 with a vision, which he sketched in his first annual dean's report: "The West has long dreamed of an indigenous industry of sufficient magnitude to balance its agricultural resources. The war advanced these hopes and brought to the West the beginning of a great new era of industrialization. A strong and independent industry must, however, develop its own intellectual resources of science and technology, for industrial activity that depends upon imported brains and

12 David Packard, *Stanford Engineering News* 17, no. 22 (July 1965).
13 The best account of Terman's war years is McMahon, *The Making of a Profession*.

second-hand ideas cannot hope to be more than a vassal that pays tribute to its overlords, and is permanently condemned to an inferior competitive position."[14]

Terman did not expect the fledgling western electronics industry, despite its rapid growth during the war, to carry Stanford financially, at least not right away. Rather, he believed that the first step toward invigorating the industry was strengthening the university's programs in selected areas of electronics. As he explained to the university's president, "Government-sponsored research presents Stanford, and our School of Engineering, with a wonderful opportunity if we are prepared to exploit it. . . . We failed to take advantage of a similar opportunity presented by the research activities of the war. We are fortunate to have a second chance to retrieve our position. It is doubtful if there will ever be a third opportunity."[15]

Terman and the core of electronics veterans he had brought back with him from the Radio Research Laboratory were especially well positioned by their wartime contacts and contracts to take advantage of those new opportunities. Their traveling-wave-tube (TWT) program exemplified the new style of Stanford electronics.[16] Improved at Bell Labs during the war by a team that included Stanford graduate Lester Field, the TWT was a microwave tube similar to the klystron but with significantly better gain and bandwidth, advantages particularly significant to countermeasures to radar. Terman kept in touch with Field's work, recognized its implications, and lured Field back to Stanford in 1947. Though supported on a shoestring compared with what he had enjoyed at Bell Labs and RCA, Field quickly established himself as one of the best men in one of the most competitive specialties of postwar electronics, developing new kinds of TWTs, increasing their power, and reducing their objectionably high noise level. He also earned distinction, in the words of his chairman, as "the best teacher in the department on either undergraduate or advanced levels," and attracted some of the best and brightest of Stanford's graduate students, including Hubert Heffner, Stanley Kaisel, and Dean Watkins.[17] In 1947 Terman agreed with the military to consolidate Field's contract, along with three others, into a single Joint Services Electronics Program contract called Task 7, the intellectual and financial foundation of the future Stanford Electronics Laboratories.

By 1950 Terman's campaign had made Stanford, if not the Harvard, at the very least the MIT of the West. With a far smaller faculty, Stanford had pulled virtually even in the number of electrical engineering doctorates awarded each year, and its program in microwave tube design was the best in the country.

14 Terman, Dean's Report, School of Engineering, 1946–47, Stanford Archives (SC 165).
15 Terman to Donald Tresidder, Apr. 25, 1947, Stanford Archives (SC 160, II, 5/20).
16 "Stanford Electronics Attracts National Attention: The Traveling Wave Tube." *Stanford Engineering News* 6, May 1950, p. 1.
17 Hugh Skilling to C. H. Faust, Dec. 30, 1948, Stanford Archives (SC 216, 28/12).

It took the Korean War to transform this academic empire into big business. In light of the national emergency, the Joint Services Electronics Program reviewed its university contracts and decided to complement selected programs with applied (and classified) contracts. Stanford, already high on the program's list for its contributions to TWT and high-power klystron studies, received $300,000 (subsequently increased to $450,000) a year for translating its basic research into practical devices and systems. For Terman the contract for applied research represented a natural extension of the basic research program, in his words, "the payoff that has come from the program of government-sponsored basic research in electronics that we have carefully built up since 1946."[18]

Virtually overnight, Stanford doubled the size of its electronics program without any significant change in content or direction. The applied program, though classified and therefore administratively distinct, enlarged, accelerated, or extended technical projects already well under way. In practice, the traffic of faculty and graduate students back and forth eroded any meaningful division between the two. In renewing Task 7, Terman inserted a clause specifying that one purpose of the basic contract was "to provide ideas which can be exploited in the development of new devices and systems in the applied electronics program."[19] Acknowledging the arbitrariness of division between "basic" and "applied," he eventually merged the two programs with the formation of the Stanford Electronics Laboratories (see Fig. 13.1).

Though the applied program did not, as a rule, develop devices beyond the prototype stage, part of its understanding with its sponsors was that it would work closely with industrial firms that did. Toward this end its administrators encouraged faculty consulting, brought corporate engineers to campus, and arranged an annual technical review for the contractors actually building the reconnaissance, countermeasures, and radar tubes based on Stanford designs.

Seeking to capitalize further on Stanford expertise, established electronics companies set up microwave-tube divisions near campus and often hired Stanford faculty and graduates to staff them. Many of Field's early students had gone on to industrial positions—Kaisel at RCA, Watkins at Hughes Aircraft, Heffner at Bell Labs—and then returned to Stanford as the applied program expanded. Other members of the Stanford Electronics Laboratory staff, like Radio Research Laboratory veteran Donald Harris, also had significant industrial experience. General Electric set up its TWT division in Palo Alto and hired Harris to run it. Litton recruited Kaisel to manage its electron-tube division. Dean Watkins, who took over as SEL's resident TWT expert after Field left for Caltech and Hughes, went into business for himself, with

18 Terman to J. E. W. Sterling, "Proposed Project in Applied Electronics," Sept. 12, 1950, Stanford Archives (SC 160, II, 13/18).
19 "Electronics Research Laboratory of Stanford University: Proposal for Extension of Contract N6onr251 (07)," July 29, 1954, Stanford Archives (SC 160, II, 14/17).

Fig. 13.1. D. A. Dunn, a group leader in the Stanford Electronics Laboratory, testing a traveling-wave tube (TWT) in the early 1950's. Perfected at Stanford University and used primarily as a radar countermeasures device, the low-powered TWT played an important role in the development of the microwave electronics industry in the Santa Clara Valley. Photo courtesy Stanford University Library Department of Special Collections and Archives.

partner Richard Johnson, developing TWT's and related devices for countermeasures, communications, and surveillance. Kaisel, too, later started his own company, Microwave Electronics. Following General Electric's lead, Sylvania established its microwave-tube division in Mountain View, just a few miles from the university. By 1960 a third of the nation's TWT business, $40 million per year (virtually all of it for defense), was located a stone's throw from campus. "Obviously, this is not a coincidence," noted Terman, "there was real technical fall-out from the Stanford activity."[20]

20 Terman, "The University and Technology Utilization," March 1963, Stanford Archives (SC 160, X, 2/11).

To encourage more formal collaboration between the university and these enterprises (what we have termed horizontal integration), in 1954 Terman created the honors cooperative program, giving local electronics companies an opportunity to send some of their brightest young engineers back to school for advanced degrees. In just three years the program's enrollment soared from 16 to 243, representing more than a third of Stanford's entire graduate engineering enrollment. Terman also enthusiastically supported the Stanford Industrial Park, the earliest and perhaps most successful effort to foster academic-industrial cooperation by developing a high-technology park on university land.[21] Varian Associates, itself a Stanford spinoff concentrating on microwave tubes for defense applications, was the first tenant, followed by Hewlett-Packard, General Electric's TWT division, Watkins-Johnson, and many others (see Fig. 13.2).

Looking back, one military administrator suggested that Silicon Valley had been no accident: "A clearly visible impact of Joint Services Electronics Program activity at university centers has been the evolution of industrial activity, usually not far from those centers, entrepreneured, manned, and carried forward by students [and faculty] who have gone into those industries."[22] Less clear, perhaps, but just as important, has been the impact of that industrial activity (and the government agenda behind it) on those university centers.

Microwave, not solid-state, electronics set the pattern for "Silicon" Valley. Until the mid-1950's, when William Shockley, with Terman's strong encouragement, left Bell Labs to set up Shockley Semiconductor in Palo Alto, microwave-tube technology dominated the electronics industry around Stanford. Few of those firms made the transition to solid-state electronics themselves, but their experience was crucial in providing a prototype for a similar integration of academic, corporate, and government research and development in the solid state.

John Linvill consciously modeled his solid-state electronics program at the Stanford Electronics Laboratory on this earlier pattern, building up a top-notch academic program with government (largely military) contracts, bringing in faculty members with industrial experience, and attracting corporate support. Linvill, himself a former member of Bell Labs, recruited most of his early staff from Bell, Philco, and RCA. To encourage closer ties with industry he initiated an industrial liaison program for solid-state electronics. In return for pledging $5,000 per year for five years, industrial affiliates got a sneak peak at Stanford research (and Stanford graduate students) through copies of technical and quarterly reports, a guest lecture or seminar at the company once a year, and an annual two-day review. Linvill lined up nineteen affiliates, including local firms like Varian and Ampex, firms with local divisions like Sylvania

21 Lowood, "From Steeples of Excellence to Silicon Valley," offers a detailed, somewhat revisionist, account of the establishment of the Industrial Park.
22 Shostak, "History of the Joint Services Electronics Program."

Fig. 13.2. Russell Varian and William Hansen inspecting their klystron tube in the late 1930's. They spent the war with Sperry Gyroscope modifying the klystron for a variety of defense applications. In 1948, they and several Stanford colleagues founded Varian Associates, the first tenant of the Stanford Industrial Park and, along with Hewlett-Packard, a prototype for later Silicon Valley start-ups. Photo courtesy Stanford University Library Department of Special Collections and Archives.

and Motorola, and national firms looking for access to Stanford like Texas Instruments and RCA.[23]

This program was in many respects a template for Linvill's later, and far more ambitious, effort at industrial collaboration, the Center for Integrated Systems.[24] Launched in 1980 with pledges totaling some $15 million from a consortium of microelectronics companies, including General Electric, Texas Instruments, Fairchild, Tektronix, Intel, and Digital Equipment, the Center for Integrated Systems was focused on the particular design and fabrication challenges of very large scale integration. Like its predecessors, the center operated as a partnership of corporate and government interests; $8 million of its initial research support came from the Defense Department. Like them also, it was aimed at keeping American electronics competitive by reshaping the univer-

23 Linvill to Pettit and Terman, Nov. 12, 1958, Stanford Archives (SC 160, III, 17/4); Linvill to L. McGhie, "Industrial Affiliates Program in Solid State Electronics," Apr. 19, 1955, Stanford Archives (SC 160, III, 56/1).

24 Johnston and Edwards, *Entrepreneurial Science,* pp. 44–45.

sity's research and graduate teaching programs around a particular target technology.

The Transformation in Aerospace and Strengthening of University–Industry Ties

If microwave electronics set the pattern for what were to be Silicon Valley's academic-industrial-government relations, the aerospace industry gave that pattern concrete form and greatly expanded its dimensions. Solid-state electronics may have given Silicon Valley its name, but the aerospace industry has traditionally been its biggest employer and customer. The rise of one aerospace company, Lockheed, and its special relationships with NASA's Ames Research Center in Sunnyvale and with Stanford's aeronautical engineering and electronics programs offer some further insights into the region's ecology of research.

Between the two world wars, the National Advisory Committee on Aeronautics (NACA) and the Guggenheim Fund had supported at Stanford one of the most productive and industrially oriented aeronautical engineering programs in the country.[25] With contracts from the NACA and a $200,000 grant from the Guggenheim Fund, William Durand and his assistant Everett Lesley made Stanford a recognized center of aeronautical research. With Guggenheim support the program added Alfred Niles, a young structural engineer from the Army's flight research center at McCook Field, and Elliot Reid, a rising star in aerodynamics at NACA's Langley Laboratory. Together they devised an important research program, introduced new courses, wrote new texts, and trained some 200 students who went on to leave their marks on the industry. Seventy-one of them completed a one-year course in either aerodynamics or structures, and half that many earned engineer's degrees. By the late 1930's Stanford had placed some 40 aeronautical engineering graduates throughout the industry, most on the west coast.[26]

In 1939, however, the Guggenheim money ran out, and the remaining NACA contracts were barely sufficient to cover expenses. To earn enough to keep the program going, Reid opened the wind tunnel to industry in 1940 and made the laboratory pay its own way. Following the example of Caltech, which during World War II had raised more than a million dollars for a high-speed tunnel from a consortium of California airframe companies, he and Niles set out in the spring of 1944 to rebuild Stanford aeronautics.[27] They

25 See Hanle, *Bringing Aerodynamics to America*, and Hallion, *Legacy of Flight*.
26 "Stanford on the Job: The Aviation Industry." *Stanford Illustrated Review*, Apr. 1939.
27 "Postwar Aeronautical Engineering Training and Research Program for Stanford University," May 16, 1944, Sterling Papers, Stanford Archives (SC 165, I, 4/4); Reid to C. L. Johnson, Aug. 3, 1944, Stanford Archives (SC 165, I, 4/4).

hoped to raise a second endowment from the companies that had benefited most from Stanford's graduates, but with expectations of a postwar slump, aircraft companies were not looking for long-term academic investments. As the chief engineer at Douglas explained, his company had always got all the Stanford engineers it needed without paying for their educations: "We have not in the past found it necessary to underwrite fellowships and this does not seem to be the time to start."[28]

By the fall of 1947 Reid and Niles had completed the last of their small commercial contracts, fired the secretary, and closed the books on twenty years of the Guggenheim Laboratory. Reid penned a poignant epitaph: "Thus, after twelve years of endowed existence and eight in the status of quasi-orphan—during which period many of the present leaders of aeronautical research and design were trained here—the Stanford establishment for instruction and research in Aeronautical Engineering, once renowned for pioneering accomplishment, now consists of two middle-aged professors, some student assistants, a pitifully obsolete wind tunnel, a library, and miscellaneous laboratory equipment of considerable value—and a hoard of invaluable teaching and research experience."[29]

All was certainly not lost, however, as the Cold War, with its billions of dollars for aircraft procurement, soon brought the industry out of its tailspin and introduced a new variable in the strategic equation—the ballistic missile.[30] Ballistic missiles changed the rules of the game as much for defense contractors as for defense analysts. Like its rivals, Lockheed found postwar commercial aviation a losing proposition. As one company president quipped, "There's money in the commercial airline business. We know because we put it there."[31] Instead, Lockheed set its sights on defense contracts, only to discover that it was poorly prepared for the unprecedented challenges of the missile age, with its hypersonic speeds, exotic materials, and sophisticated guidance systems.

With missiles becoming an increasingly significant share of the defense market, Lockheed felt it had no alternative but to learn to compete. And learn it did. In 1956 it had no missile sales at all. Just four years later it controlled 15% of the market.[32]

28 A. E. Raymond to Samuel Morris, Aug. 21, 1944, Stanford Archives (SC 165, I, 4/4).

29 Reid, "A Financial Study of the Commercial Operation of the Guggenheim Aeronautic Laboratory Between Sept. 1, 1939, and Oct. 31, 1947," Stanford Archives (SC 165, I, 4/3).

30 For the impact of the Cold War on the American aviation industry, see Simonson, *The History of the American Aircraft Industry*, especially the piece on the Korean War by Cunningham, and Rae, *Climb to Greatness*.

31 Anderson, *A Look at Lockheed*.

32 G. R. Simonson, "Missiles and Creative Destruction in the American Aircraft Industry," *Business History Review* 38 (1964): 309–10.

Behind that remarkable turnaround was a carefully planned corporate strategy of updating Lockheed's expertise in electronics, guidance and control, structures and materials capable of withstanding high temperatures, and the other key technologies of the space age by collaborating closely with the universities where much of that knowledge was being created and where the best young scientists and engineers were being trained. In short, to salvage its competitive position, Lockheed had to learn new technologies and, significantly, learn them fast or risk being closed out of the new growth market. These pressures spurred a reorientation toward and greater reliance on the university.

Lockheed established its first missile division in 1953 near Los Angeles under a retired Air Force general who, promising to run the facility "more like a university than a hardheaded business," hired top scientists, paid them top salaries, and turned them loose to follow their instincts. He not only called his facility a "campus" but encouraged close ties with Caltech, the University of California at Los Angeles, and the University of Southern California. But the general quit after a year, taking some 200 top Lockheed missile scientists with him and leaving the company with a $31 million missile backlog.[33]

Having failed to create its own university, Lockheed settled on an alternative strategy—going into partnership with one. In 1954 it shifted its missile division to Sunnyvale, where it would be near both Stanford's electronics laboratories and NACA's Ames laboratory, the postwar center of high-speed aerodynamics research, including top-secret studies of missile reentry.[34]

Although attracted primarily by Stanford's reputation in electronics, Lockheed's management recognized important advantages in a revitalized program in aeronautical engineering as well. To reconstruct the university's faltering aeronautical engineering program in its own image, Lockheed arranged to have one of its top missile consultants, Nicholas Hoff (a Stanford graduate then chairing a department at Brooklyn Polytechnic), appointed as head of Stanford's aeronautical engineering division, with the company paying half his salary and contracts the rest.[35] It also arranged for the head of the company's research program in gas dynamics to teach part-time at no cost to the university. He later joined the faculty full-time. Hoff, in turn, brought aboard Walter Vincenti, an old friend from student days and an authority in supersonic and

33 The missile division's story can be followed in "The General's Laboratory," *Time*, Aug. 23, 1954, pp. 66–67; "Scientists Take a Walk," *Newsweek*, Dec. 26, 1955, p. 60; and "Lockheed Missile Scientists Quit," *Aviation Week*, Dec. 19, 1955, p. 16.

34 Lockheed's postwar strategies are described in Lockheed Corporation, *Of Men and Stars*, and Bolton, *The Grease Machine*. For the move to Sunnyvale, see "Lockheed Moving Missile Division into San Francisco Bay Region," *Aviation Week*, Feb. 6, 1956, p. 34. For Ames, see Hartman, *Adventures in Research*, and Muenger, *Searching the Horizon*.

35 Terman, "Memo of Phone Conversation with Willis Hawkins," July 13, 1956, Stanford Archives (SC 160, III, 38/1); Hoff, interviewed by Stuart W. Leslie, June 12, 1987.

hypersonic aerodynamics from Ames. The company also opened a research laboratory in the industrial park to stimulate further ties with the university.

Lockheed's initiative could not have been more timely. As dean, Terman had watched Stanford aeronautical engineering slide from distinction to insignificance. By 1954 it was attracting only a couple of students a year, bringing in no contract money, and was, in Terman's words, "essentially dead."[36] He was about to deliver the coup de grace when a group of alumni, hearing rumors of the decision, offered to raise a "warchest" from the aircraft industry to save the program. Led by John Buckwalter of Douglas and Philip Coleman of Lockheed, they asked each major western airframe company to pledge $5,000 a year for five years to put the program back on its feet and into a position where it could once again attract outside support.[37]

With a backlog of orders and a critical shortage of trained aeronautical engineers, the industry responded quite differently to this campaign than it had to Reid and Niles's virtually identical appeal just ten years before. Douglas, Lockheed, Boeing, Convair, Northrop, North American, and Hughes all pledged support, $130,000 in all over five years. Not much by later standards, perhaps, but "mighty big," as Terman later put it, at the time.[38]

Assessing the implications of these developments for Stanford's president, Terman remarked, "These appointments have completely changed the character of the Division of Aeronautical Engineering, and have insured that Aeronautical Engineering will be a vigorous and important branch of the School of Engineering."[39] Indeed, by 1959 the division had research contracts totaling $460,000 with the Air Force Office of Scientific Research, the Office of Naval Research, and the Air Force's Arnold Engineering Development Center, 92 graduate students, and 19 graduates. That was up from $4,500, twelve students (including undergraduates), and two engineer's degrees just three years earlier.[40]

More important than the changing numbers was what they signaled about the changing direction of Stanford aeronautics. Increasingly, the department's research and teaching program reflected the technical agenda of the missile age. As Hoff pointed out in his annual division report, "The major portion of this research is concerned with the effects of very high temperatures on struc-

36 Terman, "Recent Activities in the Department of Aeronautics and Astronautics," Stanford Archives (SC 216, 39); Terman to Arthur Raymond, Nov. 11, 1955, Stanford Archives (SC 216, 39).

37 Terman, "Department of Aeronautics and Astronautics: An Example of a Successful Graduate Department," Stanford Archives (SC 160, III, 2/8).

38 "Affiliates of Aeronautical Engineering Program," Stanford Archives (SC 160, III, 2/8).

39 Terman, "President's Report, 1956–57," Stanford Archives (SC 165, IV, 1/3).

40 Hoff, "Department of Aeronautical Engineering, Annual Report to the Dean, 1960–61," Stanford Archives (SC 165, IV, 1/5).

tures, gas flow, and heat transfer as encountered in the reentry of strategic missiles."[41]

Hoff concentrated on structural behavior at extreme temperatures and updated the structures curriculum to include missiles. Vincenti collaborated with Lockheed researchers in developing the so-called "hot shot" wind tunnel for studying high-temperature aerodynamics and built up a series of unique courses around it. The department described them as "dealing with the fundamentals of those particular aspects of physics and physical chemistry, such as kinetic theory, statistical mechanics, and chemical kinetics, which knowledge is indispensable for a thorough understanding of the state of the air at very high altitudes when it is disturbed by a very rapidly moving object such as a reentry missile."[42] He also lured Milton van Dyke, one of his former colleagues from Ames, to join the department as its resident theorist in hypersonics.

To move the department into the increasingly competitive field of guidance and control, Hoff hired Robert Cannon, an inertial guidance specialist from MIT with industrial experience at North American. Cannon built up a teaching and research program, largely under Air Force sponsorship, that quickly rivaled those in structures and aerodynamics. Like Hoff and Vincenti, Cannon appreciated the importance of keeping basic research oriented toward industrial and government needs and also established close ties with Lockheed through his consulting, his teaching, and his faculty appointments. Daniel DeBra, Lockheed's head of dynamics and control analysis, and Benjamin Lange, a member of the company's Discovery satellite group, both completed theses while working for the company and later joined the department full-time. John Breakwell, a leading specialist in orbital mechanics, also came over from Lockheed.

Whenever possible, Hoff brought in corporate researchers to keep the department up to date in particular specialties. At one time or another he had an officer of the Vidya Corporation teaching a course on aerodynamic heating, two researchers from Hiller Helicopter teaching vertical take-off and landing, and an expert from United Research Corporation teaching jet propulsion.[43]

Following Terman's example in electronics, Hoff established his own industrial affiliates program, partly to tap industrial money but mostly to keep Stanford faculty and students in touch with industrial interests and opportunities. In return for an annual pledge of $5,000 to $10,000, each company got to meet faculty and students during an annual spring review, received copies of all department publications and theses, and was assigned its own

41 Hoff, "Report of the Department of Aeronautical Engineering for the Year 1959–1960," Stanford Archives (SC 165, IV, 1/5).

42 Hoff, "A Plan of Industrial Liaison in Aero- and Astronautical Engineering at Stanford University," Feb. 1, 1959, Stanford Archives (SC 160, III, 2/8).

43 Hoff to Pettit, Jan. 6, 1960, Stanford Archives (SC 216, 39).

faculty liaison officer. "With the extremely rapid changes now taking place in the development and the design of airplanes, missiles, and spacecraft, it is most important to the department to foresee new trends as fully as humanly possible and to adapt its teaching and research programs to the changing needs of industry," he pointed out.[44] Although affiliate support never amounted to more than a small fraction of the contract budget, it offered considerable advantages for hiring new faculty and getting new programs started. As Hoff once explained, "Worthwhile research projects can be begun before their usefulness can be demonstrated sufficiently to persuade the armed forces to grant research contracts for them."[45]

With a foot in the door from the earlier appeal, Hoff had little difficulty lining up participants, including Lockheed, Northrop, Hughes, and Aerojet, and later Boeing, Convair, and others. Altogether, the yearly total rarely exceeded $100,000, about as much as a good contract. But for both the university and the companies the affiliates program was always more about jobs than about money. One faculty member jokingly likened the annual meeting to a "slave market," and in fact the affiliates, especially Lockheed, did end up hiring many of the students. Thanking Lockheed for its generous support of the program over the years, Terman suggested that since "a significant fraction of the graduate students we recruit from all over the country will one day work for Lockheed . . . your investment in Stanford Aeronautical Engineering has been justified."[46]

Lockheed and other aerospace firms earned substantial dividends from their investment in the honors cooperative program as well. In the first year of Hoff's chairmanship, this program attracted 14 students, out of a total enrollment in aeronautical engineering of 21. The following years the figures were 39 of 61, 49 of 86, and 76 of 112. As the largest local employer (aerospace and otherwise), Lockheed of course dominated the program, often sending 50 students at a time.

The network linking Lockheed, Stanford, the Defense Department, and NASA reveals in useful detail the architecture of relationships of what was to become Silicon Valley. The history of this network contains the real lessons of that science region.

The Golden Triangle: A Reassessment of Stanford and Silicon Valley

Silicon Valley, as we have suggested, is widely viewed as a model for "high-tech" regional development, and legions of cities and towns have endeavored

---

44 Hoff, "A Plan of Industrial Liaison in Aero- and Astronautical Engineering at Stanford University."

45 *Ibid.*

46 Terman to Hall Hibbard, Jan. 14, 1959, Stanford Archives (SC 160, III, 8/1).

Fig. 13.3. The Stanford Industrial Park as it appeared in 1959. Photo courtesy News Service, Stanford University.

to remake themselves in this mold. In the conventional view, Stanford University is identified as the key agent in everything that follows. In other words, the prior existence of a major research university doing engineering (helped along, perhaps, by the activities of a visionary individual such as Frederick Terman) created the conditions under which a particular pattern of industrial development was generated, more or less spontaneously[47] (see Fig. 13.3).

Although this view is not exactly wrong, the history recounted here suggests that it is partial and excessively narrow. Frederick Terman may well have been the father of Silicon Valley. However, his fatherhood consisted not of creating single-handedly the conditions for its development but in knowing how to extract maximum advantage from the historical circumstances and institutional context within which he operated.

47 Scott, *New Industrial Spaces.*

What we find, in effect, is a kind of "golden triangle" linking the university, industry, and the federal government (especially the Department of Defense). Government funding was crucial in supporting the expansion of Stanford's engineering program and shaping its technological trajectory. Cold-War politics and the immediate exigencies of the Korean War determined both the level of funding and the technological priorities to which that funding was directed.

Department of Defense priorities also shaped industrial trajectories, sometimes posing new problems to firms, spurring them to expand and solidify their relationships with the university. The case of Lockheed and its turn to ballistic missiles is especially instructive in this regard because here Stanford was demonstrably not leading but responding directly to industry's requirements. Lockheed, in dire need of new technological competence, took the rather drastic step of moving its missile division from southern California to the San Francisco Bay Area. There it could benefit from the expertise of the Ames Research Center, but to tap the expertise of Stanford it had first to contribute by helping to rehabilitate the university's aeronautical engineering program. In this way, the development of industry in Silicon Valley fed back upon and reshaped the orientation of the university itself.

The story of the origins of Silicon Valley is in significant measure the story of the construction of a particular institutional nexus whose ostensible goal was the production of research and a technical system linking research to industrial production. But this process was also intimately, wittingly or unwittingly, linked to the production of a very particular kind of industrial space, which we have called here the science region.

Acknowledgments

Research for this paper was carried out with the assistance of National Science Foundation grant DIR-88-14763.

References Cited

Anderson, Roy A. *A Look at Lockheed*. N.p.: Newcomen Society of North America, 1983.

Bolton, David. *The Grease Machine*. New York: Harper and Row, 1978.

Hallion, Richard P. *Legacy of Flight: The Guggenheim Contribution to American Aviation*. Seattle: University of Washington Press, 1977.

Hanle, Paul. *Bringing Aerodynamics to America*. Cambridge, Mass.: MIT Press, 1982.

Hartman, Edwin P. *Adventures in Research: A History of Ames Research Center, 1940–65*. Washington, D.C.: NASA, 1970.

Johnston, Robert F., and Christopher Edwards. *Entrepreneurial Science: New Links Between Corporations, Universities, and Government*. New York: Quorum Books, 1987.

Leslie, Stuart W., and Bruce Hevly. "Steeple Building at Stanford: Electrical Engineering, Physics, and Microwave Research." *Proceedings of the IEEE* 73 (1985): 1169–80.

Lockheed Corporation. *Of Men and Stars*. New York: Arno Press, 1980.

Lowood, Henry. "From Steeples of Excellence to Silicon Valley." *Stanford Campus Report*, Mar. 9, 1988, pp. 11–13.

Malone, Michael. *The Big Score: The Billion Dollar Story of Silicon Valley*. Garden City, N.Y.: Doubleday, 1985.

McMahon, A. Michal. *The Making of a Profession: A Century of Electrical Engineering in America*. New York: Institute of Electrical and Electronics Engineers, 1984.

Muenger, Elizabeth. *Searching the Horizon: A History of Ames Research Center, 1940–1976*. Washington, D.C.: NASA, 1985.

Rae, John. *Climb to Greatness: The American Aircraft Industry, 1920–1960*. Cambridge, Mass.: MIT Press, 1968.

Reich, Leonard. *The Making of American Industrial Research: Science and Business at GE and Bell, 1876–1926*. New York: Cambridge University Press, 1985.

Rowland, Henry. "A Plea for Pure Science." *Physical Papers* (Baltimore, 1902): 593–613.

Sanderson, Michael. *The Universities and British Industry, 1850–1970*. London: Routledge and Kegan Paul, 1972.

Saxenian, Annalee. "The Genesis of Silicon Valley." *Built Environment* 9 (1983): 7–17.

Scott, A. J. *New Industrial Spaces*. London: Pion, 1988.

Shostak, Arnold. "History of the Joint Services Electronics Program." In David Robb and Arnold Shostak, eds., *Proceedings of the Fortieth Anniversary of the Joint Services Electronics Program*, pp. 15–46. Washington, D.C.: Battelle Laboratories, 1987.

Simonson, G. R., ed. *The History of the American Aircraft Industry*. Cambridge, Mass.: MIT Press, 1968.

Trafford Park Estates. *The Story of Trafford Park: The Home of Modern Industry*. Manchester, Eng.: Trustees of Trafford Park, n.d.

Weinberg, Alvin. "Impact of Large-Scale Science on the United States." *Science* 134 (1961): 161–64.

Wise, George. *Willis R. Whitney, General Electric, and the Origins of U.S. Industrial Research*. New York: Columbia University Press, 1983.

Reflections on Big Science and Big History

Bruce Hevly

The development of big science has been central to the diversification and growth of science in this century. As the essays in this volume demonstrate, it has attracted the attention of historians and social scientists, as well as that of the scientists themselves. This sample is meant to be suggestive rather than definitive or conclusive. Taken as a group, the studies presented here draw attention to some of the emerging themes characterizing the study of big science, indicate needs for future scholarship, and raise important questions concerning the historian's methods of studying and writing about the subject.

Perhaps the most important effort made here is the attempt to redefine the concept of big science. Although each illuminates a different aspect of the subject, these essays demonstrate the results of a common endeavor: a more fully drawn historical image of a complex human enterprise. From the sum of these parts, a more coherent picture of big science emerges, one that should serve as a basis for further study. Nonetheless, and even after hundreds of pages of text, "big science" itself remains an elusive term. With an adjective combining quantitative and qualitative senses, the phrase is conveniently murky, appropriate for an activity that few can define or describe precisely but many feel able to recognize on sight. By way of conclusion, it seems important to draw attention to the main features the authors represented here have discerned.

The canonical sources recommended some rough form of quantitative measure to identify big science. Years ago, Derek J. de Solla Price argued that each generation defines big science in comparison to what went before; with hindsight, much of the expansion of scientific activity in the modern West has taken the form of a steady increase in the social resources devoted to science. Price concluded that the growth itself is not as significant as are drastic shifts in this relatively constant rate of change. Writing from Oak Ridge National Laboratory, Alvin Weinberg proposed another idea, suggesting a rough and ready measure that defined big science as any scientific project large enough to demand a noticeable portion of the gross national product.[1] But because of their focus on such indistinct measures of size, both of these rules may be misleading. Big science is not simply science carried out with big or expensive instruments. As Robert Smith points out in this volume, such instruments, despite their size, may be used in a manner consistent with traditional, little science.

What constitutes "bigness," then, if not size alone? Big science touches many areas beyond the boundaries of science narrowly defined; that is its essential quality. It can be understood only by integrating these areas into a coherent picture, a requirement that forces historians to take seriously the fundamental task of our craft: to place the past into its proper context. Again, the work presented here suggests that the changes creating big science were not simply changes in scale. While scientific machines surely increased in size and power, as did the groups operating them, and the objects of research were perceived through ever more precise systems of measurement, data collection, and analysis, new forms of institutional, political, and social organization arose. These changes in the internal and external contexts of science constituted new procedures for the conduct of scientific work. Big budgets and big instruments are only part of the story; they represent indicators, which themselves should not be mistaken for the substantial changes they signal.

The outline of a more extended context for big science emerges through these essays, one that includes several important features. First, big science has come about through not just an increase in resources devoted to scientific research, but also through the increasing concentration of resources into a decreasing number of research centers, and the dedication of these special facilities to specific goals. Postwar research centers such as Fermilab and Brookhaven, for example, have pursued high-energy physics on a scale and with a concentration of effort unmatched by the leading academic centers, such as Caltech, before World War II. Berkeley and Stanford produced such centers only after their at times painful evolution from physics department to national facility.

---

1 Sources cited refer to the Select Bibliography, pp. 367–73. See Derek Price, *Little Science, Big Science*, Weinberg, *Reflections on Big Science*.

Second, within these centralized institutions the laboratory workforce has specialized. Laboratories have been divided not only into groups of theoreticians, experimenters, and instrument builders, but also into hierarchies of group leaders, laboratory managers, and business coordinators. The Gravity Probe B experiment demonstrates this more complex management structure, as do the actions of the group leaders who come together at facilities such as Tsukuba.

Third, big science, drawing on earlier rhetorics concerning science and power, depends on the attachment of social and political significance to scientific projects, whether for their contribution to national health, military power, industrial potential, or prestige. This continuous process of justification, which requires the attachment of science to outside goals, has influenced the researchers' understanding of their work, and ultimately its intellectual content as well. One sees this in the process of planning research strategies at MIT just before and after World War II: the idea that science could be part of a concentrated effort for the public good, through the processes and products of basic research, came to shape the goals, methods, and organization of nuclear, microwave, and solid-state physics. Here the war amplified trends already in evidence during the 1930's at MIT, Berkeley, Stanford, and elsewhere.

Thus, the apparent familiarity of big science may mask the concept's deeper meanings. This lesson, drawn from the concept's definition, is also true for the phenomenon's implications. Scholars would be wise to adopt a skeptical attitude toward pat descriptions of the relationships between science, government, industry, and technology, for example, as well as simple explanations of the workings of scientific institutions and of the characteristics of collaborative research. Whereas past studies of big science typically counted dollars and personnel, and tabulated the funding sources that nourished large-scale research, we can now see more of the causes and consequences of the growth of science. Those interested in the influence of research sponsors—industrial, military, and eleemosynary—cannot simply assume that outside financial support subverts research in some pure, ideal state. Rather, they must demonstrate such influence on the substance of science.[2] Ultimately, because of the necessity of placing big science in a broader context including the interplay of science, technology, and social forces, this subject is one that should continue to motivate and challenge scholars.

From these essays, four central themes emerge as the products of a proper contextual understanding of the history of big science, that is, an understanding developed by looking beyond measures of dollars and square feet. First, within big science, the relationship between science and technology has taken new forms, which have influenced the natures of both endeavors. Second, the social context of big science has included the interactions of scientists, engi-

2 Two important essays along these lines are Noble, "Command Performance," in M. R. Smith, *Military Enterprise*, and Forman, "Behind Quantum Electronics."

neers, and military officers, and the latter, especially, have been largely over-looked by historians up to this point. Third, precisely because of its size, big science's institutional context demands the attention of historians, and its extensive documentation supports especially productive research along these lines. Finally, the importance of collaborative research, for both scientists and historians, is highlighted here. The first two themes especially have been traditional concerns of social scientists and historians, but these essays provide new insights and the basis for fresh departures. The latter two themes are just beginning to be explored; here this volume begins to break new ground.

Within the development of big science, science and technology have had important intellectual and ideological connections. The scientists' material world is primarily a technological one, and technological needs and oppor-tunities have to be counted as strong influences on scientific practice. Similarly, within the ideology of science—an ideology articulated by the makers of sci-ence policy and the organizers of research institutions[3]—science and technol-ogy have been portrayed as inextricably linked. Within this mode of thought, science is believed to be incapable of progress without an increasingly complex technological base, and science is also believed to inevitably produce ever more advanced technology. The so-called "science regions," attempted clones of Silicon Valley and Route 128, are the brick and mortar manifestations of this ideology and its attendant rhetoric of scientific and technological prog-ress. But this ideology itself needs to be understood historically, rather than accepted as historical explanation. A deeper study of both successful and unsuccessful science regions shows that the merging of science and technology with the goal of benefiting both does not happen naturally, but rather through a process of adaptation that changes the scientific institutions concerned. Stanford's relationship with Sperry began an adaptive process of change; its relationship with Lockheed resulted in part from the aircraft maker's failure to establish a research "campus" and corporate science region independently. Princeton's overt effort to establish a science region failed.

Several chapters in this volume demonstrate the importance of understand-ing the developing interactions of science and technology. Physicists before World War II, particularly at Berkeley, Stanford, MIT, and Caltech, built research tools and experimental programs that relied at times on a well-refined sense of opportunism. Of course, opportunism in some form is essential to any successful, innovative research, which requires the ability to discern the possi-bilities for a telling experiment posed by theory and technology. But in these cases opportunism was not restricted to the translation of theoretical values into potentially observable ones; big science also depended upon scientists who could recognize opportunities to develop useful experimental techniques that also would interest potential sponsors and so assure research support. Some research techniques, then, could provide funding as well as experimental

3 See Wise, "Science and Technology," *Osiris* (new series) 1 (1985): 229–46.

opportunities. Sponsor relationships thus became part of the intellectual and social context of big science, and came to influence plans for further research.

A prime example of the product of such opportunism is the wide-ranging use of microwave techniques in physics and engineering research that continued to grow at Stanford and MIT after World War II, from roots put down before the war. Another instance described here is the development of MIT's Laboratory for Nuclear Science and Engineering, which in some ways recapitulated the development of aeronautical research after World War I at the same institution. The comparison of MIT with Cornell, a university that followed a different path during the 1930's and 1940's, emphasizes the importance of prewar institutional traditions and political economies. Under the aegis of outside sponsorship, the artifacts of scientific research came to have dual meanings, speaking to both the academic and the corporate worlds.

If the needs and values of sponsors—foundations, industrial concerns, and government bureaus—were carried into big science with the technologies they provided or paid for, then the problem of understanding the sponsors themselves assumes renewed importance. One vital avenue of inquiry explored here is the forest of boards and committees established after World War II to coordinate research and development efforts for the military, and to regulate the interaction between the military, academic scientists, and industry. Presiding over these postwar creations were brokers and interpreters such as Lloyd Berkner and William Golden, consultants such as Philip Morse, industrial research leaders such as Oliver Buckley, and the military officers who invested their careers in the products of research and development. It is becoming clear that researchers and their sponsors at times confronted each other only indirectly, through cooperative advisory and supervisory mechanisms that lent scientific work its definition and meaning, from the government's perspective, by relating scientific knowledge to the aspirations of the defense establishment.

As Allan Needell and Daniel J. Kevles demonstrate, delving into government archives as well as scientists' papers allows a more complete historical account to be written. An even better description will require further analysis of the role of military officers, who until recently have been largely overlooked in histories of big science. Too often historians have relied solely on the scientists' accounts of their relationships with military sponsors, and on the researchers' descriptions of the military's needs, desires, and shortcomings. But one can imagine easily that academic scientists being asked to volunteer their services were often told that their work was indispensable, whether it was or not.

The military, moreover, had its own interests, motives, and capabilities, often not revealed in accounts of what academic scientists were told or believed, and much work remains to be done to clarify the needs and interests of military sponsors of research and development. Summer studies, for example, are now still understood largely from the scientists' point of view, and little is known about that of the military. The military's in-house and wholly owned laboratories such as the Army's Harry Diamond Laboratory, the Navy's electronics and ordnance facilities, and the Rand Corporation are also largely unexplored by historians, although a beginning has been made in this area as well, notably by the Los Alamos history project and recent research on the development of lasers.[4]

If military officers have remained in the shadows in histories up to this point, engineers have been only slightly more visible, although this volume brings them more into the open. Clearly, since big science is dependent upon technology, engineers have played important roles mediating between science and technology, and at times between scientists and industrialists. But, in the manner of James Fenimore Cooper's stealthy natives, scientists brush away the trail they leave on their way to scientific facts, and it seems they often remove any evidence of the engineers' contributions. For example, engineers from Du Pont and other companies made important contributions to the Manhattan Project, as did engineers in the electronics industry and in manufacturing during World War II. These roles were defined by their own historical, institutional, and professional contexts, and, as David Hounshell shows, such wartime projects cannot be understood without understanding these contexts. Nor can postwar big science. Contemporary large instruments such as the Space Telescope and Gravity Probe B also reflect an amalgamation of the scientific and engineering cultures.

The Du Pont study, as well as most of the essays in this volume, demonstrates a larger point: that the relationships between science and technology, and between scientists, the military, and industry, will become more clearly understood as historians make more conscious use of institutions as units of analysis. As Lillian Hoddeson shows, wartime Los Alamos was an institution able to change the structure and priorities of its research program in response to experimental data and changing technical requirements. But in turn, these institutional factors helped to define an important physical concept: the spontaneous fission rate of a radioactive material. Institutional records document with a wealth of detail the interaction and interdependence of science, technology, and society in the scientists' work setting.

Yet institutional studies are often perceived to be history's bane. Unfortunately, all too often they have comprised myopic, monotonous chronological litanies of names, dates, and minor experimental triumphs. Participants writing their own histories often ignore the need to place their work within a context; historians often fail to take the final step in their analyses to show how institutional context affects the intellectual content of science. But this

---

4 Examples include Koppes, *JPL and the American Space Program,* and Allison, *New Eye for the Navy.* Forthcoming studies will examine Los Alamos in World War II, the development of lasers, and the history of solid-state physics.

volume proves that such analyses can and should be made, and that institutional history need not and should not be taken as an end in itself, but rather as a tool for those interested in the intellectual, social, and cultural history of science.

It is not just that the size and structure of big science demand good institutional history. (Big science is, after all, institutionalized science.) In addition, immersion in the voluminous records produced and preserved by postwar scientific institutions (budget proposals, minutes of policy meetings, records of contacts with outside researchers, and the documentation of the preparation and conduct of experiments, to name a few examples) provides the historian a detailed picture of the day-to-day context and conduct of research. The result is a more detailed view of the scientists' world, one more sensitive to its being part of a broader cultural network, and one closer to the reality of big science.

One feature of life within these institutions is of central importance: the character of collaborative research. The scientists who have contributed essays to this volume point out how populous their working environments are. The products of large, long-term experimental collaborations—scientists' reports, and scientific concepts—have undergone a complex social history before ever emerging from the laboratory. Large scientific collaborations have changed the relationship of individual researchers to their experiments and the nature of individual contributions to the process of creating new knowledge. Friction within Stanford's Microwave and High-Energy Physics Laboratories, for example, indicated the changing corporate character of research. The coordination and management of research, the sharing of key instruments, the preparing of reports and proposals for funding agencies, and the division of labor among those designing, building, and interpreting instruments and experiments all complicated the production of knowledge. If we historians are to understand the emergence of these changes—changes which the practitioners themselves recognize—we will have to recognize the ways in which our own work has come to overlap that of social scientists, especially sociologists, geographers, and economists.

Big science, then, has raised vital questions about the interactions of science and technology, the relationships between science, the military, and industry, and the workings of scientific institutions. In addition to demonstrating the state of current scholarship in the study of big science, this volume suggests fruitful areas for further research. Scholars have learned to appraise big science in new ways, but clearly there are areas that remain largely unexplored, paths to some of which are indicated by these essays. Much of the current scholarship is concerned with the first branch of academic science to expand into big science, nuclear and particle physics, and the first place this happened, the United States. The growth of nuclear physics was supported

initially by funds from a combination of sources, including industry, foundations, and state governments, and after World War II its development continued, thanks largely to generous support from the U.S. military. Because of
these circumstances, American physics has received much attention from those
interested in big science.

But other sciences, and other cultures, need to be investigated. One area
not touched upon in this volume is big biology and its relationship to the
pharmaceutical industry, which is ripe for examination. In the history of
physics beyond the U.S., the stories of CERN in Switzerland and KEK in Japan
are being written, and other large projects should be examined as well. These
studies are interesting not just because they represent big science beyond the
American context. In their examination of sites of international collaboration,
they also provide prime opportunities to compare different cultural traditions
of scientific research. John Krige, Dominique Pestre, and Sharon Traweek, for
example, show that European and Japanese physicists relate quite differently
to technology and engineers than do American physicists. At CERN, differences from America in technological style and the social status of engineers
alternately helped and hindered European physicists in competition with their
U.S. rivals. Even within the United States, historians have focused on the
culture of academic science, while industrial and military laboratories have
received much less attention. One might ask: in these nonacademic laboratories do relationships between engineering and physics differ?

If this volume raises questions about big science, it should also generate
serious discussion of the phenomenon of big history. Of the thirteen chapters
presented here, two were written by scientists for whom collaborative research
is a daily reality. Of the eleven chapters by historians and social scientists,
three were written by collaborative groups, and another four relied on research carried out as part of collaborative projects. The amount of sponsored
research in our field—from dissertations to multivolume histories—continues
to grow, and this work includes some of the most exciting and important now
being undertaken. Thus, while it seems likely that part of the intellectual future
of historical scholarship will lie along lines suggested by these studies, we
might also ask whether the future of historical practice is foreshadowed here
as well.

History, like physics at the turn of the century, has been seen as essentially
the province of individual researchers, perhaps working at times with mentors
and apprentices. But for many historians the traditional setting is beginning to
change. Should the analyses applied to the cases of scientists involved in
sponsored, collaborative research also apply to our own endeavors? Just as the
complexity of nuclear and particle physics encouraged collaborative research
among physicists, the scale of big science, its complexity, and the vast and
varied amount of the documentation it has produced, seem to dictate the

strategy of collaborative research to historians. In addition, the financial and political realities of academic life support the movement toward more sponsored research. And so the teams of historians may come to resemble, in miniature at least, the teams of scientists under study, as has already happened in some of the social sciences. Scholars engaged in such projects should remain sensitive to the impact of these arrangements on our own work—arrangements that could influence the choice of topics, modes of presentation, and training of students. We historians should not imagine that we are any more free of our own complex institutional and cultural contexts than are the scientists and engineers.

In the end, then, the history of big science is a vital issue for historical scholarship in many ways. The chapters in this volume present the emerging picture of big science as an elaborate and intricate historical phenomenon, the study of which must be carried out by those sensitive to the influences of its interdependent contextual elements: intellectual concepts, experimental tools, the impact of collaborative research, the ideology of science and technology in postwar culture, and the constraints and opportunities of sponsorship.

SELECT BIBLIOGRAPHY

Select Bibliography on Big Science

Published sources cited in the body of this book may be found listed under "References Cited" at the end of each chapter. The list below is intended as an introduction to the field, as it now exists. It consists of titles of general interest cited by the authors in *Big Science*, as well as additional items drawn from a variety of bibliographic sources. The editors wish especially to thank Allan Needell and Robert Smith, who generously shared the results of their own bibliographic project on science and the federal government in the United States.

Allison, David K. "The Origin of the Naval Research Laboratory." *U.S. Naval Institute Proceedings* 105 (1979): 119–39.
———. *New Eye for the Navy: The Origin of Radar at the Naval Research Laboratory.* NRL Report 8466. Washington, D.C.: Naval Research Laboratory, 1981.
Alvarez, Luis W. *Alvarez: Adventures of a Physicist.* New York: Basic Books, 1987.
Badash, Lawrence, Joseph O. Hirschfelder, and Herbert P. Broida. *Reminiscences of Los Alamos, 1943–1945.* Dordrecht, Neth.: Reidel, 1980.
Baxter, James Phinney. *Scientists Against Time.* Cambridge, Mass.: MIT Press, 1968.
Beer, John Joseph. "The Emergence of the German Chemical Dye Industry." *Illinois Studies in the Social Sciences* 44 (1959).
Braun, Ernest, and Stuart MacDonald. *Revolution in Miniature: The History and Impact of Semiconductor Electronics.* 2nd ed. New York: Cambridge University Press, 1982.
Bromberg, Joan Lisa. *Fusion: Science, Politics, and the Invention of a New Energy Source.* Cambridge, Mass.: MIT Press, 1982.
Brown, Laurie M., and Lillian Hoddeson, eds. *The Birth of Particle Physics.* Cambridge, Eng.: Cambridge University Press, 1983.

Brown, Laurie M., Lillian Hoddeson, and Max Dresden. *Pions to Quarks: Particle Physics in the 1950s.* Cambridge, Eng.: Cambridge University Press, 1989.

Burchard, John E. *Q.E.D.: M.I.T. in World War II.* Cambridge, Mass.: MIT, Technology Press, 1948.

Bush, Vannevar. *Science—the Endless Frontier.* Washington, D.C.: U.S. Government Printing Office, 1945.

———. *Modern Arms and Free Men.* New York: Simon and Schuster, 1949.

———. *Pieces of the Action.* New York: Morrow, 1970.

Cini, M. "The History and Ideology of Dispersion Relations: The Pattern of Internal and External Factors in a Paradigm Shift." *Fundamentia Scientia* 1 (1980): 157–72.

Compton, Arthur H. *Atomic Quest: A Personal Narrative.* Oxford: Oxford University Press, 1956.

Conant, James B. *My Several Lives: Memories of a Social Inventor.* New York: Harper and Row, 1970.

Constant, Edward W. *The Origins of the Turbojet Revolution.* Baltimore: Johns Hopkins University Press, 1980.

DeVorkin, David. "Organizing for Space Research: The V-2 Rocket Panel." *Historical Studies in the Physical and Biological Sciences* 18 (1987): 1–24.

Dickson, David. *The New Politics of Science.* New York: Pantheon, 1984.

Dupree, A. Hunter. *Science in the Federal Government: A History of Policies and Activities.* 2nd ed. Baltimore: Johns Hopkins University Press, 1986.

Edge, David O., and Michael Mulkay. *Astronomy Transformed: The Emergence of Radio Astronomy in Britain.* New York: Wiley, 1976.

England, J. Merton. *A Patron for Pure Science: The National Science Foundation's Formative Years, 1945–1957.* Washington, D.C.: National Science Foundation, 1982.

Forman, Paul. "Behind Quantum Electronics: National Security as Basis for Physical Research in the United States, 1940–1960." *Historical Studies in the Physical and Biological Sciences* 18 (1987): 149–229.

Forman, Paul, John L. Heilbron, and Spencer Weart. "Physics *Circa* 1900: Personnel, Funding, and Productivity of the Academic Establishments." *Historical Studies in the Physical Sciences* 5 (1975): 1–185.

Foucault, Michel. *Power/Knowledge.* Ed. Colin Gordon. New York: Pantheon, 1980.

Franklin, Allan. "The Discovery and Acceptance of CP Violation." *Historical Studies in the Physical Sciences* 13 (1983): 207–39.

———. *The Meaning of Experiment.* Cambridge, Eng.: Cambridge University Press, 1986.

Galison, Peter. "Bubble Chambers and the Experimental Workplace." In Peter Achinstein and Owen Hannaway, eds., *Observation, Experiment, and Hypothesis in Modern Physical Science,* pp. 309–73. Cambridge, Mass.: MIT Press, 1985.

———. *How Experiments End.* Chicago: University of Chicago Press, 1987.

———. "The Evolution of Large-Scale Research in Physics." In *Report of the HEPAP Subpanel on Future Modes of Experimental Research in High Energy Physics.* DOE/ER-0380. Washington, D.C.: U.S. Department of Energy, 1988.

Geiger, Roger. *To Advance Knowledge: The Growth of American Research Universities, 1900–1940.* New York: Oxford University Press, 1986.

Genuth, Joel. "Groping Towards Science Policy in the United States in the 1930s." *Minerva* 25 (1987): 238–68.

Gillmor, C. S. "Federal Funding and Knowledge Growth in Ionospheric Physics." *Social Studies of Science* 16 (1986): 105–33.

Godement, Roger. "Aux sources du modèle scientifique américain." *La Pensée* 201 (Oct. 1978): 33–69; 203 (Feb. 1979): 95–122; 204 (Apr. 1979): 86–110.

Green, Constance MacLaughlin, and Milton Lomask. *Vanguard: A History*. NASA SP-4202, Washington, D.C.: NASA, 1970.

Greenberg, Daniel S. *The Politics of Pure Science*. New York: New American Library, 1967.

Gruber, Carol. *Mars and Minerva*. Baton Rouge: Louisiana State University Press, 1975.

Guerlac, Henry. *Radar in World War II*. Los Angeles: Tomash; New York: American Institute of Physics, 1987.

Hagstrom, Warren O. "Forms of Scientific Teamwork." *Administrative Science Quarterly* 9 (Dec. 1964): 241–63.

———. *The Scientific Community*. New York: Basic Books, 1965.

Hanle, Paul. "Astronomers, Congress, and the Large Space Telescope." *Sky and Telescope*, Apr. 1985: 300–305.

Harwit, Martin. *Cosmic Discovery: The Search, Scope, and Heritage of Modern Astronomy*. New York: Basic Books, 1981.

Hawkins, David. *Project Y: The Los Alamos Story*. Los Angeles: Tomash, 1983.

Heilbron, J. L., and Daniel J. Kevles. "Mapping and Sequencing the Human Genome: Considerations from the History of Particle Accelerators." In *Mapping Our Genes. Federal Genome Projects: How Vast, How Fast. Contractor Reports*. Vol. 1, pp. 160–79. Washington, D.C.: U.S. Office of Technology Assessment, 1988.

Heilbron, J. L., and Robert W. Seidel. *Lawrence and His Laboratory: A History of the Lawrence Berkeley Laboratory*. Vol. 1. Berkeley: University of California Press, 1989.

Heilbron, J. L., Robert W. Seidel, and Bruce R. Wheaton. *Lawrence and His Laboratory: Nuclear Science at Berkeley, 1931–1961*. Berkeley: Office for History of Science and Technology, 1981.

Hermann, Armin, John Krige, Ulrike Mersits, and Dominique Pestre. *History of CERN*, Vol. 1, *Launching the European Organization for Nuclear Research*. Amsterdam: North Holland, 1987.

———. *History of CERN*, Vol. 2, *Building and Running the Laboratory*. Amsterdam: North Holland, 1989.

Hewlett, Richard G., and Oscar E. Anderson, Jr. *A History of the United States Atomic Energy Commission*, Vol. 1, *The New World, 1939–1946*. University Park: Pennsylvania State University Press, 1962.

Hewlett, Richard G., and Francis Duncan. *A History of the United States Atomic Energy Commission*, Vol. 2. *Atomic Shield, 1947–1952*. University Park: Pennsylvania State University Press, 1969.

———. *Nuclear Navy, 1946–1962*. Chicago: University of Chicago Press, 1974.

Hirsh, Richard F. *Glimpsing an Invisible Universe*. Cambridge, Eng.: Cambridge University Press, 1983.

Hoch, Paul. "Crystallization of a Strategic Alliance: Big Physics and the Military in the

1940s." *Program, Papers, and Abstracts for the Joint Conference of the British Society for the History of Science and the History of Science Society,* Manchester, England, July 11–15, 1988: 366–74.

Hoddeson, Lillian. "Establishing KEK in Japan and Fermilab in the U.S.: Internationalism, Nationalism, and High Energy Accelerators." *Social Studies of Science* 13 (1983): 1–48.

———. "The First Large-Scale Application of Superconductivity: The Fermilab Energy Doubler, 1972–1983." *Historical Studies in the Physical and Biological Sciences* 18 (1987): 25–54.

Holton, Gerald, ed. *The Twentieth Century Sciences.* New York: Norton, 1970.

Hounshell, David A., and John Kenly Smith, Jr. *Science and Corporate Strategy: Du Pont R&D, 1902–1980.* New York: Cambridge University Press, 1988.

Hughes, Thomas P. "The Science Technology Interaction: The Case of High-Voltage Power Transmission Systems." *Technology and Culture* 17 (1976): 646–62.

———. *Networks of Power: Electrification in Western Society, 1880–1930.* Baltimore: Johns Hopkins University Press, 1983.

Humphrey, Hubert H. "The Need for a Department of Science." *Annals of the Academy of Political and Social Science* 327 (1960): 27–35.

Irvine, John, and Ben R. Martin. "Assessing Basic Research: The Case of the Isaac Newton Telescope." *Social Studies of Science* 13 (1983): 49–86.

———. "Basic Research in the East and West: A Comparison of the Scientific Performance of High Energy Physics Accelerators." *Social Studies of Science* 15 (1985): 293–341.

Johnston, Robert F., and Christopher Edwards. *Entrepreneurial Science: New Links Between Corporations, Universities, and Government.* New York: Quorum Books, 1987.

Jungk, Robert. *The Big Machine.* New York: Charles Scribner's Sons, 1968.

Kargon, Robert H. "Temple to Science: Cooperative Research and the Birth of the California Institute of Technology." *Historical Studies in the Physical Sciences* 8 (1977): 3–31.

———. *The Rise of Robert Millikan: Portrait of a Life in American Science.* Ithaca, N.Y.: Cornell University Press, 1982.

Kargon, Robert H., and Elizabeth Hodes. "Karl Compton, Isaiah Bowman, and the Politics of Science in the Great Depression." *Isis* 76 (1985): 301–18.

Kevles, Daniel J. "Scientists, the Military, and the Control of Postwar Defense Research: The Case of the Research Board for National Security." *Technology and Culture* 16 (1975): 20–47.

———. "The National Science Foundation and the Debate over Postwar Research Policy, 1942–1945." *Isis* 68 (1977): 5–26.

———. *The Physicists: The History of a Scientific Community in Modern America.* 2nd ed. Cambridge, Mass.: Harvard University Press, 1987.

———. *In the Name of Eugenics.* New York: Knopf, 1985.

Knorr-Cetina, Karin, and Michael Mulkay, eds. *Science Observed.* London: Sage, 1983.

Kohler, Robert E. "Science, Foundations, and American Universities in the 1920s." *Osiris* 3 (1987): 135–64.

Koppes, Clayton R. *JPL and the American Space Program: A History of the Jet Propulsion Laboratory.* New Haven: Yale University Press, 1982.

Krige, John, and Dominique Pestre. "The Choice of CERN's First Large Bubble Chamber for the Proton Synchrotron (1957–1958)." *Historical Studies in the Physical and Biological Sciences* 16 (1986): 255–79.

Latour, Bruno. *Science in Action*. Cambridge, Mass.: Harvard University Press, 1987.

Latour, Bruno, and Steve Woolgar. *Laboratory Life*. Beverly Hills, Calif.: Sage, 1979.

Leslie, Stuart W. "Playing the Education Game to Win: The Military and Interdisciplinary Research at Stanford." *Historical Studies in the Physical and Biological Sciences* 18 (1987): 55–88.

Leslie, Stuart W., and Bruce Hevly. "Steeple Building at Stanford: Electrical Engineering, Physics, and Microwave Research." *IEEE Proceedings* 73 (1985): 1169–80.

Livingston, M. Stanley, ed. *The Development of High-Energy Accelerators*. New York: Dover, 1966.

———. "Early History of Particle Accelerators." *Advances in Electronics and Electron Physics* 50 (1980): 1–88.

Lowen, Rebecca Sue. " 'Exploiting a Wonderful Opportunity': Stanford University, Industry and the Federal Government, 1937–1965." Ph.D. diss., Stanford University, 1990.

Lowood, Henry E. "From Steeples of Excellence to Silicon Valley." *Stanford Campus Report*, Mar. 9, 1988, pp. 11–13.

———. *The Silicon Valley: A Research Guide and Bibliography for Historians of Science and Technology*. New York: Garland, 1991.

Martin, Benjamin R., and John Irvine. "An Evaluation of the Research Performance of Electron High-Energy Accelerators." *Minerva* 19 (1981): 408–32.

Marvin, J. R., and F. J. Weyl. "The Summer Study." *Naval Research Reviews* 8 (1966): 1–28.

McDougall, Walter A. *The Heavens and the Earth: A Political History of the Space Age*. New York: Basic Books, 1985.

McMahon, A. Michal. *The Making of a Profession: A Century of Electrical Engineering in America*. New York: Institute of Electrical and Electronics Engineers, 1984.

Mendelsohn, Everett, and Merritt Roe Smith, eds. *Science, Technology, and the Military*. Sociology of the Sciences Yearbook, 1988. Dordrecht: Kluwer Academic Publishers, 1988.

Merton, Robert K. *The Sociology of Science*. Chicago: University of Chicago Press, 1973.

Morse, Phillip. *In at the Beginnings: A Physicist's Life*. Cambridge, Mass.: MIT Press, 1977.

Moyer, Albert. "History of Physics," *Osiris* (2nd ser.) 1 (1985): 163–82.

Mumford, Lewis. *The Myth of the Machine: I, Technics and Human Development; II, The Pentagon of Power*. New York: Harcourt, Brace, Jovanovich, 1967, 1970.

Needell, Allan A. "Nuclear Reactors and the Founding of Brookhaven National Laboratory." *Historical Studies in the Physical Sciences* 14 (1983): 93–122.

———. "Berkner, Tuve and the Federal Role in Radio Astronomy." *Osiris* 3 (1987): 261–88.

———. "Preparing for the Space Age: University-Based Research, 1946–1957." *Historical Studies in the Physical and Biological Sciences* 18 (1987): 89–110.

Nelkin, Dorothy. *The University and Military Research: Moral Politics at M.I.T.* Ithaca, N.Y.: Cornell University Press, 1972.

Newell, Homer E. *Beyond the Atmosphere: Early Years of Space Science.* NASA SP-4211, Washington, D.C.: NASA, 1980.

Pestre, Dominique, "Comment se prennent les décisions de très gros équipements dans les laboratoires de 'science lourde' contemporains: Un récit suivi de commentaires." *Revue de Synthèse* 4 (1988): 97–130.

Pickering, Andrew. "Against Putting the Phenomena First: The Discovery of the Weak Neutral Current." *Studies in History and Philosophy of Science* 15 (1984): 85–117.

———. *Constructing Quarks: A Sociological History of Particle Physics.* Chicago: University of Chicago Press, 1984.

Price, Derek J. de Solla. *Little Science, Big Science—And Beyond.* New York: Columbia University Press, 1986.

Price, Don K. *Government and Science.* New York: New York University Press, 1954.

Pursell, Carroll. "Preface to Government Support of Research and Development: Research Legislation and the National Bureau of Standards, 1935–1941." *Technology and Culture* 9 (1968): 145–64.

Reagan, Michael D. *Science and the Federal Patron.* New York: Oxford University Press, 1969.

Reich, Leonard. *The Making of American Industrial Research: Science and Business at GE and Bell, 1876–1926.* Cambridge, Eng.: Cambridge University Press, 1985.

Reingold, Nathan, ed. *The Sciences in the American Context: New Perspectives.* Washington, D.C.: Smithsonian Institution Press, 1979.

Riordan, Michael. *The Hunting of the Quark.* New York: Simon and Schuster, 1987.

Roland, Alex. *Model Research: The National Advisory Committee for Aeronautics, 1915–1958.* NASA SP-4103, Washington, D.C.: NASA, 1985.

Rosholt, Robert L. *An Administrative History of NASA, 1958–1963.* NASA SP-4101, Washington, D.C.: NASA, 1966.

Rowland, Henry. "A Plea for Pure Science." *Science* 2 (1883): 242–50.

Sanderson, Michael. *The Universities and British Industry, 1850–1970.* London: Routledge and Kegan Paul, 1972.

Saxenian, Annalee. "The Genesis of Silicon Valley." *Built Environment* 9 (1983): 7–17.

Schweber, Silvan S. "The Empiricist Temper Regnant: Theoretical Physics in the United States, 1920–1950." *Historical Studies in the Physical and Biological Sciences* 17 (1986): 55–98.

———. "Shelter Island, Pocono, and Oldstone: The Emergence of American Quantum Electrodynamics After World War II." *Osiris* (2nd ser.) 2 (1986): 265–302.

Seidel, Robert W. "Accelerating Science: The Postwar Transformation of the Lawrence Radiation Laboratory." *Historical Studies in the Physical Sciences* 13 (1983): 375–400.

———. "A Home for Big Science: The Atomic Energy Commission's Laboratory System." *Historical Studies in the Physical and Biological Sciences* 16 (1986): 135–75.

Servos, John W. "The Industrial Relations of Science: Chemical Engineering at MIT, 1900–1939." *Isis* 71 (1980): 531–49.

Sherry, Michael S. *Preparing for the Next War: American Plans for Postwar Defense, 1941–1945.* New Haven: Yale University Press, 1977.

Smith, Merrit Roe, ed. *Military Enterprise and Technological Change: Perspectives on the American Experience.* Cambridge, Mass.: MIT Press, 1985.

Smith, Robert W. *The Space Telescope: A Study of NASA, Science, Technology and Politics.* Cambridge, Eng.: Cambridge University Press, 1989.

Smyth, Henry de Wolf. *Atomic Energy for Military Purposes.* Princeton: Princeton University Press, 1946.

Stewart, Irvin. *Organizing Scientific Research for War: The Administrative History of the OSRD.* Boston: Little, Brown, 1948.

Stine, Jeffrey. *History of U.S. Science Policy Since World War II: Report to the Task Force on Science Policy, U.S. House of Representatives Committee on Science and Technology, 16 October 1985.* Washington, D.C.: U.S. Government Printing Office, 1986.

Stuewer, Roger H. *Nuclear Physics in Retrospect, Proceedings of a Symposium on the 1930s.* Minneapolis: University of Minnesota Press, 1979.

Sullivan, Walter. *Assault on the Unknown: The International Geophysical Year.* New York: McGraw-Hill, 1961.

Sullivan, Woodruff T., III, ed. *The Early Years of Radio Astronomy: Reflections Fifty Years After Jansky's Discovery.* Cambridge, Eng.: Cambridge University Press, 1984.

Tatarewicz, Joseph N. "Federal Funding and Planetary Astronomy, 1950–1975: A Case Study." *Social Studies of Science* 16 (1986): 79–104.

Teich, Albert, and W. Henry Lambright. "The Redirection of a Large National Laboratory." *Minerva* 14 (Winter 1976–77): 447–74.

Traweek, Sharon. *Beamtimes and Lifetimes.* Cambridge, Mass.: Harvard University Press, 1988.

Treitel, Jonathan Alexander. "A Structural Analysis of the History of Science: The Discovery of the Tau Lepton." Ph.D. diss., Stanford University, 1986.

U.S. Congress, House of Representatives, Committee on Science and Technology. *World Inventory of "Big Science" Research Instruments and Facilities.* Washington, D.C.: Library of Congress, Congressional Research Service, 1986.

Van Allen, James A. *Origins of Magnetospheric Physics.* Washington, D.C.: Smithsonian Institution Press, 1983.

Weinberg, Alvin. "Impact of Large-Scale Science on the United States." *Science* 134 (1961): 161–64.

———. *Reflections on Big Science.* Cambridge, Mass.: MIT Press, 1967.

———. "Scientific Teams and Scientific Laboratories." *Daedalus* 99 (1970): 1056–75.

Westfall, Catherine. "The First 'Truly National Laboratory': The Birth of Fermilab." Ph.D. diss., Michigan State University, 1988.

Wilson, Robert W. "My Fight Against Team Research." *Daedalus* 99 (1970): 1076–87.

Wise, George. *Willis R. Whitney, General Electric, and the Origins of U.S. Industrial Research.* New York: Columbia University Press, 1985.

Wood, Robert C. "Scientists and Politics: The Rise of an Apolitical Elite." In R. Gilpin and C. Wright, eds., *Scientists and National Policy Making,* pp. 41–72. New York: Columbia University Press, 1964.

Index

In this index an "f" after a number indicates a separate reference on the next page, and an "ff" indicates separate references on the next two pages. A continuous discussion over two or more pages is indicated by a span of page numbers, e.g., "pp. 57–58." *Passim* is used for a cluster of references in close but not consecutive sequence.

Drell, Sidney, 73
DuBridge, Lee, 14f, 170, 173, 308, 316, 325–26, 329f
Dunn, D. A., 343
Du Pont Company, 10–13; and Manhattan Project, 12f, 237, 243–54 *passim,* 284, 360; plastics research at, 13, 244, 254–60 *passim;* and synthetic rubber, 51–52n11, 239; corporate strategy of, 236–38, 253–54, 258–60; fiber research at, 237–45, 254, 258–60, 284; and marketing, 244–45, 258–59; and relations with University of Chicago, 245, 247–51; and conventional explosives, 247, 253
Durand, William, 346

Economic relations: and Great Depression, 28, 164; and patent rights, 50, 54–55, 60, 74, 144; in Japan, 110ff; and New Deal, 154, 254; in democratic society, 157; and marketing of products, 244–45, 258–59; and corporate acquisitions, 253–54; and antitrust laws, 254; and permanent war economy, 260; and civil aviation, 297. *See also* Commercial applications; Funding; Sponsorship
Education, 94, 104; and transfer of skills, 31, 33, 288; and international exchange programs, 113–14, 118, 162; and minorities, 125; and women, 125–26; and particle accelerators, 134, 137; and physical science curricula, 160, 162; and engineering curricula, 174–75, 180; and G.I. bill, 176
Ehrenfest, Paul, 162n51
Einstein, Albert, 168, 218
Eisenhower, Dwight D., 132, 326f, 329ff, 332
Electrical engineering: at California Institute of Technology, 22–24; at Lawrence Berkeley Laboratory, 22; at Stanford University, 22, 24n6, 48, 56f, 61, 339, 341; and corporate

sponsorship, 23–24, 25, 51n11; at MIT, 160, 169, 171; and scientific-industrial relations, 338–44
Electric power industry, 22–23, 25, 48
Electronics industry, 25, 339–45
Employment, *see* Workforce, scientific
Engineering: allied with scientific research, 5, 21, 31, 33, 63, 93–94, 174–75, 220, 267, 286–87, 340–44; distinguished from scientific research, 5, 90, 92–95, 250–51; of Berkeley accelerators, 22–25, 31, 33, 38–41; of CERN accelerator, 90, 92, 95; and educational curricula, 174–75, 180; of Gravity Probe B, 223–26. *See also* Electrical engineering; Mechanical engineering
Entrepreneurialism, 36, 93, 151, 179, 202, 220
EPCOT Center, 334
Europe: research practice in, 5, 33, 35, 89–90, 92–97; physical sciences in, 86–97 *passim;* gap between science and engineering in, 90–95 *passim;* scientific status in, 103; and participation in Hubble Space Telescope, 189. *See also* CERN
European Space Agency, 10, 189
Evans, R. Monte, 247
Everitt, Francis, 10–11
Everitt, W. L., 298n20
Experimentation, *see* Research practice and methodology
Explosives research, 247, 253, 268n5, 270–71, 272

Fairbank, William, 215, 219f, 221–23
Faraday, Michael, 336
Farwell, George, 274, 277
Fascism, 152, 154, 157–58
Federal Telegraph Company, 25, 36
Fermi, Enrico, 150, 174, 250f, 275, 278, 280, 285
Fermilab, 7, 14, 105, 133ff, 356
Feynman, Richard, 167, 169n86, 173
Field, Lester, 341f
Fisk, J. B., 298n20

military sponsorship, 59, 61, 170, 177–79, 180, 315, 329; at SLAC, 65ff; in Europe, 81, 86–97 *passim;* in Japan, 100–101, 106–8, 112–19 *passim,* 167; and scientific status, 115; experimental skills in, 150–51, 172–73, 286; and educational curricula, 160, 162; at MIT, 160–61; at Cornell University, 161–65, 169; in Germany, 162, 166f. *See also* Particle accelerators
Physics departments: at California Institute of Technology, 26; at Tohoku University, 110; at Cornell University, 150, 161–65, 169, 177; at MIT, 150, 159–61, 169. *See also* Stanford University, physics department at
Pickering, Andrew, 83
Piore, E. R., 298n20
Plastics, 13, 244, 254–56, 258–60
Political relations: and Cold War, 14–15, 94, 152, 196, 299, 301–2, 307, 310; at CERN, 80–82, 190n14; and democracy, 102–3, 157–58, 189; at KEK, 109–12; and communism, 111; and liberalism, 111, 153, 158; and fascism, 152, 154, 157–58; and New Deal, 154; and social inequality, 157; and atomic weapons, 168; and coalition building, 184–85, 189, 191n16, 195, 208; and government policy-making, 189–92; and technocracy, 293, 306
Positivism, 153
Pratt, H., 298n20
Preisswerk, Peter, 79
President's Science Advisory Council, 132f. *See also* Science Advisory Committee
Price, Derek, 187, 356
Princeton University, 195–96, 358
Project HARTWELL, 14, 301–2, 316, 327–31
Psychological warfare, 297, 301f
Public relations, 35, 194
Pugh, G. E., 218–19
Purdue University, 173

Pursell, Carroll, 293n6

Quantum mechanics, 150, 160, 162, 174
Quarles, D. A., 298n20

Rabi, Isidor, 79, 150, 330, 332
Radar research, 4, 56, 174, 265, 295, 340; at MIT, 37, 174, 265, 295; at Stanford University, 60, 62
Radiation Laboratory, *see* Lawrence Berkeley Laboratory; Massachusetts Institute of Technology
Radio astronomy, 9, 14, 185, 291n3, 309
Radioisotopes, 22, 27f, 30, 35ff
Radio research, 74, 294–95, 296; at Lawrence Berkeley Laboratory, 22, 25, 31; at Harvard University, 56, 298n20, 340–41; and Cold War, 301–2
Rand Corporation, 196, 317, 360
Raytheon Company, 285
RCA laboratories, 169, 340ff, 344f
Reagan, Ronald, 112
Reid, Elliot, 346–47, 349
Relativity, theory of, 36, 212, 216, 218, 221
Research and Development Board, 298, 317–23 *passim,* 328
Research Corporation, 26–27, 38
Research practice and methodology: and scale of instrumentation, 4, 37, 67, 69, 97, 145, 179, 335; in Europe, 5, 33, 35, 89–97 *passim;* in United States, 5, 33, 35, 89–97 *passim,* 101ff, 287–88; anthropological interpretation of, 6, 100–101; in Japan, 6, 100–101, 113–14; and individual autonomy, 7, 30, 33, 38, 76, 142, 185f; technological determinism of, 31, 33, 87, 89–95 *passim;* 136–37, 145; commercial determination of, 38, 51n11, 54, 74, 144, 239–41, 243, 254–55; military determination of, 38, 59–61, 62, 83–84, 260, 288, 313, 316, 322, 359; organizational

Library of Congress Cataloging-in-Publication Data

Big science / edited by Peter Galison and Bruce Hevly.
 p.   cm.
Papers from a workshop held at Stanford in 1988.
Includes bibliographical references and index.
ISBN 0-8047-1879-2 (cl.): ISBN 0-8047-2335-4 (pb.)
 1. Physics—Research—History.   2. Research—History.
3. Research, Industrial—History.   I. Galison, Peter Louis.
II. Hevly, Bruce William.
QC30.B54   1992
507.2—dc20
91-9818
CIP

⊗ This book is printed on acid-free paper